IN THE ARMS OF ADAM

a diary of men

James Randall Chumbley

Xanthus Press
• Savannah •

Library of Congress Catalog Card Number: 97-60127

ISBN:0-9638295-7-2

Printed in the U.S.A.

Cover design by Bob Thomas

Xanthus Press
309 East Park Lane
Savannah GA 31401
Tele/Fax 912-234-5698
xanthuspress1@worldnet.att.net

Many of the characters' names and some of the locations in this
book have been changed to respect their privacy.

Life is like a big abstract painting.
In the beginning, you start out painting with primary colors.
As time passes, some of the primary colors stay clear,
while the rest begin to run together becoming muted
and making new colors. Those primary colors are
the influences waiting for us in life,
the muted colors, however,
are the colors of our souls.

To my mother, may she find the sanity that was lost in the violence.

To my sister and brother, may truth, acceptance and forgiveness bring us together where the fury tore us apart.

To my father, may his cycle never be repeated in our lifetimes, and to his peace.

There are several people I would like to thank for their encouragement and support, which served to greatly help me in completing this book. I hope they know how deep my gratitude runs: Brad, Charlie, Darron, Herbert, Mace, Mary, Michael, Patricia, Susan, and Wil. And of course, the characters, who moved me to write.

There are places and things you do not know about.
They are inside of me.
Just as I cannot look deep into your soul,
nor can you mine.
I do not pretend to know what is right for you.
Don't tell me what I must do or what road to follow.
It is time to stop.
Let me be free.
Let me be at peace with what I feel and let me find comfort in
the arms my soul requires.
Let me be in the arms of ADAM.

Many times while writing this book, I'd reach a particular point and stop, unsure whether to travel back into the mists of time. The thought of returning to such an obscure place made me fearful I would be unable to find my way back to today, losing the cushion of safety the years have falsely provided. That fearful place is the childhood I discarded long before I became a man. Any reservations of returning were mainly due to unsureness about certain people and events in my life, that to this day, remain a haunting bevy of questions. And perhaps most unsure of myself as to whether I could rejoin the pieces of the puzzle, some scattered and others lost, that make up my life. The task of searching out the pieces would result in regaining a past I tried to abandon and exposing truths I tried to conceal. After all, what difference would it make if this book were finished? What about my life would be of interest to others?

I have always known I am one of two things: Either a fool or more than an ordinary man. At times, as we all surely are, I could be a bit of both. Feeling less than ordinary most of my life, it has been hard believing the latter. Yet, if I could somehow communicate my feelings with clarity, maybe I could better see where I've been or at least have a better sense of where I am. An artist by nature and a painter by trade, one thing has kept me coming back to writing instead of giving up: An explosive passion in the deepest parts of my soul to express in words, what I dare not depict on my canvases. It is probably the essence of life to know oneself better or view a different landscape than the one being lived. Many times I was skeptical if my passion could overcome the self-hate resulting from the always present familiar demons walking close by my side that consumed me during my youth. Ultimately, I decided that finishing this book for myself would be the true test of that passion.

From the first word I put on paper, I realized that writing was a long and arduous task. I have never been very good at finishing things, despite a flow of ideas and quick starts. Why put myself through another test? It's usually dangerous for one to dig into the dark past. Why summon those demons from forgotten years of a lost childhood long buried? Why turn on the light of harsh reality?

Yet, I needed answers that only they could provide. It was as if they were fighting one another, waiting for the proper medium to leap out. Only then in the harsh light of reality might they disappear forever. I remember making a special trip to the drug store near my apartment just to purchase a journal to begin expressing the thoughts overflowing in my head. Standing in front of shelves full of all types of paper and notebooks, I wondered which color notebook to purchase and whether the four dollars and fifty cents would be well spent. Finally deciding on red, it was as if the color somehow blended with my passions. I carried that red notebook with me for weeks before I penned the first words that had been such a part of me for so long. It was now time to start on the road back.

IN THE ARMS OF ADAM

a diary of men

So few can see the truth.
It is covered up with the disgust of our prejudices,
years of prejudice from generations before.
We are not responsible for ills passed on to us,
but we are for what we leave to the future.
It is time to give something good to tomorrow
and extinguish the wrongs of yesterdays.
Bring ourselves out of the darkness
and into the light of truth.

wilson

In the Arms of Adam

Innocence is the child
blameless
stolen by the father
taken
lost is the childhood
forgotten.

Laying in his hospital bed, Todd brought it up again.

"See, Randy, if you'd loved me as much as I loved you once way back when, I might not be in this hospital bed today," he said jokingly, his head appearing to rest comfortably on the pillow.

But I think a part of him was serious and for a moment I wished things had been different. In the hallway, two nurses conversed with a doctor, and other than the beeper of an IV machine going off in the next room, the Intensive Care floor was quiet. Todd's eyes focused on me occasionally, but mostly he looked at the ceiling as we talked. I sat on the edge of his bed. His hand shook slightly in mine as I held it as gently as I knew how. Now and then, the red flashing light on a monitor next to the bed caught my attention as I dug deep inside of myself probing for the right things to say. In searching for words that would make everything sound okay, a sadness came over me webbed in guilt. Even though I knew Todd meant no animosity by his statement, I felt it for myself. It should have been me in that bed instead of Todd. I had risked so much to find a big, strong man, but I was fine and he wasn't. We could have been together, but I had to have something else, when the best possible man was right here in front of me dying. A lot of years had passed from the time we first met, to that moment of harsh realization in the Intensive Care Unit of Crawford Long Hospital. I had ran the gamut of men, looking for someone to replace my father and in some ways, my older brother as well.

"Do I look any older to you, Randy?" Todd asked, interrupting my brief mental diversion from the hospital room. "How long have we known one another...it's been eighteen years, hasn't it?"

I nodded and then looked away from Todd, thinking the years had gone by in a flash. What should normally seem like a large part of a lifetime had slipped away. I had been too busy running away from eighteen years ago, that I hadn't realized, until that very moment, I was almost two decades older. But how could that be? It seemed only a few years ago that our friendship began.

As well, it had been almost that many years that had passed since I stood by father's open grave and heard the rifle shots echo through the leaf barren trees up into a cloudless blue sky. The Honor Guard — seven soldiers in dress uniform — stood in a row, stiff as boards. Each with three rounds in his rifle. Twenty-one bullets rang out in succession, making three loud shots. And in truth, there was a fourth shot, silent to all but me. The first muffled shot — the one entering my father's mouth — rang in my ears that day, as I looked up to watch the bullets hit the sun.

Like a flash from a camera, the service burst in my head, and then it was gone. I looked back at Todd for a moment, watching his eyes fight their desire to shut until they closed. The hospital noises faded and I found myself drifting back to a long forgotten day.

It was early fall. The remnants of summer had returned after a short cool spell, the heat still trying not to give in to the first cool days as the year slipped its way into October. A few green leaves clung to the tree tops, resisting their cycle of life. They were changing their color, losing lushness as if being choked by the very source which once gave them life. The green palette meeting the sky now transformed by the vibrancy it once held so proudly in spring and carried into summer. Hints of yellow, orange, gold, red and auburn crept across the palette, eventually turning it brown. In the onset of death there would be beauty before the last leaf turned and eventually fell to the ground.

As each year came and went, that October remained constant in my mind. I knew of its approaching without the aid of a calendar and without the seasons' hints of its arrival. There is a clock of months, weeks and days ticking inside me. I know it's coming; a battle ensues, a struggle over life and death and the first casualties fall from the trees.

The house was quiet that morning; a palpable kind of quiet. Everything seemed backwards that day. It was dark, as if dusk came to greet the dawn. There is a difference between the darkness that greets the day and the darkness that ends it. As light breaks through the black of morning there is hope and a sense of cautious certainty, unlike the darkness before night that brings despair and confusion. Yet, that morning there was no light breaking on the horizon, nothing to mark the junction between earth and sky. Instead it brought uncertainty. With morning came the night and the end of a troubled, lost soul. A man long dead before he pulled that trigger. Daybreak would come late this day, no light moved across the rooms of this house. The morning air brought a chill to the bone as gray autumn clouds filled the sky hovering just beyond the tree tops, shielding the new day's light. By midday the air turned as the sun burned its way to blister the ground and soak up the last bit of moisture from the fallen leaves.

No, I wasn't physically there. Three hours before death came into the house, I was already gone. But somehow a part of me was there, my soul remained trapped, locked inside those walls, unable to gain freedom. Even today, so many years later, it still lingers there, trapped like warm air searching for a crack to escape through.

My father placed the shaft of the rifle between his dry lips. His hands shook slightly, a combination of the drunk the night before and the moment at hand. This sad life would soon be over. In a matter of seconds, a burdened life of pain was finished, but now all this was passed on to those left

3

behind. He never had a chance. He wasn't a survivor. His search ended and mine for a father began.

Certainty came to the small house on Shirley Drive. A shot rang out into the air and the outside light slowly drifted into the living room where my father's body lay on the sofa, a thick red stream running from his mouth and the back of his head. His hands cradled the rifle he'd held so close to his chest. Like a soldier, his grip had barely loosened. An unusual number of leaves fell from the forest of trees surrounding the house that day. The trees now stood barren; it would be an early fall.

As a boy, I was never allowed to shut and lock the door to my bedroom. Only my father could close it, then it would be shut at his convenience and for his reasons. But most nights it remained open. The only way that door could be closed was in my mind. In the deep darkness of night there was quiet. In the early hours of morning the yelling ceased and an uneasy calm settled through the house. My soft prayers were always the same: Let a long night push daylight away forever. With sunrise, it would all begin again.

I tried to stay awake as long as my six-year-old eyes allowed. Glancing furtively past the open door of my bedroom, I wanted it to close, to lock me in as much as to bar intruders and keep out what was happening on the other side. The longer I lay awake looking into the darkness, the longer peace would be possible. If sleep came too soon, the night slipped by and my haven of darkness would be lost to the first light of day. My waking dreams were of freedom, of a life far away from all the fear and sadness. In my dreams, I was brave enough to escape, to break away.

Falling into resisted sleep, my dreams of liberation tempted to my real imprisonment. Day-to-day life was relived through monsters that disrupted any peace. The house echoed with their yelling voices, their scuffling bodies and the sound of their glasses hitting the counter tops and tables as their poison slowly contaminated my soul.

Here was a child, a reluctant prisoner to alcohol. It ruled my young life. Little did I know then, how alcohol would dominate the rest of my days. What an unfair judgment to place on one so young. To have never taken a drop of alcohol except from the lips of my parents, yet I would pay for their sins and even possibly the sins of their parents, thus unconsciously continuing the cycle of inner pain and misery and making it mine.

I always imagined the day I grew up and left home would be a wondrous beginning for me. A magical day where the past would be sealed away in some protective place preventing the truths and harsh experiences from escaping and touching me again. The past would be lost, like a bad dream you remember in the first waking moments, but as the hours of the new day take hold, any remembrance of the nightmare is forgotten. That day would be a rebirth, like a butterfly breaking out from the cocoon which bound and restrained it, my breathless break for freedom meant leaving the confinement and tortures of the bottle which so crippled the souls of my parents. This freedom dearly dreamed of night after night, year after year, still alludes me. After all these years, the cocoon has turned internal. Its fibers intertwined with the very tissues of which I am made, infecting the blood running through my body like an invisible virus, gradually hardening my heart and turning my mind against me. I sometimes feared the only freedom would be in the ultimate darkness; the only peace will be after my last breath was taken from me. Only then would there be the quiet and peace I longed for in the darkness of night.

A child's mind can do a lot of things and my mind somehow chose to lock out as much of what was happening outside, as well as inside, my room as it possibly could. I heard the anger in my father's voice and the fear in my mother's cries. Her fears became mine and I was helpless, we all were helpless. At thirty-seven years of age, facing the looming death of a dear friend, I find myself standing at the threshold of the unlocked door of my father. A door I had walked out of many years ago. As the door resisted separation from the jamb, it creaked, crying not to be pulled open and releasing the ugly memories it had kept shut away for a childhood. The sounds it made were like those of an interior door of an old abandoned house. The wood, as my soul, had weathered and become swollen from the dampness of winters come and gone. And, as the door finally broke the seal of years of dust and dirt, echoes of a brutal man's voice yelling and a helpless woman's crying once again filled the darkened corners of my mind. A damp musty odor pierced the air of the cobweb draped room and the taste of fear rolled over my tongue. Try to imagine stepping into a pitch black room and you would be stepping into my childhood. I survived by running away outside of myself and learning to forget — survived by mentally locking that door. Seconds before a car crash, many of those involved forget what happened. My childhood was those few seconds. Like a car crash, one leaving few scars on the outside, but many inside. Leaving many lapses in my memory, some purposeful.

Sitting next to Todd, watching him come in and out of sleep, I realize the foundation I have been standing on is shaky. At present, it can no longer hold me up as an adult. It's too weak and the realities are festering like pus in an open wound, pushing the infection up to the surface and breaking through the skin. Since childhood, I continually pushed everything deep down inside of me until I became nothing but an emotional trash dump. On the outside I tried to make everything look fine, while the inside of me decayed. But now, the truth is lying in front of me. I have to face it before another decade passes, before I find myself in Todd's place. My structure of childhood is damaged and must be rebuilt if I am to go forward out of the darkness to stand in the light. The images are still difficult to recall from memory. A part of me is still trying to protect itself from the truths, trying to push the refuse deeper and deeper, but my capacity level has been met and I can hold no more. The trash is pushing through my skin.

A combination smell of rubbing alcohol, and something undetectable drifted into the hospital room. Todd seemed unaffected by it, shuffling his feet while he slept. Triggering the nose of my mind, the association made me remember the smells surrounding my father all those years of my child-hood: Earth and grass, beer and whiskey. I was intoxicated by the smells; they held an invisible power over me. In an afternoon, he easily consumed at least 12 beers before he started in on whiskey. The beer, an appetizer; the whiskey, his main course.

He was unpredictable. A man who would be calm and hermit-like one moment, violent the next. His large, square hand hit as heavy as a hammer and his belt cut as sharp as any knife. Odd, I can no longer remember the sound of his voice, but I still recall its booming harshness. As he screamed because of some irritation innocently inflicted on him, I can see the spit fly from his mouth. In slow motion, his mouth moves, spilling out anger, eyes piercing, rolling in his head, his teeth biting the air like an aggravated attack dog. Like the ogre in a child's fairy tale, he feeds on the weak and virginal. The young dare not make a sound while he sleeps lest he storm from his room ready to silence the air. But mine was hardly a fairy tale and he couldn't be pressed between the pages of a book, later to be placed on a shelf out of harm's way.

In the hell of it all, there was a man trying to be a father. It would be unfair of me not to acknowledge this side, truly believing he tried, but at the same time realizing his deepen-ing madness held too tight a grip on him. The man remem-bered yesterday as a nightmare, is seen now as a man struggling to do the best he could. For he was two different people, one trying to be a father and the other trying to sur-vive his own monsters. With the magic brew of evil witches, alcohol turned a father into an ogre.

The more he drank, the greater the chances were to experience his madness and its wrath. Poised to go off at any moment, he was like the trigger of a gun, and I felt the bullet's sting. Other times, the potion would turn him sweet and loving. There were occasions my younger sister, Sandra, our older brother Stephen, and myself, would return home from school to find a caring man. He would have ice cream and cookies waiting on the table. The next day, we might find the demons once again held him in their grip. This was the man we called Father. That other man waiting at the door with offerings was a stranger to our house, one who never stayed very long. But as Hansel and Gretal discovered, the sweetness was a disguise concealing rage. Sometimes I think he abused me because I triggered something in him at a particular moment which would set him off. There was no pattern to his actions. Like a roller coaster ride, never knowing what each day would bring. When he was sober, but that was seldom, he became reclusive, and the ogre retreated into his cave.

My father ruled us like we were in his private army. A veteran, decorated with a Purple Heart in the Korean War, he was a Sergeant who couldn't separate himself from his years in the military. A career Army man, he found order in the harsh military life — a part of his history that I learned in my early years. He lied about his age, and at sixteen, entered the Army in 1943, during the second half of World War II.

After the war, an Army buddy of my father's, Jack, was dating a young woman named Dot, who was friends with my mother. At the time, Jack and my father were stationed at Fort Benning, Georgia. Dot and Jack thought my mother and father should meet. After several months of letter writing and the exchange of pictures, my father made a trip to Fayette, Alabama. On September 27, 1952, less than two years later, they were married by a Justice Of The Peace in Columbus, Mississippi. Almost a year after that, my older brother was born just before my father was sent to France, where in the small town of Vassoncourt I was conceived.

His was the face of contentment, this child with green eyes and brown wavy hair who came into this world on that twenty-first day of June, in the year of nineteen hundred and fifty five. The second son of Martha and Wilson was named James, after the apostle, but he would be called Randy, for his middle name was Randall. Everything innocent and hopeful filled those big eyes staring out into the world, safely cradled in the arms of his mother.

The cries expelled by him as he took his first breaths outside his mother's sheltering womb would become a familiar sound. As the years advanced, these cries turned inward to the deepest part of his young soul. His would be a lost childhood.

He grew outwardly handsome and sturdy, but the seasons came and went without the boy much marking their passing. Fall leaves covered the ground, but he never ran to stir them under his feet. The winter chill filled the air, no match for the growing coldness within his sweet being. When Spring filled the landscape, his eyes looked past the greenness, and his ears failed to hear the melody of newly hatched chicks. Summer, the season of his birth, came and went with little celebration. The chicks grew their wings and flew off into the summer sun, but he remained lost in a childhood unable to fly free.

It was to survive that he learned to travel inward, to remove himself from the ever present family torment. His would be a youth filled with loneliness, depression, fear and disappointment. In addition, his life would be consumed with an unending search for love; a search to find a father, a search to fill a void, and a search to come to terms with the contradictions of his manhood. He would be different, apart from those around him. His emotions would separate him from others and what he was taught to believe, ensuring an even lonelier walk through a large portion of his life. Searching to find freedom from the confusion of what his heart said was right for him and what the society he lived in said he must be. Adding more turmoil to finding himself, he would be haunted by a silent past locked away deep in his subconscious. He would struggle to pull the truth from the dark room of his mind, which for years remained locked. An explosion of emotions resulted, leaving a young boy to find his way through them.

In 1964, my father retired from the military and we moved from Columbus, Georgia to Warner Robins, where he took a Civil Service job as a security policeman at Warner Robins Air Force Base. So geared to the military life, he found it hard to adjust to being a civilian. The bottom fell out and the abuse escalated. He began drinking more and more to ease the separation. The life he knew in the military became increasingly a part of our lives, even more so than when he was still enlisted. Our home became his barracks, his base of operations and he was the Sergeant-in-charge. At age nine, I was fully inducted into his army.

The army life was no longer there to protect him from that which he was hiding. I always sensed he was running from something in his memory. And now, without the uniform to cover him, he felt naked and something in his past was catching up with him. His mother never married; my father was a bastard born out of wedlock. And thus, the sins of the parents became very much the child's — something I suspect haunted his existence. But my father's family was never spoken of. My mother always told us never to ask questions. All we knew was that his mother died just days after my older brother Stephen was born. She never saw her first grandson. I don't even know her given name, if that is any indication just how little she was mentioned. Nor were there siblings, aunts, uncles, cousins or childhood friends to call or drop by the house on a lazy summer day or after church. No one to add color to his blank past.

Much of the truth about my father died with his mother, the rest forever lost the day he killed the only remaining witness. Conceivably, by killing himself, he was finishing what he felt should never have begun. It's a part of our history we will never know, a portion of the answers which could possibly help explain the madness behind the man we called Father. Behind our house was a large tool shed. It was red with white trim, resembling a big doll house. My father kept all the yard equipment there. He slept in a bed set up on one side of the shed when things weren't going well between him and my mother. Somehow the shed came to symbolize my father. It set back from the house, sheltered by low hanging limbs of tall trees and shrubbery. The neighborhood was quiet with rows of small brick and wood houses built on evenly divided lots. With a red brick front and white porch, the small three-bedroom house was the second dwelling on the right, around the corner from Rumble Junior High School. The side and back were constructed of wood and painted the same colors as the shed. As most of the houses in the neighborhood, it sat close to the street. The city put in sidewalks a year before he died. Initially, it had been a two bedroom house, but the previous owners added on a living and dining room and turned the original living room into the third bedroom — my parents room. It was the best house in which we had ever lived. In the backyard, a tall magnolia tree towered over the house and in the spring it exploded with white flowers filling the air with a sweet aroma. A long wavy row of monkey grass separated the driveway, which circled behind the house, from the trees and flower beds. Red and white azalea bushes filled the backyard, providing a playground for the resident birds and squirrels. The yard was kept as spotless as any Army base. Shirley Drive abruptly ended into a cemetery, which at first gave my brother, sister and me the creeps, but we got used to it.

During the afternoons and evenings, Father sat in a lawn chair on the concrete patio extending out from the shed and drank his beer and whiskey; while smoking Lucky Strike cigarettes from the pack he always carried in his shirt pocket. Leaning next to him was the BB gun he used to terrorize the birds and squirrels out of the fruit trees. At times, I stood at the rear windows of the house and watched him like he was a stranger who had wondered into our yard. When he called to the house for me, as he often did, I went out and sat next to him as if tied to him by an invisible rope. My older brother roamed the streets with kids in the neighborhood and my sister stayed close to our mother. I couldn't escape and play with other kids my age; I had to stay and play with him. It was a miserable playground.

"Every man should fight for his country. It should be mandatory for all men to serve in the Army," he would start in, reminiscing.

Continuously, he talked about manhood until his words were no longer clear to my ears. I listened until his words ran together and the foulness of the witch's brew rode on each breath. Hour after hour, day after day, I helped him in the yard and sat with him on that concrete patio thinking I would never grow up and get away. I felt trapped, the rope closing tighter and tighter around my body.

He worked and talked about being a man and how I had a long way to go before acquiring manhood, as if it was a station in life he thought I would never achieve. They were just words meaning nothing to a child. But, maybe he knew then about me, maybe he was never sure about himself.

"Take your shirt off son, be a man and get sun on your back," my father would say as we worked in the yard.

Hating to remove my shirt, I fought not to cry in fear of being called a crybaby. Praying every time he wouldn't ask me, but he always did. He insisted. And I always fought the tears, feeling stripped and raw as his eyes examined me, then occasionally commenting I was too womanly.

It bothered him when adults remarked that I was too pretty to be a boy — zeroing in on my inadequate masculinity somehow apparent at that young age. Surely, my Grandfather Nash's comments stung the worst. "Are you sure he's a boy, Wilson? He is just too pretty. Doesn't that boy ever get dirty?" he would say in a hillbillyish, dirt farmer's voice.

Once when my father took Stephen and me to the barber shop, he ordered that we both get crew cuts. My hair was longer than most boys my age. I raised such a fuss and cried so much the barber could hardly cut my hair. Father was livid. "It makes you look too much like a girl; you're not a girl, are you? Boys don't have long hair and boys don't cry. I can treat you like a girl if you want!"

He made me walk the two miles home from the barber's, while he drove alongside with Stephen, referring to me as "little Miss Prissy," from the car. He meant to humiliate me and it worked. My vision was blurred by tears — the crying only making my father madder. "Look at the cry baby, Stephen, look at your brother the cry baby," he yelled out the car window. The more he taunted, the more the tears fell from my cheeks. I kept my head to the ground. The hot afternoon sun baked the road. The echoes of children playing just feet away from where I was walking alongside the car filled the summer day. In one yard, the neighbors' kids were playing kickball. Their ball bounced off a chain link fence stirring up a cloud of dirt as it hit the grass-barren ground with a thump. If only I could disappear so the other kids couldn't see my humiliation hanging thick in the air like a cloud around my head. If only I could run faster than the car and get away. But he would get me sooner or later, he always did. Upon returning home, he took his belt to me. After that, he never allowed my hair to grow longer than a few inches. In my father's eyes, I wasn't turning out like a regular boy, but there was nothing regular about anyone in this family. Other people's comments questioning my gender added fuel to the fire that raged inside of him.

There is an overwhelming awareness that follows me from the past to present day. At a very young age, I came to know the feel of my father's skin. It was warm and his dark coarse hair raked against my body. He had a muscular build and could hold me still with one arm. I can almost feel the sweat from his body running onto me. His breath, reeking of liquor, filled my lungs. The sharp recollection comes to me in an instant and leaves just as quickly. My memory is faint until a casual reminder — such as a smell or the face of a stranger — produces all too clearly, the face of my father. I struggle to recall more, but the perception I have is one of loss. Any recollection comes from a distant memory; I no longer know the little boy who experienced it. My guilt, at times, causes me to question if it may have only been a series of bad dreams, figments of imagination. Why would a man who was so obsessed with his son's manhood subject him to such a dark contradiction? From this quagmire, even now, I still protect my father, as well as myself, from the truth. But, it's hard to know the truth if one cannot remember clearly, and I cannot see through the deep, thick fog of my childhood. Without doubt, there are vague memories of contacts which should have never taken place between a boy and his father. But then, nothing in this relationship was right.

What actually happened may never come to the surface in the pool of lost memories in which I swim. But what I do know is that innocence once drown there in suffocating water that was seldom calm. And as the questions float to the top, I see his bewitching stature and his sea blue eyes, framed by night black hair in the reflection of my mind. Something was taken from me, as very well may have been ripped from him when he was a child like me. A seduction that became a rape of innocence. Did he find the innocence in me he'd lost somewhere when he was a boy? I know his innocence was taken by circumstance unknown to me. My father had no father — did he search out as I have done to fill an emptiness? Did he search for a protector, as I have done? He was a child from the hills of Tennessee, a boy of sixteen fighting a war in a far off land which should have only been fought by men. He lied about his age to run away from something or someone. The feelings inside of me must have come from him. Innately I have learned them through him. I am therefore left wondering; who is the guilty one? Perhaps he was too weak and I was the evil one, a demon child; was it I who turned him to madness? What about my face brought back his own childhood to haunt him? To understand such questioning you have to know the heart beating in me, and this is something no one can comprehend.

How did I know to touch myself there, as I lay in the lukewarm water? The door to the bathroom is closed. In fear of my dirty deed being discovered, I listened for sounds that might announce the approach of someone in the house. Quietly, the water almost milky from the dissolving soap, wraps my young girlish body. My knees stick out of the white water as I move my finger in and out of me. The water ripples noiselessly between my legs spread as wide as the tub will allow. My other hand squeezes my fatty nipples, my desires wanting them to be suckled. What desires brought my finger inside of me, pushing it in as far as it would go? What desires made me want my father's penis there instead of my finger? Why is my memory so black, void of any light?

Part of me won't allow the truth to surface in my memory. There are bits and pieces, of course, but none of them seem to fit well together. I feel like I am an unknown, and trying to call up the past is a fruitless task. I would gladly leave it all behind in the darkness, but those bits and pieces will not go away and let me rest. I am haunted by things in the past I can barely recollect. Maybe it would have been better if those memories never surfaced and died with my father and remained dead. Yet, their memory had a greater power over my being than breath had in the flesh of my father. They have followed me long since his death, and have visited me in the dreams of many a long night. And now, they are visiting me again as I sit watching Todd die. But even the dreams will not give the whole truth, coming to me like a riddle in the middle of the night, implying the deeds and desires of my father. Or were they the desires of a little lost boy? How did they make me the man I am today? There are still times the riddle wakes me in a sweat of panic. I overwhelmingly feel the need to lock the bedroom door, my sleep disturbed by reminders of a dark past invading the consciousness of my mind. I lie still in the bed. Only my eyes dare to move around the room. My ears listen intently to the quiet in the air. In a moment, I'm faced with the reality that I'll always be surrounded by the weight of the past.

It's too quiet, as if something is about to happen. Even

though I know I'm alone in the house, I make my way from the bed to the opened bedroom door. I peer through the nightness, studying its blackness remembering the rapid beats of a little boy's heart. Reaching for the knob, I find some comfort in closing the door, in the sound made as the lock snaps secure. I'm safe again from the physical presence of my father, safe from the wilderness outside my door. I repeatedly checked the lock of my bedroom door. A riddle I have yet been able to answer.

Todd's friend, Sylvia, peaked her head into the room. "How is he doing?" she asked. A sweet-looking young woman, reminding me a little of my sister, Sandra. Sylvia was outgoing and funny, like Sandra, but she seemed to be holding something back. Holding something in reserve that she didn't want to let anyone know about. Again, like my sister.

"Why don't you ask me yourself?" Todd quizzed her, coming out of his nap.

I got up from the chair, offering it to Sylvia, and stood in the corner across from Todd's bed. She had chestnut hair almost the same color and length as Sandra's. They could be sisters, I found myself thinking as I watched Todd and Sylvia talking. As an adult, my sister told Mother about Father's sexual abuse of her. I hoped Mother would never find out. Sandra and I had agreed this knowledge would send her over that edge she had clung to for years. She had enough of her own memories to torment her. Mother's drinking and mental problems were taking a big demand on our adult lives. Drunk, she would call us at all hours ranting and raving about the past. The next day, not remembering making the phone calls or anything she'd said. After awhile, it got to the point Mother didn't have to be drunk to call. It was making our lives miserable. We all tried to help, but nothing seemed to stop her from self destructing — not even the hospital stays in the mental wards or the drugs seemed to be working. Finally, exhausted from Mother's complaints about her sad life, Sandra divulged Father's abuse in hopes that Mother would back off and realize we were all in this mess together — that she wasn't the only one who suffered. The knowledge didn't change things — the late night drunken calls continued. Stephen, Sandra nor I got any rest from the past — Mother continued to relive it for all of us. But what Mother didn't seem to understand was that we were living it as well — we had been living it all along.

The sad part is I understand my mother's madness and I share it with her. In many ways I have become her. Perhaps, just like eye color is inherited, so is madness. And the part of madness that wasn't passed on through the gene pool, I learned. But that understanding wasn't enough to help her. Images I carry of my mother are not whimsical ones. Her face swollen, fearful of his next strike, eyes black and blue and her arms covered in bruises, imprints, where his hands grabbed or struck her with great force. Puffy bloodied lips, where his fist struck to command her silence. Knees shaking, all our knees were shaking in dreaded fear of him. I hear her voice crying out in the back of my head, calling out telling us to run, but it is she who needs to flee. There were times when she did try to run, when the constant beating cornered her like a desperate animal trying to escape the jaws of a predator in the night. When her body couldn't take another blow, when her heart and soul desired freedom.

He usually waited until the appearance of night to strike, as if knowing his actions would be shielded in the darkness. By then, the combination of beer and whiskey had well fueled the anger inside of him — all three making a volatile mixture. The eruption was eminent. But where would she go in the dimly lit street, running through the neighborhood on bare feet, her bruised body covered only by a torn slip? The barking of dogs echoed in the street and a few porch lights popped on in the night. Which direction should she run? Sometimes to a neighbor's, but they didn't want to become involved. My father's drunken episodes kept them away. Instead they peeked through their curtains and cracked front doors. They no more wanted to confront him than we did.

The police were seldom called. And when they were summoned, Father met the officers in the front yard. He talked and joked with them, and then the officers left after giving Father a slap on the back. Or, sometimes she waited outside, hidden in a corner of the night, until he either left the house or we signaled Father had gone to bed. We called quietly out into the night, three little children, "Mommy, Mommy, he has gone to bed." The beastly ogre had gone to bed, withdrawn to his cave. And if Mother did run, he might go after her in his car, searching the streets to bring her back from where she was running. His car moved alongside of her trying to cut her off. The car's taillights exploded in the blackness of the street as he jumped out and grabbed her, pushing her into the car. But most of the time, Mother stayed and took the blows, seldom striking back. There was little room to run. If she had left, he would have beat us more. So she stayed. We were his possessions. To do with as he pleased.

Why did no one come to save us from him? Where were the heroes I watched on television who were saving everyone else? They were real, weren't they? Where was the Caped Crusader? Why didn't Robert Conrad take time out from fighting evil, corrupt villains from "The Wild, Wild, West" and come help me? Where was my protector when I needed him? Where was Andy Griffith, the fatherly and wise sheriff who could set my father straight? How I envied Opie. I waited for them to save the day...but they never came. But I still waited even into adult life to be rescued, looking into the faces of the men I passed on the street, in the bars and in my bed for a hero. Instead, as a child, I found comfort in my dog, Rex — a collie and shepherd mix. He looked just like Lassie to me and like any boy, I loved my dog. Rex was something to love and in which to find loyalty. Every night before going to bed I called to him from my bedroom window. His big paws rested on the window ledge. I petted him until my mother came into the room to check on me. When Rex was still a puppy, I snuck him into my room after everyone had gone to sleep. Eventually, my father caught on and that was the end of that. Rex stayed outside. He was a companion for the little boy I once was. I sat with him in one of the holes he had dug at the edge of the backyard. The yelling inside the house would carry out to the yard, but when I was with Rex, things didn't seem so bad. He was my friend and a distraction. The first thing I did when returning from elementary school each day was play with Rex. Then one day, I came home, and Rex was gone. Without real explanation, my father said he gave the dog away to a friend who had a farm. That was the first time I understood what real hate for another person felt like. My father had given away the only friend I had. For days, I looked for Rex, hoping he would find his way home. Many nights after, I cried myself to sleep under two pictures of Rex taped to the headboard of the bed.

Mother called me immediately after her conversation with Sandra, wanting to know what I knew about any sexual abuse. Her concern was that she should have figured it out when it was going on, but she had been blind to it. Now she was confronted with what she had always known. The truth had been released from once silent lips and Mother had to somehow filter further betrayal of her husband. Just the thought that something might have happened was enough to believe it was so. "It all added up," she said over the phone, speaking in such a bitter tone as if he was standing there next to her. And he was; his grave couldn't confine the past. She would have no solace in knowing this truth. As an adult, I don't blame her for not knowing then, she was living in her own hell with him. Mother said she could remember times when I cried hysterically after my father left my room. Then I called for her. But we were all crying because of him, crying on the inside and our tears were drowning us. I turned cold and numb as her words struck my ears, painting a distant picture. But Sandra's remembrances are as vague as mine. Father stopped her in the hallway when she was eleven, just the two of them in the house. "I have to check to see if you've started your period," Father said to her. Then he proceeded to put his hand down the front of her pants, pushing his finger up her vagina. She focused on the grids of the floor heater next to her feet. The sexual abuse continued up to his death. Today, Sandra still has sensations of the heavy smell of his Mennen after-shave mixed with the odor of Falstaff Beer on his breath. Flashes pop in and out of her head, flashes of his bare chest, flashes of her lying with him in the bed, baseball games on the radio playing in the background. In the back of her mind, Sandra sees a little girl riding in the car with Father at the wheel, as the woods roll by and then the picture fades. The girl in the car is her, but she can't remember what happened to that little girl or what happened when the car stopped. It was her turn to have the rest of her life destroyed.

"I remember some things, but I try to forget. Sometimes it's better to forget you know," Sandra has told me. "Remember Randy, how you used to always want me to stay at Bridgett's house when we were little?" I didn't remember Bridgett or that she was a childhood friend of Sandra's. She had to remind me and even then I still couldn't place her. "You never wanted me to be alone with Daddy," Sandra explained. "Mother spent a lot of time in bed because of her nerves...remember the time Father moved out of the house into that tiny trailer. When he came to get me, you always insisted on going too, so you could keep an eye on me. Then he had to move back in the house because there just wasn't enough money. You used to watch me like a hawk...you were afraid of something and now I know what it was. You knew because it had happened to you, that bastard. We would find places to play so Daddy couldn't find me," Sandra continued. "You would always fix my hair for me...you took care of me, remember?" She told me of a night long ago. I must have been ten years old and she seven at the time. Father had been drinking and I wanted Sandra to stay at Bridgett's. Bridgett's mother had called to say Sandra couldn't spend the night because she hadn't any pajamas or clothes for school the next morning. Apparently, after dark and after Father had passed out, I rode my bike through the worst part of town to take Sandra the items she needed to spend the night.

"And, remember Rex?" Sandra asked. "I know how much you loved that puppy. You know he killed Rex, don't you? He just made up that story about giving your dog away. He brought home his gun from work when he was a security guard on the Air Force Base. He took Rex to the woods and shot that poor little dog in the head. I was sitting in the car and heard the shot. I know that's what happened...I'm so sorry."

During the years of unspeakable conduct, the activities of our father weren't always consciously apparent to any of us. As he violated and brutalized each of us, somehow we allowed our spirits to leave our bodies. We took our hearts and hopes and placed them away on a shelf high enough where he couldn't reach them. And, somehow, we left them there on that shelf, forgetting we had them, misplacing our souls. By escaping in such a way, we misplaced the knowledge of a large portion of our lives. I only realized many years later, as an adult, my father had also inflicted his damage on Sandra. Up until then, I thought she'd been spared most of the physical abuse, not realizing, all along, he was taking her soul.

One afternoon several years out of college and living in Atlanta, I was driving in my car trying to come out of a depression I had been in for weeks. It was a common practice; I drove, like a frightened little boy running, without any destination. Battles with depression had been ongoing. I usually toughened them out by sleeping for days. Or, when I mustered up enough self-confidence, I ventured out to find someone who would sexually alleviate my pain. But the emptiness I felt during my depressed states was sometimes intensified after the sexual encounters and I was left alone again. Just hours before my drive, I'd spoken to Sandra over the phone. In our conversation, as with many previous ones over the years, I had picked up on how depressed she sounded and how much she mirrored my lack of self-esteem and sense of worthlessness. As always, I tried not to let on to her the state of mind I was in. But it was apparent she and I had felt the same for many years. Her words were drowning in alcohol as she spoke, and I saw the mirror image of myself in her words.

Up to that conversation with my sister, every hour of the waking day over the past weeks had been filled with self hate. I couldn't stop telling myself how worthless I was, and every time I looked in the mirror, all I saw was the ugliest vision of myself. I spent most of the time in my bedroom with the door closed and the shades drawn. Sleep was the only thing I could do well. I wasn't good enough to be in the world outside. Once in awhile I got out of bed and walked through the dark apartment to the dining room window to peer through the shades. The sunlight rushed into the room making my eyes squint. Looking down to the street, I watched people walking to the park across from where I lived. I desperately wanted to be one of them — like the kids playing kickball while I walked in shame alongside my father's car returning from the barber shop. Days passed, I couldn't make myself go outside. Soon I couldn't distinguish the hour without looking at the clock or tell whether it was day or night without opening the shades.

Thoughts of death preoccupied my mind and I relived my father's suicide as if it were my own. Should I take my life as he did? But that would almost be redundant, he had already taken it. Ironically though, I was still breathing and my blood was still moving through my veins. The pain was still as intense as when I was a little boy — that poor little scared boy that I still was. Where would I find a gun and where would I shoot myself? I could go to the kitchen and get a knife and plunge it into my heart that had stopped beating a long time ago. The bathtub would be the cleanest place and it would be better for those who would find me, less of a mess to clean up. My blood would empty my body and escape through the drain — clean and easy and finally my body would be free of the virus of madness. But the tub would be hard and cold. I would rather find comfort in my bed where it was soft and warm, but the mess would be too great. I wouldn't want to leave such a mess like my father had left for me. I could wait until dark and drive my car on a lonely stretch of highway. Driving fast, I would count the telephone poles, as I had done so many times before. And when I got to number twenty-six, one for each year of my life, closing my eyes and pressing the accelerator to the floor, I would crash into it. The rest would be left up to God. I trusted He wouldn't fail me, as I had thought He had done before, when I had prayed for Him to take me in my sleep. Then He could give the life in my body to someone who could make better use of it. If I succeeded, no one would know I'd followed in my father's footsteps and ended my life. But that would be the end of hope and I have lived on hope alone. Finally, I forced myself to open all the shades in the apartment and remove myself, for at least awhile, from the darkness that surrounded me.

It was too much torment for the tender years of a child too accept. The ultimate violation is the one which takes the trust away from the heart of a child. Once trust is stolen, like the innocence, there is little chance for it to be regained. Trust is the only thing a child has to give to the world. That child's trust is the same as his love and when trust is taken, then so too is his love. I was left with nothing, no trust and no love, especially for myself. My father's control and abuse was my world. Even after growing up, I was unable to separate my adult world from the world of my father's dominance and violence.

I grew cold and hard from the brutal beatings and violations, but I was still fragile on the inside. They were a routine part of life. You just try to forget about them both and somehow they become "normal." But your soul never forgets the way your conscious mind will. A child doesn't understand. There's this big person, upon which survival depends, inflicting things on you and you don't know what to think or do. As a result, one becomes another person and abandons the abused one.

Now, I know, I was an object for my father to vent his own madness and frustrations on. I was a small convenient source to lash out at. Surely, in truth, he was really lashing out at himself; I was merely the helpless recipient of the physical pain. Only later in life would I come to know the psychological implications. He had to deal with the mental torture, adding to his madness. I don't believe he wanted to do those things, he couldn't control himself. He very well may have experienced the same things as a child himself. It was probably all he knew.

Up to now, Todd's life had been a good one. From what he told me, his family history was very different than mine. Of course, I never really came out and told Todd of the lost years of my childhood. And for some reason, until now, I never thought about them, much less shared the truth with anyone. The past was just always with me, like an invisible emerging cloud. Not even a good friend like Todd really knew. How do you put a past like that into words so someone can comprehend the reality of what transpired? How do you explain blackness? How do you admit to another adult that you're still holding on, even reluctantly, to the past?

Growing up, I guess I came to hate my father. I had hoped he'd realize the horror his alcoholism was inflecting on all of us, my mother, sister, brother, and myself, and stop. He brutally beat my mother, and when we tried to intervene, he turned on us. Some things I can remember clearer than others, but it's the inner pain and loss, the by-product of the abuse which has remained clearest in my mind. Each day I carry them with me. Pain and loss have been my companions.

There are times when I still look through the eyes of that little boy I never came to know. I find myself back in my room in the house whose outer walls hid what was happening on the inside from the outside world. It was night. Perched in my bed on my knees, I looked from the dark room into the hallway lit by the light in the bathroom. The house was filled with yelling. It started like a gunshot breaking the silence of a peaceful night. I had a feeling it was coming, like a sixth sense triggering an awareness learned years earlier; something in me knew this night would be like too many before. Although, I could never be certain, the chemistry of the day seemed to evoke eruption into the night. That day, things seemed too good to be true.

I was amazed the whole neighborhood hadn't been disturbed by the violent voices filling the lateness of the night. Looking back today, I'm sure the neighbors knew what was going on in our house, but in the late 1950s people didn't interfere with a man and his castle. I could hear my mother run from one end of the house to the other with my father chasing after her.

"I'll kill myself if you touch me," screamed my mother. I caught a glimpse of her nude body's silhouette in the light of the bathroom as she ran down the hall.

"Mommy, Mommy," Sandra called from her room.

"Stay in your bed and go to sleep," Father yelled at her. But how could any of us sleep? Stephen was quiet in his bed trying to pretend sleep.

"Don't run from me, damn bitch," yelled my father as the same light from the bathroom caught his nudity as he pursued her.

I could hear my parents tussling in the kitchen. Utensils spilled to the floor out of a drawer, which had been violently pulled open and off its tracks. Suddenly, my mother's bare footsteps sounded on the floor heading back in my direction.

"I told you if you touch me again, I'll kill myself. I'll kill myself with this butcher knife," she screamed at my father again.

Again she ran by my room down the hall, the steel of the knife reflected the bathroom light. I was frozen, not knowing what to think, afraid of how the night would end.

As my father came after her, the erection of his penis, like a weapon, was obvious passing the lighted bathroom. Mother must have gone one way at the end of the hall and my father another. For a brief moment, she escaped his reach. With the knife clenched in her fist she ran back to the bathroom and closed the door. Now the hallway was dark and I couldn't see what was happening. I heard my father run up to the bathroom door trying to open it.

"Martha, unlock the damn door or I'll kick it in," he yelled, as he continually tried to force it open.

"Stay out of here or I'll kill myself," she said again and again...

My father's body hit against the door until finally he succeeded in forcing it open. The light spilled out into the hallway, exposing their nude bodies struggling over the knife. Mother held the knife high above her head. Its blade pointing downward toward her breasts and his chest. He had his hands around hers, trying to take the knife from her. They were both out of breath, their bodies were weakening from the struggle. At any second I expected the knife to plunge into one of them.

I closed my eyes and covered them with my hands in total disbelief of what was taking place. I couldn't watch anymore and even at that tender age, there were no more tears to cry. The knife clanged as it fell to the linoleum floor. I opened my eyes just as they were each trying to reclaim it.

"Stop, please stop!" I remember screaming.

They were so wrapped up in their madness, they had been unaware of my witnessing the chase and the struggle. My plea luckily was enough to make them stop.

"Go to sleep, Randy!" my father said, with irritation in his voice as he left the bathroom and retreated to their bedroom.

My mother went in the other direction toward the kitchen. In their embarrassment, they had left the butcher knife where it had fallen from their hands.

The door to their bedroom closed behind my father. Moments later, Mother went to my sister's room. The house was quiet now. My eyes focused on the knife laying on the floor, expecting one of them to come back for it. After a few minutes, which seemed like hours, I eased out of my bed and walked in the direction of the bathroom. My bare feet chilled by the cold floor, I nervously stared at the knife, listening for my parents. In slow motion, without command from my brain, my hand picked up the knife and carried it into my bedroom.

"What are you doing?" Stephen whispered, as he sat up in bed.

Standing just inside the door, failing to answer him, I looked around the room for a hiding place to put the knife so my parents couldn't find it. The reality that the kitchen drawers were full of knives didn't occur to me. It was only important at that moment to hide this one. I slid the knife under the dresser out of sight and crawled back into my bed, pulling the covers to my ears so I could listen to the silence.

Hiding knives, razor blades, and other sharp objects later became a common practice, especially after my father's suicide. Depending on her mood swings, which were greatly influenced by drinking in combination with prescription drugs, I held suicide watches over my mother. On some occasions, I had to take her to the Emergency Room to get her stomach pumped. She would get drunk and threaten to kill herself. At first sign of a bad swing, I would run around the house hiding all the knives and razor blades from her. Several times I took them from her very hands. I'd learned early on where to hide them. Even to this day, in my own home, I do not leave kitchen knives on the counter. I always make sure they are put away out of sight.

Before Sandra, Stephen, and I separated ourselves from one another, we used to plan running away. We would meet in the backyard making a list of what to take: Cookies, toys, clothes, our piggy banks, and our bags of candy stashed under ours beds from Halloween. We wondered if we should tell Mother, maybe she would come. How could the three of us go and leave her with him? She would have to come too, and of course, Rex. We would wait until Father went to sleep, or passed out in front of the television and sneak out of the house. There was no decision of where we would go, or how far to get away. Whether our escape would be to the next block, town or state, that was never decided. Anywhere would have been fine, we just wanted to leave, already having left in our minds. Stephen had talked about us camping out in the woods behind the house. That way, we could sneak back into the house when Father was gone and see Mother and get more food and stuff. We had built a fort back in the woods on the other side of the ditch, sometimes playing there with the next door neighbor kids. Mother always said they were worse off than us. They were the Tailors, five bratty kids, four boys and a girl. Mrs. Tailor wore a lot of make-up, at least that's what Mother always said. Mr. Tailor was a trucker, not home very much. And when he was away, Mrs. Tailor stayed out late, sometimes phoning Mother from the motel and bar down by the railroad tracks to check on her kids. But, it was our fort and we let the Tailors play there. If we decided to hide out there from our father, they would have to keep quiet and not let him know. But, they wouldn't talk to him, they were afraid of him too.

Ours was a sad household. The sickest thing was that we protected our father, as much for his sake, as for our own. We didn't want anyone to know the shame of it all. So, we tried to act like the perfect family. What liars we all became. He taught us how to be liars. Father's boss called from the Air Force Base when he didn't show up for work, wondering where Father was. Mother would cover for him, saying he was under the weather. But we knew he was out drunk somewhere.

Pursuing childhood friendships comfortably or having kids over from school was obstructed by the fear they would find out our secrets. We all lived in so much shame that we came to believe everyone else was better than us. After awhile, I stopped trying to make friends. I envied the relationships between the other boys at school and their fathers, resulting in daydreaming that my father was someone else.

I remember being very small and he was so big in his

army fatigues and t-shirt; one of my father's friends. The sun was high in the sky as he hit balls to the other boys from the apartment building where we lived while Father was stationed in Germany. I peaked around the corner of the building out of sight of the playing field. They were having fun. My hand was full of small rocks. I would look round the side to see if he could see me and when I thought he wasn't looking, I threw a rock at him. Luckily, I didn't have a very good aim. It must have taken six tries before I was successful. Quickly, I ducked back behind the building pressing my body against the bricks so as not to be discovered. When it was safe and he had returned his attention to the other boys, I threw another rock and then another. Each time ducking behind the building my heart beating rapidly. Soon enough I was detected, but I wanted to be. His arm came around the corner and grabbed me.

"What are you doing, Son?" he asked.

"I'm just playing."

"Throwing rocks at people isn't a game. Do you want me to tell your father?"

My father was in the apartment fighting with Mother. She had sent me outside to play.

"No," I mumbled. "I want you to be my father."

I ran home to find my mother with a black eye and my father drinking beer in front of the television.

I fantasized about another family rescuing me and taking me away from our house and the misery there. Those fantasies grew into a life in my mind very separated from the life my body was living. I was waiting for my real family to find me. When I was just a toddler, my real family had stopped off in Warner Robins and I'd gotten lost. Somehow, getting stranded here with this family. My real family was good and my father was the best father in the whole wide world. He didn't drink or hit us. One day, he would knock on the door and swallow me up in his big arms and take me home.

Even when I was very young I knew Father was a troubled man. At times, I felt sorry for him. Attempts to please him seemed like a wasted effort even though we all tried. What pleased him one day wouldn't the next. As children, we thought, if we could just make him happy with us, then, all the fighting and problems between him and our mother would stop. We got used to things always being upset. It would be odd if too much time passed without something bad happening.

By the time I became a teenager, neither my heroes, nor my make-believe family had come to rescue me and the abuse continued. Even when things were quiet, the threat hovered, lurking, waiting to strike. The verbal abuse escalated and was bad enough by itself: "You stupid idiot, you will never be anything...I'll tell you what to do, you fuck...Did you hear me?...Do I have to kick the hell out of you?...You stupid shit...I'm going to make you sorry...You won't be able to sit down for a week...What did you say to me?...Wipe that smirk off your face or I'll knock it off." The words hurt as much as his fist or the sting of his belt, as much as blood spilling from broken skin. Once a beating stopped, I was safe for awhile. It was better to know it was over than to wonder when it was coming. There was a kind of relief induced from the throbbing pain left on my body from the belt buckle. After the beating, the rhythmic pulsation on the flesh soothed me to sleep.

Time and time again, I wanted to believe things would change and I could trust him, but it was foolish to dream. There were times when he showed remorse and I was hopeful for the future. The remorse was too soon lost and he reverted back into the beast. It was that dream though, that hope, that one day things would be better, which helped me not give up on life. Dreams of going away to college, getting a job and moving out of that house filled my days. Too many times it seemed that that moment would never come. There were times I thought I would never live to be an adult — none of us would ever make it out alive. I was in a hurry to grow up and escape. Growing older proved not enough, though. Thirty-something years later I realized I had dreamed a large part of my life away. And in the process, overlooked the love of Todd.

There were no family vacations to the beach or Disney Land and only an occasional trip to Grandmother's house in Alabama. And those always ended with a fast retreat to Georgia because of some family squabble. There was always a turkey and an unanswered prayer at Thanksgiving. At Christmas, there was a decorated tree surrounded by presents, but there was no celebration in our hearts. We went through our charade, but the holidays just made the realities of our lives much clearer. I spent hours sitting by the tree staring at the lights hoping for a miracle.

The holidays did command short periods of quiet in our house, and then the bottom fell out again. Peace in our house crumbed like burnt Christmas cookies. The pressure to act like a "normal family," was just too great. It was something I could bank on — holiday season after holiday season. Hope of the season was soon lost, things were back to what I understood as "normal" in my life.

My father got drunk and stayed away for several days, as was common. We were amazed how he kept his job. Every time he left I found myself hoping he would never come back. Deep inside knowing it would be the best thing for us — if he just disappeared from our lives, then perhaps Mother could find us a new father. It was a child's fantasy, and one not free of guilt. When he returned, the house filled with the old familiar smell of booze. Mother snuck around the house drinking, like it was a big secret, but she was only fooling herself. She hid the bottles in the bottom of her bedroom closet, and kept her glass in one of the kitchen cabinets spending inordinate amounts of time crisscrossing between the two. It's amazing the things one keeps in the closet for years and years of their life. It appears to be a popular hiding place for a lot of things. Father would cut her off, trying to control her drinking — more for himself, while he had no control of his own. They fought and then made-up, back on that roller coaster ride again. Sometimes Mother made Father's favorite meal of fried oysters, okra and corn bread, as they got drunk together. And then, to no one's surprise, the fighting started up again. The older I got, the more I tried to intervene. However, by doing so, I did or said something he didn't like — taking his belt or hand to me, the same was true for Stephen.

I always hoped the day would come when I wouldn't submit to the buckle of my father's belt. As it repeatedly sliced its way into my skin, I tried to think of that day. The more I cried, the harder the belt came against me and the deeper the buckle cut.

"If you continue to cry, I'll keep whipping you," my father would say.

As I grew older, the cries gradually withdrew. My face turned deep red, eyes welled up with tears, but never enough to be noticed by him. I gritted my teeth to trap the cries within my mouth, not allowing them to escape to my father's ears. With each blow I prayed it would be the last against my skin, but another one came and then another and another... I wanted to cry out for someone, cry out to God to make him stop. It took awhile for the bruises to heal, sometimes the old ones were barely gone before the next beating. My father's beatings became a lesson in not showing emotion.

I learned early on there was no point in running from this man. First attempts to flee were futile. Later, when I ran into the house and locked myself in the bedroom, he'd break down the door. There were hiding places under the beds, in the closets, or on the side of the house, but they only offered temporary sanctuary. Running from the house bought some time, but that was all it got me. If he didn't come after me, then he would be waiting until I returned. It was better to get it over with, to know it was over.

I spent the last few years of my father's life avoiding him as much as possible, staying out of his way. Spending time at the public library, or staying after school to help the teacher, anything, not to go home. Stephen slipped in and out of the house, coming home only when he could be sure Father was gone or asleep. The years of consumption of large quantities of alcohol had weakened him — age was catching up. And, he as well, spent more time away from us, no longer calling me to come and sit with him on the patio off the shed. So we left him sitting there drinking and smoking like he was the neighbor next door. The bruises on my mother's face and body gradually disappeared and seldom returned. Things began to quiet down for longer periods of time without eruptions, but there was always an air of mistrust in our house; it had been apparent to us from years past we couldn't trust him. The lapse of violence didn't make us feel secure.

By my junior year of high school, the brunt of the abuse had seemed to pass, and I had long left the intensity of those memories behind, or had thought so. My father and mother became strangers in the house — invisible to one another — hardly ever speaking. The yelling stopped, except for an occasional outburst, but I was old enough by then to stop it without fear of getting hit. And I think he knew if he tried anymore, I would pick up the closest thing to strike back. He either slept on the living room sofa or in the shed. Sandra spent time away as well, at girlfriends' houses, but sometimes was still coaxed away for a ride in the car. We continued to act around him as if we knew nothing abnormal had ever taken place. Even after the past beatings, I tried to act like the flesh of my body hadn't been torn and bruised. I don't think he ever realized how much I hated him. In his mind, for the most part, I'm sure he thought our life was normal. But the word "normal" has meanings that greatly depend on whose life you're living. As well, the years of excessive alcohol consumption attacked his mind. His fear of the realization of the madness, seemed to make him forget the abuse in those last years, as we had tried to forget. Toward the end of his life, we all became strangers, to ourselves, to each other and the past.

The summer before my senior year of high school, I had been thinking about college knowing we didn't have much money. I remember telling my father how I wanted to go to college and asked if it was possible. He told me not to worry.

"I'm a veteran, Randy. If anything happens to me, the Government will pay for your education...don't worry, you will go to college. You're a smart boy, you need to make something of yourself. Make something better than I have made of myself," surprisingly he said. Encouraging words like those were rarely spoken by him. In some tangled way, I believe he saw hope for himself in me. Months before his suicide he had become more reclusive, hardly ever coming into the house.

Just before the end, he disappeared on a drunk. Something told me this time, he wasn't coming back. A few nights later, Stephen called at my part-time job, where I was a short order cook, to tell me Wilson had come home. He had caused an auto accident, hitting a woman's car. Luckily, no one was badly injured. Two of Father's policemen buddies brought him back to the house. I couldn't find relief in the news he was back. I remember being very upset and afraid he had hit the mother of someone from school. Or, perhaps, more so afraid I would never be free of him. Either way, I was sure to be embarrassed the next day at school with kids talking behind my back. In my mind I could hear the other kids say, "Randy's drunkard father hit so and so... what kind of loser family are they?"

That night, he was sleeping on the living room sofa when I came home. The smell of alcohol met me at the back door. Father's inebriated snoring carried into every room. The next morning, he was still there. I couldn't see him from the kitchen where I was standing, preparing to leave for school. Stephen left the house early that morning. I was still angry fearing embarrassment later at school. As Sandra and I were getting ready to leave, he called to us to come in to see him. It was a pitiful call — undemanding like we had been used to. The voice I heard wasn't the voice of my father. Sandra went in to say good-bye and found him vomiting blood into a paper bag. I stayed frozen to that spot, not responding. I waited in the kitchen out of view a few minutes and then hollered at her, "Hurry up, we're going to be late for school!" My feelings were right when he left the last time, he wouldn't be coming back and I would never see him alive again. It was his last good-bye.

We learned that later that morning, my father called a taxi to take him to a sporting goods store. There he bought a rifle and shells. In his confusion and distress he forgot to sign the check, which the store didn't catch until the next day. They called Mother to honor the check, but she refused. I believe the gun was eventually returned to the store. Nonetheless, the taxi brought him home. He then must have gone to their bedroom, where we later found he had placed all his government papers and financial documents on his desk. He made a list of people to call and meticulously laid out his uniform and medals from his military service on the bed. After he had finished, he went back to the living room, laid down on the sofa and pulled the trigger. During this time period, Mother had been resting in Sandra's room. She thought the muffled shot coming from the other end of the house was the BB gun. She wondered what on earth he was doing with it in the house. Cautiously, she came to investigate and found him.

He was still alive when the ambulance arrived, choking on his blood. Even at his own hand, he was leaving this world in the same violent desperation as he had lived it. It wouldn't be the quick easy death he had planned for himself. The life in his body drained out on the way to the hospital. My father was pronounced "Dead on Arrival" at the Warner Robins Air Force Base Hospital. Perhaps he killed himself because it was the only way he could stop the abuse, stop his own demons once and for all. Part of him wanted to be a good father — the part that had cookies and ice cream waiting for us on the table when we came home from school. It was this part of him that pulled the trigger.

We were called out of school. When I came home, I saw what was left of my father: The deep indention in the sofa left by his body from sleeping there over years of estrangement from Mother, spilled blood from his body seeping into the sofa and the carpet and bits of tissue ripped from his head by the exploding bullet. His last violent act was inflicted on himself. I often wonder what was going on in his head the moment before he pulled the trigger. I'm sad when I think of what must have gone through his mind in the final seconds of life; those last moments must have been hell for him — not much different from the life he lived. Later that afternoon, someone from the funeral home had arrived to find me trying to clean up the blood before my mother and sister came home from the neighbors. "Cold water works best," he said. Stephen had taken off in his car, I wasn't sure where. Unaccompanied by emotion, I took a bucket and sponge and cleaned up the blood and tissue and flushed it down the toilet. It was Father's blood on my hands now instead of my own from his violence. I didn't cry until the funeral, then I wasn't sure why.

A single black limousine followed the black hearse along a state road into Columbus. Dried leaves fallen on the road crackled under the tires as the cars whistled over the black top. We had been the only cars on the road for the solemn hour and a half drive, which seemed to last for days. The trees outside changed shape as we sat silently dressed in dark clothes with little expression on our faces, never looking into each others' eyes. Mother's parents and her brother attended the small service held earlier in the chapel of the Mortuary in Warner Robins, where tears of relief rolled on my cheeks. But no relatives accompanied us to Columbus and my father's final resting place. Only a third of the pews were filled, some with friends of Mother's, but I couldn't remember ever seeing them before. A few of my father's drinking buddies attended, sitting in the back of the room, but no one from his twenty-plus years in the military came. I sat with my mother, Sandra, and the funeral director, and looked through the back window of the limo at Stephen's '57 Chevy following behind us. There was room in the limo for him, but he preferred to drive his symbol of freedom, fully protected from our father in its armor.

The cars drove through the gates of the military cemetery, passing by rows upon rows of white markers. Oak trees lined the road shading the moving car from the October sun. The car's shadow slipped over the grass and head stones, until it stopped near a tent-covered open grave. Stephen parked a few car lengths behind, keeping a safe distance as he had always done. The director told us to wait as two men in the hearse opened its rear door and removed my father's coffin covered in an American flag. Now, Father would be were he belonged, among others who fought in many of the same battles, many years since passed, in far off lands. And now, after his body was lowered into the cool Autumn ground our battle with him would be over. I heard my mother make a small whimper and then bury her face in her hands. She sobbed. Was she crying out of relief or grief? Relief that maybe the abuse was finally over, or for grief, that the man lying in the coffin was her husband — someone she had once loved a very long time ago? Was she reliving the abuse or the beginning moments of their meeting and crying for lost hope? Was she remembering the time she pulled out a photo of him from one of his first letters before they met? My grief was for her.

The director opened the car door and reached in for my mother's hand. She looked beautiful in this moment of grief; she had always been beautiful. Sandra exited the car next, followed by me. Stephen joined us and we followed the director to the grave where my father's coffin hovered. We sat in a row: Stephen, then Sandra, our mother, and then me. We sat among strangers: The minister, the funeral director and his assistants, a representative from the military and members of the Honor Guard. And the biggest stranger was lying in the coffin in front of us. As the minister stood over the coffin and spoke words of peace and God's understanding, I wondered where God's understanding was when my father was beating my mother and us. Where was God when I prayed to Him as a little boy? The minister's words filled the air as my mother and sister cried. Like bookends, Stephen and I sat soundless. I watched the minister as he talked until I no longer heard his words. His mouth still moved, but instead of his voice, I heard the crispness in the air and it seemed louder than anything that had ever entered my ears before — louder than the shrilling voices I had been so familiar with. The crispness of the moment screamed. As leaves from the trees fell around us, my eyes followed some of them to the ground. I closed my eyes and began to pray for the four of us and for my father until I did feel God around us, in the air, watching us sitting under the trees. And there was forgiveness in my heart. For a moment, in my mind I saw my father sitting in a lounge chair on the concrete patio by the shed.

Years later, after I had finished college, the Fire Department came and tore down the shed behind our house because it was a fire hazard. I remember standing in front of where it once stood, thinking to myself it's gone now, it's over. The weeds, and the vines from the trees had already started to regain possession over the plot of empty ground where the shed once stood.

It was almost as if the secrets had never happened. The beatings were just a faint throbbing on my soul and the violations made to my young body were someone else's nightmares. For a moment, the shed had never stood; the misery had never taken place. I had done a good job of blocking these experiences from my conscience. My efforts were in vain. Little did I realize the consequences to be paid in the future for trying to forget and little did I know the blind path I would soon walk. At least for now, as I stood on the dirt which once made witness to the deeds, he had left this place, and there was no longer earth and grass, beer and whiskey in the air.

stephen

When Todd and I first met, he made his attraction obvious. In many ways, we came out together; Todd took much easier to the life than I. We were never lovers, though perhaps we should have been. Instead we became friends. That was of my doing. The friendship lasted from the day we met up until now. As I held on to Todd's hand, a nurse walked back into the room. Her white shoes squeaked on the floor as she leaned over Todd's head to check the IV. Somewhere a phone rang. In the time span of our relationship, I met a lot of men I thought were right for me. Those men didn't stay very long in my life, but Todd did.

Before our first meeting, I would see him out with his friends around town. He loved to dance, and boy, could he move on the dance floor. If there is a talent to that, then Todd had it. As the music surrounded him, he took it into his being, expressing his inner self. I think you can tell things about a person by the way they dance. It shows how they interpret their surroundings, how they feel on the inside. Todd did that, showing his style and personality. As he danced, he showed his excitement for life.

He was short in stature, but his attitude and broad smile, sparkling eyes and thick, long brown hair, made him bigger than life. If you knew him, you would call his personality bubbly. Todd was always fashionably dressed, often times in a tweed blazer and tie. Todd looked good in tweed. Before we met, I stood back in the crowd, like I always did, and watched him. Everyone was his friend and I wanted to be his friend, too.

There was no mistake that Todd would make a great partner for someone. He was a very giving and sensitive person; our friendship proved this to me. Once in awhile over the years, Todd brought up the idea I missed out on a good thing with him, and we always laughed it off. Now, he was implying the thought again in the hospital. But I had always preferred to look at him like a brother. In some way, trying to replace the real brother I had lost in the turmoil of growing up. Finding a connection I had lost with my own brother.

There is a connection linking all of us, bridging us to one another, holding us together in an invisible bond. Like endless miles of invisible string tied around our hearts, connecting us to our beginnings. So, no matter how far we wander, the cord is always there. Wherever we are, we remain tied. I was trying to regain that connection I had lost with Stephen through Todd.

For two brothers to have been spawned from the loins of one father and have shared the same womb and suckled the same sweet breast milk of a loving mother, no two brothers could be more different. From the beginning, our paths were in opposing directions. We were more strangers than brothers, more foes than friends. Somewhere early on, our link was severed. One was tougher while the other more sensitive. One had the force of the lion, the other the softness of the lamb. One became the hunter and the other the prey.

I don't know if poison can taint lives from the womb. A poison not unlike the one that was raging inside of Todd's body. Was our mother infected by the semen of our father, or by the events which took place after the conception? On a grander scale, I truly believe it was from a series of events carried from semen to semen and from womb to womb of many generations. Perhaps the lives of children are sculpted long before biological conception takes place. The course of two brothers was laid out before we ever entered this world.

Whistles echoed off the gymnasium walls as the coach

called the boys to gather along the white line of the basketball court. As the two team captains began their selection from the group of boys before them — one by one — the line became smaller and smaller. The more athletic boys were always picked first, leaving the less talented and usually frailer ones embarrassed and toeing an imaginary spot on the ground.

I stood there among the other junior high boys, looking up at the steel beams supporting the roof of the gym, listening for who would be the next one picked. Anticipating who would be spared further humiliation as the captains mulled over their decisions in forming their winning teams. We, those left standing on the white line, were the weak, the ones a world apart from those more sturdy in sports standing across from us. We were the ones who couldn't perform a single chin-up; barely able to keep up in calisthenics, struggling to perform the required number of push-ups. We were the ones who lagged behind during the first half lap of running the football field with two and a half laps to go, finishing what seemed like days after the rest. Gasping for air, we huffed and puffed our way over the finish line, not with applause from the others because we'd finished, but with ridicule that we were last. I wondered how it felt to be one of them looking at us, the less superior ones, the ones not as well coordinated, with smaller builds, the ones they sometimes referred to as "girls." And I was more of a "girl" than any of those left, except for maybe Kenneth Hanes; we would be the last ones picked. That was a given.

A pigeon had become trapped inside the building unnoticed by the activity below. Birds habitually flew in through the double doors, often propped open to allow air to circulate throughout the gym. Its wings beat together as it frantically darted from beam to beam, desperately confused and trapped, looking for a way out, looking for its freedom. Loose feathers, lost to the struggle, floated to the gym floor. It was a foreign place for both of us, and one I immensely dreaded when the third period bell rang at precisely eleven a.m. I grew smaller as the team captains' voices echoed in the vastness of the gymnasium, calling out the names, their arms pointing at other boys as the line grew shorter and shorter. My eyes turned from the pigeon to watch the second hand on the large wall clock across the gym slowly move. With each tick my agony grew more fierce. If only I could make the hands move faster, put everything in fast motion and fast forward myself into fourth period. I understood the pigeon's desperation, as I looked at the clock and somehow could relate to its need for freedom. I wanted to call up to the pigeon to follow me as I ran to the large doors leading out of the gym. I would push the doors open and the pigeon would fly free and I would fly free with it.

Only forty-five minutes left until fourth period, I thought, as I looked at the clock and then back at the pigeon. We would play for thirty. Most likely, I would stand on the side lines along with Kenneth and a few others, unless the coach made the team captain put us in the game. Ten minutes to shower and get dressed back into our school clothes and I would be free from the mortification, at least for another day. I pulled at the Phys Ed uniform that never quite fit my body as nicely as my more athletic adversaries. I looked more like a thirteen year old girl just in the beginning stages of puberty developing breasts. I had a better chance of getting a date with one of the team captains, than getting picked to be on their team. It was easy for the captains to make the first selections, but they had to give more thought to those who remained. The selection was now a joke to them. Neither captain wanted any of the few boys left standing on their team. The concern now wasn't who could play the game well, those had already been picked, but who would screw up the least.

Then the joking really began with a lot of snickering and pokes to the ribs from the boys already chosen. All for our benefit, the ones left on the line of shame. It was an embarrassing situation to be one of the few left standing on the white line made worse still by my older brother being one of the team captains. If he didn't want me, then the other surely wouldn't call my name. Though we had the same color of brown hair, that was our only resemblance. We didn't even look like brothers, his eyes were brown like Mother's, mine were green. No one in our family had green eyes, Sandra's were blue like Father's. Stephen's nose was broad with a scar across it from daredeviling on his bike when he was five years old. He had another on his right leg just below the knee, long and deep where he had fallen out of the magnolia tree. If it had been me, I would have cried, but Stephen never cried. I can't remember him ever crying. From cheek to cheek, a wide sweep of red and brown freckles ran across his round face. One of Stephen's middle teeth had a big chip, but that was how he was, a roughhouser and the scars, scrapes and chips were just a part of the package.

Mother used to dress us up like cowboys with matching red vests and chaps with white fringe. Sandra had a red cowgirl skirt and we all sported black boots and red hats. The three of us were the posse riding off into the sunset in front of the house on our bikes, our pretend trusty steeds. Sandra and I still had training wheels, but Stephen didn't need them. Being the older of the three, he naturally was the leader until we stopped playing together. One day, I can't really remember when, we just all stopped.

Stephen was big for his age, towering over the other boys in gym. Even in elementary school, his square, stocky size made him a natural at football. The line was now down to two boys, Kenneth and myself. All the tough guys made fun of Kenneth, much more so than of me. Other boys joined in the ribbing to feel like a part of the group. It made them feel better about themselves or possibly it just took the focus off of them. But no one came to Kenneth's rescue. Others, like myself, stood by quietly wanting to tell the bullies to stop, but too afraid to speak up. Speaking up would provide invitation for the hot flame of humiliation to be refocused. Tall and skinny, with black hair, he was about the most feminine looking guy in school. Kenneth just joked it off as he dodged the wadded paper balls and school debris thrown at him daily as he walked between classes. No one knew or cared what a nice guy he really was. They were too busy making fun of him, building up their own egos, turning themselves into men. I feared that brief time between classes in the school hallways. I kept my head down, my body curved inward and my eyes to the floor. Paranoia at being called names or being shoved or laughed at because somehow you were perceived as different. I hurried like a frightened rabbit to find safety in the classroom.

The football captain and several teammates would threaten to hold Kenneth down and empty a bottle of Nair hair removal into his gym shorts. It was routine for them to call him names in the shower, forever shaking their penises in Kenneth's face. I didn't want to be in Kenneth's shoes. I wanted to make them stop, but I knew they would only make more fun of me. I just stood off in the corner of the shower hoping they would stop, and always hoping I would go unnoticed; wondering where the coach was and why he didn't intervene. He knew what went on, but he treated it like the joking was some rite to manhood and it would turn us all into men.

But a shower was required after Phys Ed class. The coach always said, "No shower, no passing grade." So, if a boy could take the humiliation of the showers, the joking, the penises, the bullies, the shoving and even the threat of Nair in your pants, then at least there was an "A" rewarded in return. Some education that Phys Ed. One of the most attractive things about the college I later attended was that Phys Ed was an elective. Two years of sports were required in high school. This prompted me to take it my freshmen and sophomore years in order to get it out of the way, preferably during the last period to avoid those showers. A physical ailment or handicap would get you pardoned; how I used to pray for one. I became the artful dodger, darting from my gym locker to the showers and back, barely getting wet. As I had done so much of my existence, I imagined myself invisible to the other guys and hoped they would show mercy on me. It shamed me for them to see my nudity, as if by seeing, they would somehow know my secrets. I didn't want them to see the marks left on my body; current ones, as well as those already healed, where the emotional torment left by them were as visible to me as the marks freshly made. At all cost, the truth had to be kept secret, my body clothed, and my family protected.

Beginning of each new school year, I sat in the classroom in a heavy outer coat. That coat kept me warm from the chilly mornings that introduced Fall, but by noon, the heat of the day moved in as is unfailing with southern weather, quickly suffocating the coolness. Too self-conscious of my body, I kept the coat on all day. Sweat ran down my face. I felt the pools collect under my armpits as streams rolled against my skin. Still, I wouldn't remove the coat. My father's comments about my body had taken root: "Your ass is like a woman's," he had said many times, instructing my mother to find a winter coat long enough to cover my derriere.

The team captain's procrastination only encouraged the joking from the others. Kenneth and I stood there each taking the humiliation, in our own way. I looked for the pigeon. Unable to see it, I listened for the sound of its wings flapping over the laughter, hoping it had flown free. Finally the coach stepped in to assume his authority: "Randy, you play on Stephen's team ...and Kenneth you on..."

The joking quickly ended and the teams took their places on the court. Kenneth and I stood together again on the side lines, relieved, for the time being.

I wasn't an adequate athlete by any standard, but after all it was just a game. One had to have some measure of confidence in oneself just to get out there with the other boys. But to be rejected by your own brother was a hard ball to swallow. I felt as though Stephen didn't want to have anything to do with me, that I was a constant embarrassment to him. Perhaps he saw the same things in me that my father did all those years; my father's opinions of me became Stephen's. I wasn't as tough as they. In their eyes, I was better suited to play dolls with my younger sister behind a closed door than to try and master a basketball on the court or learn how to throw a football. It must have been a hard thing for Stephen to realize his little brother was a sissy. He must have feared I would be a reflection on himself and his manhood, as I believe my father viewed me.

One might reason the hell we lived in together would have brought us closer for survival's sake. That we would join in an alliance against the foe, our father, but that wasn't the case. We ran in opposite directions as fast as we could, stretching the cord as far as possible. To be close to one another meant having the constant reminder of what was happening at home. Every time we looked at one another there was an instant connection to the alcohol, to the pain and to the torture of living imprisoned by the bottle. Subconsciously, we stayed away from each other avoiding the painful reminders of where we came from. As with Kenneth Hanes, we stood silent, afraid to speak, afraid we would have to suffer more. As with the joking, we hoped the abuse would be over sooner if we were quiet and let Father have his way.

Many times I wondered why my brother never protected me from my father. I wanted to run to Stephen and hide behind him, shielding me. He could lash back at our father. He was bigger and stronger. And the older Stephen got, the less he stood for the beatings; he fought back, but he was too busy fighting for his own life in the hell we lived. I can't blame him now for not always protecting me, for not being the brother I wanted him to be. It was every man for himself in our house of hell. He was unable to save me.

Stephen left me behind as he absorbed himself in sports, in cars and his friends. His friends became more important to him than his little brother, or at least I saw it that way. As he grew stronger and bigger, he stayed away. He became just another big kid at school, as I watched him from across the cafeteria at lunch time never glancing in my direction. The battle between Stephen and my father was a personal one. My father believed in divide and conquer; perhaps an old military tactic. Of course, my mother, Sandra and myself all had separate battles with my father under the same roof. Stephen was the one who fought back the hardest, he was the one who had a better chance of bringing our father down. By age ten, he had reached the point where he had been hit enough. Stephen would kick at our father as the belt whipped against his legs. His screams were cries of rebellion, of fairness and decency, for we were living under the rule of a dictator. Learning early how to be a warrior, at age fifteen, Stephen pulled the broom handle from our father's hands and turned it on him, hitting him as hard as he had been hit. For a few seconds our father cowered as Stephen struck the handle against his back. Undetected, I watched them from the jalousie windows of the kitchen, rooting for Stephen, hoping he would defeat the dictator. They went at it like Medieval warriors with fire and hate in their eyes, voices screaming, spit flying from their mouths, like hungry dogs after the same bone. Surely Stephen would win, would beat our father to the ground to make up for all the years of fear and sadness he had placed in our hearts, and for all the pain he had inflected on our flesh. They pulled and tugged at the bone until Stephen finally threw it aside and ran down the driveway toward the street, almost tripping as he fled. The hate in his eyes had turned to fear as Stephen came to the realization that there would be no victors in this battle. Our father, his shirt torn and dirtied, stood and watched Stephen run until he was out of sight. Then he retreated to the shed, picking up the bone as he went. Stephen became more of a stranger to the house after that battle.

I wanted to be more like Stephen — strong willed — not so afraid. He must have been terrified of Father at times, and possibly, there were times he feared for his life, but he wouldn't let the enemy see that fear. He had the blood of a rebel in him. Fighting his way out of the madness of childhood, he was often not afraid to strike back when he thought he had a chance of winning. Maybe that is where he lost some respect for me. I wasn't a fighter and I wouldn't stand my ground; always the first to cry in battle.

Fighting was a natural thing in our household. We learned it very early from the physical wars waged between our parents. My father destroyed our mother's life, all our lives and beat us down, blow by blow. As children, our little bodies and minds absorbed this reality. Like a huge sponge sucking up the hate, anger, fear and misery, we gradually learned to repeat the cycle our parents repeated from their youth. They unknowingly passed on their wretched legacy to another generation.

Siblings are known to fight, it's a part of growing up, but there was too much anger and hate in the blows we inflicted on one another. Stephen always won; there was no contest. I reminded him of his own fear of our father and of the weakness fear brings to one's mind and soul. I know now Stephen was taking out his frustrations of our father on me when we waged battle. In an impossible childhood, we were playing the games our parents played. But those games couldn't be easily put away in the toy box. Like a familiar riddle from a popular children's game, repeated years later from memory, the riddles we sang weren't as easily forgotten and not remembered out of fondness and joy. The words to the riddles were too freshly printed in our souls, cut too deeply in our flesh and sung too often. Our riddles were cries and screams in the night. Stephen had to strike back at someone and I was always available. I didn't hit as hard and as long as our father. It was miserable catching hell from both of them — it destroyed my confidence. I wasn't strong enough to let it go at such a young age. I desperately wanted my brother's love and protection.

I did look up to him. Stephen wore his red letters, "WRH" for Warner Robins High, proudly on a thick white sweater. He played all the sports: Football, baseball, and basketball, and of course was good at them. Terrible at sports, I could never hit, catch or throw any ball. Athletics were the only thing in life of which he could be proud. Wearing that sweater was a symbol of honor, freedom, and accomplishment. A lettermen sweater made of invisible armor to keep the sad, hateful forces of home life at bay. For Stephen was a different person when he wore it, different from the one constantly fighting our father. And when he wasn't wearing it, I would sometimes sneak into his dresser and try on his suit of armor. It smelled like Stephen, the rich, almost sweet odor I associated with a boy becoming a man. My body filled with excitement as the combination of the whiteness of the sweater and the smell of Stephen surrounded me. Stephen was becoming a man more each day. Our father's violence pushed him into early manhood. Looking in the mirror, I hoped to see Stephen in my reflection, wanting to be just like my big brother. Why was I unable to escape like Stephen? Stephen was popular, liked by everyone all through school. He was the class clown as well as the football jock. If ever I was acknowledged, rare as that was, it was as "Stephen's little brother." I know he was affected by our life, but Stephen somehow managed to push forward, trying to break the cord tying us to our father.

I often did his homework or let him copy mine when we were in the same class. Stephen had dropped back several years in school. As well, I let some of his friends on the football team copy my work, hoping they would like me better so I could feel a part of things. I wanted them to need me, to think I was important and stop making fun of me. Stephen stopped studying and began to stay away from home more, only coming to the house to change clothes or to eat and sleep. The violence between Father and my brother intensified as Stephen grew older. It was easier to stay away than to wage war.

I had turned completely inward during my high school years. On the outside, I continued to act out a "normal" life, wanting what I thought the other kids had. Today, I realize of course there were others who had similar misery in their own homes, but at the time I thought we were the only ones. We were the "redneck" family everyone made fun of. My brother, sister and I were the poor little "white trash" kids who belonged to the town drunk that beat his wife every Saturday night after coming home from the bar. This was the picture of my family I tried hard to cover up. We were dirt. On the outside, I was funny, so as not to let the sadness of my inner self out for everyone to see. But each yearbook picture shows a boy living a lie. The empty expression in the eyes told the sad truth. I so wanted to be popular and fit in like Stephen, but I couldn't overcome the insecurities which had become the very part of how I saw myself, also caught by the camera. I couldn't wash the dirt off my skin, I wasn't able to remove the shame. I walked the halls of Warner Robins High School, glancing sideways at the popular kids with my head down. There was no point in joining any of the student clubs or campaigning for student government. Those kids were clearly "better" than I. My picture would never be in the "Who's Who" section of the annual with broad smiles and heads held high. I would never be Most Liked, Best Dressed, or Most Likely to be Anything. As a result, I killed the boy named Randy and someone else took his place, but even the replacement wasn't good enough.

Stephen dated lots of girls. They sent him notes in class, met him between periods, cheered for him at his games, and called him at home when he was there. I wasn't sure how I felt about girls. Guys were referring to me as a "girl," as my father had. I wanted to like girls, but none of them seemed to notice me, at least not the ones I noticed. I had already found Stephen's stash of sex magazines in the bottom drawer of his dresser. When no one was home, I would lock myself in the bathroom and look at still shots of men and women having intercourse before I even knew what intercourse was. Looking at the pictures excited me, but I was uncomfortable with the excitement, many times sickened by it. The thought of sex made me feel ashamed and dirty, loathing my existence. But I still hid in the bathroom from time to time to look at the pictures. I started masturbating as I looked at them with intense guilt, racked with remorse; revisited by remote images of repressed associations. I continued to look at the pictures until the sweet, sick feeling in my belly began to hurt and the feeling turned to fear.

My first year in high school, I developed a crush on Mary Ann, a military kid like myself. She had long blond hair and blue eyes. Mary Ann was quiet, like me, so we talked and studied together. Soon I was walking her home from school. After weeks of escorting Mary Ann home, I wanted to ask her to "go steady." One weekend when the carnival came to town we went together. I bought a cheap bracelet with my initials for her and brought it to school on a Monday. I was planning to pop the big high school question before first period. Unable to muster up the nerve, I put it off to the next period. Then until lunch and then until after school. Each day that week I tried to ask her but failed to gather up the courage. By Friday, I had failed miserably in asking the question, "Will you be my girl?" That afternoon, as usual, I walked Many Ann home. I had to ask her before we got to her house, I told myself over and over in my head. Just get it out, just ask her! But, like each day the week before, I was too afraid, too unsure of myself. Finally, just before arriving at her house, I cowardly slipped the bracelet in her coat pocket without her noticing. On the following Monday, Mary Ann showed up at school wearing the bracelet. I had a million questions to ask my brother about having a girlfriend, but by then he was less and less around. Mary Ann moved away soon after with her family, her father getting transferred. We kept in touch by writing for the rest of the school year and then that slipped away.

There are a few good memories of my brother I have cherished over the years: The time I was fooling around with the '57 Chevy Stephen had been working on behind our house. It was blue with a white top and mag wheels. The engine cranked up loudly as Stephen turned the key in the ignition and wheeled the car out of the driveway leaving black tire marks in the street. He had told me never to fool with his car. Trying to impress a girl in our neighborhood, I ignored his warning. Within seconds of starting the car, there was a small explosion and it caught fire. Dousing the fire with baking soda, I hoped he would never know. And if he did, I knew I would have to hide from him for a week. He found out later that day what I had done, the burnt out engine and the white power giving me away. But he never hit me. We had both been hit enough.

When I was fifteen, Stephen tried to show me how to drive his car, a stick shift. I had no coordination with my feet. I kept stripping the gears, but he was unduly patient with me as I drove the car late one night. He was concerned and attentive, qualities not often experienced under our roof, except by our mother when she could grab a ray of hope and hold onto it for awhile. How important Stephen's car was to him! And what a feat it was for him not to get upset with me. He worked on that car all the time; it was his escape and he saw it as his freedom from our father. Like the lettermen sweater, it was a symbol of emancipation. Stephen could drive away from all the pain inflicted by our father, at least for awhile he could ride free. I felt very close with him sitting next to me in the car. He was spending time with me, taking an interest, and for a little while, he was acting like a brother. And, for a few moments we had freed ourselves from our father.

The brief memories of an older brother reaching out to the younger in some gesture of love and brotherhood have always given me hope. When they happened, they served as relief from the emptiness, a warm gust of air to ease the coldness lingering inside of me. In a way, it teased a desire for more, sending me out in search of someone who could be there for me.

Stephen's inability to spend time with me and take me under his wing far outnumbered the times he did. But, that wasn't his job. Neither he nor I, understood my need for his guidance to overshadow the evils of our father. Instead, he was a big brother who, for whatever reasons, chose not to pick me to play on his team in Phys Ed class, chose to make fun of me in public, to humiliate me in front of other boys. Brothers do those kind of things, but there were more punches to my stomach than pats on my back, more rejection than acceptance, more distance than closeness. Like the time we were playing volleyball: I missed the ball several times, he walked over to me on the court yelling and punched me in the chest while calling me a sissy along with a few other "choice names." And there were similar times as well, where a little brother saw the face of anger on his big brother's body, the face of his father, and the feeling of helplessness overwhelmed his confused world. He struck me with the anger of our father and I took it with the same emptiness, as if my father had been hitting me, removing myself from the experience as I had done so many times before. The cord between us had been pulled so thin that it nearly broke.

Before we knew it, our childhood passed without much bonding. We became too different, but we had always been. Differences we had at birth were accelerated through our boyhoods. The years passed quickly as we rushed to grow up and get away. The sooner we grew, the less chance, as in the wild of some species, of the father eating the young. As we passed in the halls at school, we only became reminders of what was waiting at home. We lived within the same walls, rarely conscious of what was happening in each other's worlds taking place under one roof. Before we knew it, we were adults and went our detached ways. In reality, the split came long before maturing into our own manhoods.

The picture I have of my older brother is of freckles on the face of a young boy. Recollections locked away behind the door of my childhood along with the memories of my father. We shared many things: The same bedroom, the same dining table, and the same school. We felt the same sting from the brutal belt of the same father. We felt the same fear. In reality, though, we might as well have come from two different families. For fear of our father separated us, made us enemies in the struggle to survive.

The sad truth is that there weren't many pleasant memories, only nightmares. I'm haunted by mine, and I'm sure, he is still haunted by his. I grieve for the memories that might have been, if only things had been different in our house and under our roof. I wish the few good moments hadn't been overshadowed by the smell of booze on the breath of our father and the bruises on our flesh.

Stephen dropped out of high school but later went back and earned his diploma. He built a career and made a success of himself. He married and has fathered three children. He survived the beatings. Yet, I'll always remember my father chasing him around the back yard repeatedly hitting Stephen on the back with a broom handle. Somehow he went on to find himself and build a better life. Although I have not had a great deal of contact with Stephen and his family, from what I can sense, he is a fine father to his children. He learned what not to do from Father's example. Stephen learned from the nightmares and went forward, and I hope, ended the legacy of our father.

He filled the void left by our past with his career and family. Whereas I tried to fill the gap by looking for someone to replace the males in my life. We were separated by the touch of our father. Stephen had the luck of being older. In some ways, spared by the virtue of not being the gentle prey my father needed. He wouldn't have been silent as I had been. I have seen the face of both my father and brother in many of the men I have been with. I searched them out.

The connection runs as fluid as the water which flows over the earth, sometimes smooth like still water and others like the rapids, tearing roughshod at our souls, but always flowing like the very blood running through our veins. It is a pattern of life, a parallel to the very creation of man being duplicated over and over again. Every time a child is born, the connection continues, the thread is lengthened. It is the brotherhood of man.

mr. jones

I had suspected Todd was sick a few years earlier. Something in his eyes. I could sense it. He looked thin and tired, saying he'd just been working too hard, but I could tell his eyes had lost their sparkle. In order to respect his privacy, I didn't ask any questions. I knew he would tell me when he was ready. I just didn't want him to wait too long. I wanted to be there for him if he needed me.

Todd was a rare individual, a beautiful wild flower growing in a field of daisies. Born with a tremendous talent and the desire to do wonderful things, he possessed great passion for life and lived to see beauty in all things around him. Todd was a skilled artisan, owner of a company specializing in creating faux finishes. He created wonderful murals of bygone periods and restored furniture to an immaculate condition and beauty. I have never seen anyone do more with a can of paint than Todd. There was an innocence to the subjects he painted; an innocence I had lost long ago.

I stepped out of Todd's hospital room to make space for two friends stopping in to visit. Walking out the double doors of the Intensive Care Unit, I got a drink of water from the fountain. The sun rushed through the large windows of the waiting room, where other visitors were gathered, awaiting their turn. I leaned against the glass, looking down the three stories at a young guy cutting the grass in the courtyard below. It was Springtime, the time of passion. New life abounds after the long, cold sleep of winter. A young bud pushes up through the chilled earth, reaching toward the warmth of the beckoning sun. It is a miracle, a time of hope and renewal. And a time to make the dreams of our winter's sleep come true. The days are again growing longer and the sun's light becomes brighter as spring unfolds. It's life blossoming before us. As this new life begins around us, another one fades from sight. His passion slipping away and his dreams losing out to the harsh realities of the times. He is fighting for his life and the battle appears to be lost.

Before there was an illness; before there was a word that could mean death to gay men and especially young ones; before they were aware, there was something out there invisible to the eye that could and would destroy many of them if they ventured out to find intimacy, connection, joy, ecstasy and love; before they knew how to protect themselves, and before anyone ever read or heard the word AIDS, there was a wonderful life called Todd.

His was an innocent search, journeyed by most, whether male or female, heterosexual or homosexual, to fulfill the need for companionship. It was a human exploration, mirrored in nature that has been ventured from the beginning of man. Regardless of sexuality, companionship is something that shouldn't be denied anyone, but there was one thing that would change the life of a splendid young man, as it did thousands upon thousands more.

The various discussions in the waiting area concerning sick friends and family members faded as I continued to watch the landscaper work. A boy accompanied by his mother walked down the sidewalk leading from the building to the parking lot just out of view from the window. The little boy pointed in excitement to the lawn mower, saying something to his mother as she pulled him along by the hand. And again, I tried to remember the little boy that I once was; innocent like the spring air, innocent like that little boy on the sidewalk.

The world is made up of those who protect the innocent

and of those who take it away. There are people who shelter the sweetness of youth from the harsh realities living among us and people who take it for themselves. Why these thieves take without regard for the innocent I do not know. But, when they go, they leave nothing behind except pain and despair. After they are done, there is little innocence left. In their cunning, they drain from the well of all things trustful and pure, and when they have sucked it dry, they move on to victimize again with no remorse. Hopefully there are far more protectors.

If you're of the innocent, there is rarely a place to run for help. You're alone and you wonder what you have done to bring this upon yourself. Is it your fault? Do you deserve for this to happen to you? And if you tell, will they blame you? The shame you feel will then be written on your forehead for everyone to read, and all of those who see it will tell others. So, you begin to believe this is the way things are in life. You take the blame upon yourself and cradle it in your soul. You spend your time trying to figure out how to change so it will not happen again. You walk cautiously through life, quietly on its perimeter, so as not to disturb the past again. You walk in confusion and in silence.

I couldn't run to my father; he was one of them. He was the enemy. Although, at the time, I didn't understand nor perceive him as a taker, I just somehow knew there was no one to turn to, and if there were, he wouldn't be the one. I had to be silent again and make some sense of things. But there was no sense to be made by a little boy out of what was happening to his innocence. Unable to trust, like a lamb in a pack of wolves I cautiously made my way to the outside where I could see them coming.

The Jones' lawn was one of the biggest in the neighborhood. Mr. Jones was extremely friendly and I remember Mrs. Jones as a very sweet, extremely overweight woman. A little older than my parents, they seemed nice enough. She had been struggling with diabetes for many years. Mrs. Jones moved slowly and clumsily through the house, her weight impeding. The large print dresses she wore fitting loosely on her accentuated her size. Her terry cloth slippers revealed the swollen ankles below her varicosed legs that were usually swollen as well. She often sat, instructing Mr. Jones to bring things to her, to keep from having to struggle up from the table or chair from where she may have been sitting. So motherly, she always invited me in for juice and cookies before, and usually after, cutting the lawn. Mr. Jones was considerably smaller in girth than his wife. He always dressed in dark colored pants and white shirts that pulled at the buttons around his round belly. A jovial man with graying hair at the temples and thin on top of his head. I remember him as "touchy" with his hands, the many occasions he patted my chest or rested his hands on my small shoulders as I sat with Mrs. Jones eating my treats. His light eyes darted as he flashed a warm smile. I quickly became comfortable with them. Their house was quiet and warm, not like my own a few blocks down the street. One of the nicest in the neighborhood — always painted — the yard was well kept, thanks to me. Two nice cars parked in the driveway, always washed and shiny. A big welcome mat at the front door. The house was warm and had a complete feeling. Unlike our home, there was a sense of order, every piece of furniture, every knickknack seemed to belong, as if they were made for it. And the house was clean and smelled like roses. Going to the Jones' house was like going to visit June and Ward Cleaver, except Mrs. Jones didn't look anything like Mrs. Cleaver. I came to enjoy being around them and fantasized they were actually my grandparents. Fantasy played an important part of my young life; everyone had a better life than mine. Oh, if I could only change places with another boy my age, what a life I would have. But, even I knew if it was possible to exchange my life with another, someone still had to live the life I was living and that wouldn't be a life I would wish on anyone.

Stephen had been cutting lawns in our neighborhood since he was eleven. When he took a regular part-time job three years later, my father thought I should step in to fill his shoes. Not particularly happy with the idea, but like everything else, I obeyed my father's wishes. Depending on the size of the yard, my pay was between five and ten dollars. Being small for my age, I wasn't especially well suited for the job. The lawn mower was old and hard to crank at times. It had made the rounds before Stephen inherited it, and was now, nearing retirement. But I cut four to five lawns a week, plus whatever other yard work the owners requested. Summer had kicked in early with an intense south Georgia heat, making the job sticky and miserable. The yards seemed to go on forever. After my first week of cutting and raking, pruning and dragging limbs and other chores, I became sick of the smell of grass. My father thought this through and decided it would help make a man out of me, as if the sweat, dirt and nausea went "hand in hand" with manhood.

Toward the end of that first spring of cutting grass, I was reluctantly coming to accept my state of self employment. Of course, there was really no choice in the matter. I knew if I quit, Father wouldn't be happy with me; keeping everyone happy was my unacknowledged job. That was decided for me early on in life, along with acting as the little peace keeper.

In one way it was good — it kept me out of the house and away from my father's rage. But getting dirty — really sweaty and grimy was the downside. Unlike many boys, I hated dirt. I never made mud pies or ran through puddles, always avoiding things that made me feel soiled. For a little boy the money seemed good, and each day I started out clean, my hair combed and my clothes freshly washed, except for those old worn-out pair of tennis shoes; I took pride in my appearance. It had a lot to do with feeling so worthless — the natural result of my home life. A bath and clean clothes always seemed to make everything better. Washing and scrubbing away the filth and covering myself with something clean gave temporary relief.

And I saved every dollar, except for what was needed to

pay for gas and oil for the mower. At the end of the day, I allowed myself the ten cents for a ginger ale from a vending machine outside a "mom and pop" store in our neighborhood. It was a small reward, giving me comfort as I shook grass cuttings and bugs from my clothes and hair on my return trip home. The mower jiggled and rattled as I pushed it up the street past lawns I had cut earlier and others waiting to be cut tomorrow. In my head I added up the day's receipts as I pushed the mower along. Money was my ticket out. And, if Father went off and never came back, we'd need all my money to get by. I would take care of things. We could get by without him, we'd been doing it for a long time anyway.

As June rolled around, the old lawn mower had cut its last lawn — a good enough excuse for me to stop. But my father decided to buy a new one so I could continue my entrepreneurship. The new mower was self-propelled, making the job a little easier. After its introduction, I spent many afternoons cutting the Jones' lawn. Mr. Jones was one of my customers who had me do a lot of other work around the yard and house. Retired and with a history of back ailments, there was little he could do. A six-foot tall hedge running the length of their backyard was a dragon to be slain. Taking up most of a day to trim its sharp teeth, requiring me to climb up and down a ladder to tame the green monster and make him obedient. Every time I trimmed it, I fell into the jaws of the hedge, cutting up my hands and legs on the thick, rough branches that formed its skeleton. Each time, I swore to myself would be the last at slaying the dragon or I had to charge double.

One morning while cutting their lawn, I noticed Mr. Jones watching me from a window in the house. Before quickly turning to see him standing there, I could feel his eyes on me. At first, I didn't think much of it. Maybe he was just making sure I was doing a good job. As the summer progressed, his gaze grew more intense. I began to feel uneasy, sometimes he stood in the window in white boxers and a t-shirt stroking his privates. His watching spooked me. Instinct told me there was something not quite right but I ignored its warning. I continued to come to their house. Up to that point, they had been so nice to me.

Later in August, I was helping Mrs. Jones with some cleaning in the house, moving furniture and putting away things in the attic. Mr. Jones was away that morning but arrived soon after we had finished. I was sitting at the kitchen table eating a very large piece of cake when he came in. Mr. Jones had just bought a new gun and inquired if I wanted to go for a ride. He would show me how to shoot it.

Sitting quietly in the car, Mr. Jones drove the blue Buick out of town and turned onto a country road. After driving a short distance, he then pulled over to the side, the car's wheels cut into the gravel.

"Do you want to drive the car?" he asked.

"Don't know how," I cautiously responded. "Can you teach me?"

"Of course I can, it's easy," Mr. Jones answered, with the encouragement of a grandfather.

I could hardly contain my excitement — my first chance to get behind the wheel of a car. He exited the car as I slid over in anticipation behind the large steering wheel. After some basic driving instructions, he moved the seat all the way forward; although, I still had to strain for my right foot to reach the pedals. My head peeked over the wheel. Scared, but not enough to stop, I was actually driving a car for the first time. Slowly, I pulled the car back on the stretch of deserted road, unintentionally wheeling the tires in the gravel and dirt. Eyes forward, heart rapidly pumping, my sweaty hands gripped the big black steering wheel. I watched the white dividing line, but had trouble keeping the big car between it and the edge of the road. Mr. Jones grabbed the wheel to help steer, all the while instructing me to look down the middle of the road and not concentrate on the line. The car weaved along as it made a succession of spurts, lunging forward and quickly stopping briefly as I badly maneuvered my foot between the brake and gas pedals. Concentrating as hard as I could, I tried again to control the car. This was a big step for me. If I could drive, it meant I was growing up, and if I was growing up, I could move away. And, the sooner, the better, for me.

Because Father never allowed my mother to drive, I needed to learn. I planned to be prepared when he left and never came back. Mr. Jones would let me use his car to drive my mother, I knew he would. But, my good intentions weren't helping me drive the car any better that day. It seemed the harder I tried, the harder it was to keep the Buick headed straight down the road. The car was too big to handle and the realization I wasn't growing up annoyed me.

Mr. Jones instructed me to pull the car over. His hand grabbed the wheel again as I tried to steer the car. It struck me that driving a car wasn't as easy as I had imagined. The disappointment hung on my face. I wouldn't be growing up today.

With a pat on the leg, Mr. Jones reassured me I had done a good job with my first day of driving. Sliding closer to me, he reached over and turned off the ignition. Then, extending his arm past me, he opened the car door sliding us both out the driver's side. I stood outside the car as Mr. Jones walked to the trunk. Opening it, he pulled out a gun case. I followed him across the street to a clearing in the woods. This was a great day I thought, the first time to drive a car, even if I wasn't as successful as I had hoped, and to shoot a gun too. These are all the things "normal" little boys must think about and do. Now, I was doing them too. What a nice man; he would make a terrific grandfather.

As I basked in the moment, Mr. Jones pulled the hand gun out of its case and began loading it. Carefully showing me the gun and explaining how to hold it, he aimed at one of the trees and fired. The shot rang in my ears as I covered them with my hands. After several shots, he asked me if I wanted to try.

The gun was heavy, heavier than I ever expected. Like

the car, I could hardly hold it steady. Again, Mr. Jones instructed me on what to do as he molded my hand to the gun. I wanted to call him grandfather as I listened to him talk. With my hands cupped in his, I pulled the trigger. The gun jerked into the air, throwing me back against Mr. Jones. Steadying my arm as I settled my feet, he told me to fire again.

"That's real good, Randy. I think you have the hang of things," he nodded, continuing to hold my body to his.

As the gun fired again, I could feel the next jerk as strongly as the first, loosening my body away from Mr. Jones. He pulled me back against him.

"Oh, I think that's enough for today," he said, as he took the gun from my hand.

Disappointed, I followed him back across the street, asking him if I could drive the car again.

"Maybe, we'll see," he responded.

We got back in the car and he laid the gun case on the floor, pushing it under the seat. He sat there for a minute looking around the deserted area and then at me.

"Well, can I drive?" I asked, hoping to redeem myself from the first try.

Mr. Jones looked away without responding. He continued to look around and I began to feel uneasy, wondering why he hadn't started the car.

"You're such a pretty little boy," he said, reaching over to put his hand on my leg.

"I think we need to go now, you should take me home," I said, panicking on the inside, my fear increasing as Mr. Jones continued to look at me that way.

"My dad knows where I'm at," I proclaimed, knowing there was no truth to the statement.

Mr. Jones leaned over quickly, putting his mouth on mine, I felt his tongue trying to push through my mouth. As I squirmed, attempting to get away, his hands grabbed me. Firmly, he began pulling at my shorts, trying to unzip them. I didn't know what to do, afraid to do anything. Mr. Jones' tongue kept pushing into my mouth as he slid his hands over me.

With big scary eyes, he grabbed my hand pulling it to his exposed crotch. He kept repeating the words, "You're such a pretty boy, you're such a pretty boy." Words my grandfather had said, the very words my father hated to hear in reference to me. My mouth was now covered with his saliva, and I wanted to wipe it off, but I didn't have a free hand. Finally, I kicked him away while reaching for the car door. Angry with my continued resistance, he jerked my hand away from the handle. I was surprised by my own opposition, since I never tried to escape my father. Like a cornered animal, I struggled for freedom, knowing I was to become his prey. No one really knew where I was kept entering my thoughts.

"Stop, stop, please stop. You're scaring me," I called out.

"Sh, sh... it's okay," Mr. Jones hissed, but I knew it wasn't.

Managing to pull away at last, I opened the car door as I kicked at him again. I jumped from the car and ran down the road, not sure of where I was or which way to run. I just ran.

Mr. Jones pursued me in the car. He pulled up along side of me, and ordered me into the Buick.

"No, you're going to hurt me, I want to go home." I cried.

He softened his tone, assuring me he would take me home and not hurt me.

"No, I'll walk back," I kept telling him. "Leave me alone!" The car sped up, passing me and then cutting me off. He jumped from the car and grabbed me.

"Get back in the car!" He demanded, with a beet red face. "I won't hurt you!"

"No, No, I'm not going with you," I yelled, as he opened the door and pushed me back in the car.

I froze, my heart beating so fast I thought it was going to jump out of my chest. I hugged the door, wondering what to do, wondering if I should jump out of the car again before it started to move.

"I'll take you back; but you can't say anything to Mrs. Jones or your parents. You must never say a thing," Mr. Jones insisted, as he wiped a bead of sweat from his forehead.

"I won't say anything, just take me home," I promised in nervous relief, unsure if I should trust his words.

The car's tires spun off the gravel as it moved onto the road. Not another word was spoken on the way back, except for Mr. Jones reiterating to me not to say a word about what had just occurred. Still, I pressed my body against the car door and never let go of the handle. I dared not directly look at him. Keeping my head straight forward, I watched for any fast movement from the corner of my left eye. I didn't want him to be my grandfather anymore, I just wanted out of the car and away from him. He pulled the car in the driveway of his house and I leapt out, leaving the door open. I ran all the way back home. I couldn't say anything to my parents. How could I?

Mr. Jones stopped calling when the grass was getting too high, he left that up to Mrs. Jones. I continued to cut their lawn for the remainder of the summer and into early fall. I felt sorry for Mrs. Jones. Her husband continued being friendly, but I made sure he wouldn't get another chance at me. Understandingly, I was very nervous around him. I knew what he did was wrong, but somehow I felt I was responsible, that I had done something to make him act that way. I had no choice but to continue as if nothing had happened. I would handle the situation myself. If I stopped cutting their grass and continued to do the rest of the yards in the neighborhood, things might look strange. How could I explain things to Mrs. Jones? She would see me pushing the mower past her house and wonder why I suddenly stopped cutting theirs. She might call my mother to ask why, and I couldn't explain it to her either. My father would surely become involved and that meant he would rage at me.

I didn't hang around their house like I had customarily done and never went inside unless Mrs. Jones was home. That seemed a pretty safe strategy because she seldom left the house, except to go to the doctor. I came in for my juice and cookies or cake, but I always watched for Mr. Jones out the corner of my eye. He still watched from the windows and as always, I felt his eyes on me. When I looked over my shoulder he would be staring. So, after awhile, I stopped looking, always certain he was watching. I had to just wait until I grew up and was on my own, then I wouldn't have to do things I didn't want to do anymore.

The next spring, Mr. Jones died of a heart attack. It was just Mrs. Jones now. I didn't have to dread cutting their lawn as much nor relive the past summer. I could feel safer in the house again, but it was never the same after that day. Once or twice, while cutting the lawn after his death, I caught myself looking to see if he was standing at the window, looking for his ghost. My search has been for a protector, but I have not found one.

dennis

Even though I had looked toward Todd as a brother and a true friend, he was more than that. In my plan, he would always be around. Never thinking AIDS would touch his life and take that friendship and the security I felt with it away. Standing at the window of the waiting room, I wasn't sure if I was more upset with Todd's illness or the reality I was going to lose the strength and safety he meant to me. I had other friends, but no one could take his place. Todd and I were each other's support group. We held a mutual admiration that had developed many years ago. And, because of that, our friendship didn't require a lot of maintenance. He always listened to me when I had something on my mind and usually gave me sound advice. I tried to do the same for him. We knew we were there for each other whether there was good news to share or when something was wrong. Over the years, I had slowly become reclusive, virtually dropping out of the gay social scene, but Todd kept close tabs on me always trying to pull me back into life.

Jane, Todd's secretary, came walking down the hallway in my direction, carrying what appeared to be a large basket of fruit. At fifty-seven years old, her gray hair, sloppily pulled back in a ponytail swung behind her like a little girl's. Jane's strides were larger than she would normally make, but she wanted to comfort Todd as soon as she could get to his side. In a hurry, she barely noticed me, offering a quick nod as she passed, then turned the corner toward Todd's room. A tough exterior, she was quiet the opposite on the inside. Todd referred to Jane as his second grandmother. When Jenkins, Todd's business partner, told her to stop sending in Todd's insurance payments, Jane pulled from the back of the check book to make them. There had been some trouble between the two with the business, and since Todd wasn't able to go into the office, the cash flow was dwindling. The word was, Jenkins was telling clients to pay cash or make the checks out to him. Jane tried to look after Todd's interest the best she could. Todd, not Jenkins, had started the company, and the clients brought in their business because of him. Oddly, I remembered she had the same last name as my old landlady, Mrs. Thomas, of years ago, when I moved away from home.

She met me at the entrance of the Massey apartment building. Its large glass and iron arched door led onto a polished black and white tiled lobby floor. Built by a famed architect, Neel Reid, the Massey was a grand old building I had admired for years while in college.

"We like to keep things quiet around here," Mrs. Thomas explained, positioning her hands on her wide hips. "We only let a small number of students live here. There are a few young professionals but most of the apartments are occupied with older retired people. You understand. So, they don't like a lot of noise," she smiled, as older many Southern women do when instructing young folk.

"I understand. You won't have any problems with me," I assured her. "This is such a wonderful building. I'll love living here."

My efficiency apartment was on the second floor. One large room with hardwood floors, a kitchen off to the side, a bathroom, a walk-in closet, and the best feature, white French doors leading to a small wrought iron balcony with a view of the parking lot. My footsteps echoed off the walls of the empty apartment as I explored each corner of my new home. At twenty-two, fresh out of college, I was finally out of my father's house. I had saved all my money from working the night and weekend cook job I had since high school. Stephen was now the manager, having been promoted my sophomore year. I made the substantial deposit and princely first month's rent of two hundred and thirty-five dollars and quit flipping hamburgers and making strawberry pies. Now I worked in the Men's Department at Macy's in the Macon Mall. At first, I didn't have any furniture to fill the apartment, but I didn't care. I would sleep on the floor. Empty or not, it was my home. Besty, a local girl I had been dating, soon loaned me a love seat hide-a-bed. I had a small stereo, and Mother surprised me with a drafting table for graduation. A three foot corn plant, an apartment warming gift from Monica, another girlfriend, stood in the corner where it would gather the afternoon sun streaming through the French doors.

Besty and Monica hated each other. Besty graduated two years earlier from Wesleyan College for Women. Monica, an art major like myself, was in her senior year there. They were both pretty but very different. Besty was fashionable. Tall and slender with short brown hair cut high on her neck falling longer against her angular face; which framed a pair of light blue mischievous eyes. Whereas, Monica was shorter, long straight black hair to her shoulders, with dark round absorbing eyes. She was more comfortable in jeans and t-shirts which showed off her girlish curves. Their personalities were as different as their appearances. Besty more loud and aggressive, and Monica more pensive. Besty was my first serious relationship, and it went on for six months or so. I met her at Macy's, where she worked in the Display Department. I liked that she was outgoing, a take charge kind of person. Her personality was everything I imagined was deficient in mine. I was nervous at first, but, as with everything else, Besty took charge. With her, I briefly could forget my secrets. The first time we were making love, I wanted so to please her, to do everything right and not let anything stop me from feeling like a man. Being a virgin, I followed her lead. Luckily, Besty was aggressive.

Wrapped around each other, I cautiously asked, "What about birth control?"

"It's a little late to be worrying about that now, Randy. Don't you think?" Besty replied.

"Well, maybe we should stop," I said, anxiously.

"Don't worry, I'm using a diaphragm," she said, her laugh larger than life. "The girl always has to worry about that, the guys only think with their penis."

"Sorry, Besty," I said, feeling irresponsible.

"That's okay, at least you asked before we were done. Now shut up and kiss me," Besty said reassuringly.

As much as I wanted to be in charge, Besty took command. I never told her it was my first time, but I'm sure she knew. The closest I'd gotten to having sex was at sixteen years old. Linda, wild and a year older, drove a blue Plymouth Duster. We were making out in the back seat of her car behind the elementary school on a moonless night in June after eating at a drive-in. In the heat of young passion she stopped to reach into the fast food bag, pulling out the plastic utensil cover. Linda then discarded the contents on the floor. I wasn't sure if she was serious about using it, but I knew it wasn't her first time. Luckily, a police car shone a bright light in the back seat interrupting what was on her mind. Linda knew the officer, it was a small town. She pulled herself together and stepped out of the car to converse with him. I was scared as I scrambled to button my shirt, but not sure which I was afraid of more: The police, makeshift condom or sex.

At first, I liked being in bed with Besty naked, which we did a lot. But, for some reason sex made me feel ashamed, as if I was doing something wrong. Besty was free and eager, in fact, it was hard to keep up with her. I wanted to be like her, free of guilt, or at least able to understand from where the guilt originated. After awhile, things began to slow down between us. At times, she became aggravated with my lack of enthusiasm not understanding how one minute I was an eager beaver and the next uninterested. It was me, my guilt, but at the time I just wasn't sure what the problem was. I lost interest.

When Monica discovered Besty and I weren't dating on a regular basis, she started dropping by a lot. Often, we went dancing together for hours into the late night and then ended up at her parents house raiding the refrigerator. They owned a bakery, so there was an endless supply of cakes and cookies, and besides, her mother was a great cook.

Dancing was an escape, another way to express myself. By 1978, disco was alive and well in Macon and it grabbed hold of me. Every Friday and Saturday night, Monica and I hit the dance floor. Dancing was a lot like running from the past; with both, you never got as far away as you had hoped.

I moved into my apartment on Valentine's Day. The woman living in the unit next door had been leaving notes on my front door writing she was anxious to meet her new neighbor. I had spent most of the morning moving the drafting table, love seat and plant from one side of the efficiency to the other, deciding which meager arrangement looked best. Around four o'clock that afternoon, I heard a knock at the door. It was Besty with a plant. I wasn't expecting her, we hadn't seen each other for several days, and hadn't spoken much either. The tension made it a little uncomfortable. I needed to step back and see how I was digesting my new life away from home. I was hoping she wouldn't be taking back the love seat anytime soon.

"Besty, what are you doing here... how are you?" I said surprisingly.

"Just fine Randy. I brought you this Valentine's plant for your new place," she said, proudly holding up a flowering plant.

"It's great. Does this mean you're not mad at me anymore?" I asked.

Before Besty could respond, there was another knock at the door. It was Monica with a bottle of wine. The look on both of their faces when they saw each other was fierce and I was in the middle.

"Monica, you remember Besty don't you?" I asked.

"Yes, of course. Besty how are you?" she politely inquired. "Am I interrupting something?"

Besty made as insincere a smile as she could.

"No, Monica." I quickly recovered.

"Why don't you both have a seat, and I'll open this great bottle of wine you brought," I suggested calmly.

"Guys, I just remembered, I don't have any glasses. You two sit tight and I'll run next door to see if my neighbor is in and borrow some," I instructed, telling them about the notes. I left Besty and Monica glaring at each other on the love seat. My neighbor's door was only a few steps away. I knocked, praying she was home, only imagining how I was going to deal with the two women I had just left together in the same room. They would either kill each other or kill me, one or the other when I came back. I smelled disaster.

I knocked again. Still no answer. I was ready to give up and return to my apartment and sudden death, when surprisingly, a soft voice called from around the corner.

"Is someone knocking on my door? I'll be right there."

Turning around, I saw a handsome elderly woman carrying a small grocery bag.

"Hello, do you live here?" I asked.

"Yes. I'm Fielda Goodmen, young man," she answered.

"Hi. I'm your new neighbor Randy, and I have a slight problem," I pleaded.

"Well, come right on in and tell me about it, Son," she instructed motherly.

"Mrs. Goodmen," I said.

"No. No. Call me Fielda, please," she insisted.

"Yes ma'am, Fielda. I have these two girls in my apartment," I began to explain.

"Well, aren't you a lucky young man," she said, with a wink.

"No, you don't understand. They don't like each other and are sitting alone in my apartment. One brought me a plant and the other a bottle of wine. I was going to open the bottle and offer it to them, but realized I didn't have any glasses," I stated, almost out of breath.

"Oh, I see. Well go get them and bring them over here," Fielda insisted. "And don't forget the bottle of wine," she added.

"Are you sure Mrs., I mean Fielda?" I asked.

"Quite. Now go ahead," she said, as she motioned me off with her hand.

Upon returning, I surprisingly found Besty and Monica in what appeared to be light conversation over school days.

"My neighbor is great." I interrupted. "You have to come over and meet her. She has invited us over. Someone grab the wine."

For the next two hours, Fielda charmed and entertained us in her apartment. Larger than my efficiency, hers was a two bedroom filled with antiques and mementos which she eagerly shared with us during our visit. We finished off Monica's wine, plus another one Fielda opened. I immediately liked Fielda. She was very grand in a spunky grandmotherly way and she had come to my rescue. While living next door, Fielda often invited me in after I came home from work. Still working at the department store, I hadn't decided what to do now that I was out of school. I wanted to do something with art but I just wasn't sure where to go with it. Jobs in illustration weren't opening up, and there was really very little available in the job market to begin with. I continued working at my drafting table, pulling together a portfolio and trying to make some connections around town. Aspiring to perhaps get work as an album cover artist, I started hanging around Capricorn Records, the recording company for the Allman Brothers. The best I got were tickets and backstage passes to some concerts; invitations to a few parties and a bad hangover from waking up in a strange woman's apartment.

After many months of not knowing in what direction to head, I decided to go back to school. Thinking I might explore a career in education, I enrolled in graduate school at Mercer. Above all else, I knew how to fill my days studying. I remembered my recent graduation day and wondered if I was still searching for myself — still as lost as I was the day I graduated.

The August sun filtered through the tall oaks that stood strong and majestic on the campus of Mercer University, a private, Baptist-supported school in Macon, Georgia. Summer session was over and there was excitement in the air as soon-to-graduate students ran around trying to get in their proper order before entering the chapel. Their long black gowns stood out against the landscape, colored by the deep green grassy lawns and red brick of the Gothic style Willingham Chapel, where I had spent many afternoons in class on the upper levels. Shortly, I would be seated in its basement auditorium, where I would patiently wait to finally receive my diploma. Several yards away on a slope stood Newton Chapel, where Baptist services were held every Thursday. Postured with its pointed arches, rib vaultings and flying buttresses on the north end of the campus, it watched over the student body like a benevolent guardian leading the way to educational advancement and religious enlightenment. The warm sun added light to the landscape surrounding the Georgian architecture of the Religion and Philosophy building. As the days slowly slipped into September and summer lazily came to an end, the heat was losing some of its intensity.

Parents, siblings and friends looked on proudly, smiling and waving at their graduates, dressed so handsomely in the traditional black caps and gowns. Cameras clicked as families gathered to lock these archival moments for the family photo albums that would surely be placed on coffee tables, tucked away in trunks in attics or positioned in bookcases. Some photos of this day's event would be sealed in picture frames to be placed in mothers' and grandmothers' homes, freezing moments that would be remembered fondly again and again. For it was a day of voyages, for new adventures into the uncharted future of many young lives. They were schooled and polished for the real world that awaited at the other end of the diploma line. A day worked, studied and dreamed for four years, had finally arrived. I stood alone alongside the crowd, holding my cap to my side, quietly watching the activity around me. There were no cameras pointed in my direction, no relatives hurrying to slap me on the back and congratulate my accomplishments. Shielded by tree branches, I stood under one of the arched windows of Willingham Chapel, where three years ago, I had sat and first looked out over the campus during English 101. Back then, I was taking in a whole new world, one very different than the one I had left. It was the first day of Fall quarter and my first quarter of college. From that same window, I watched the leaves of my season of freedom softly roll along the grass of the campus, pushed by the dancing wind as I vaguely heard my professor's voice in the background.

My father had been in his grave for eleven months. Of all that he had taken from me during his life, he finally gave something in his death as he promised. The money to go to college came from the Army through the GI Bill for dependents of Veterans. It seemed just, as I had served in a different kind of battle — the war of my father. I had paid my dues. I made my bed every morning as a child, like a good soldier, with military corners so tight you could bounce a half dollar on it — a practice my father often performed. I had lived in his barracks and did my duty to him. But now, I had been discharged by the firing of a gun. I was now a civilian, no longer under the command of Sergeant First Class, no longer an enlisted boy and no longer on active duty. In my new uniform of khaki pants, blue button-down collar shirt, cordovan penny loafers and a belt to match, I had scrubbed myself clean for the first day of what I thought was a new beginning.

How ironic I attended a school designed by the influences of religion. All the things associated with religion had been absent in our home. Faith, principle and belief in anything was hard to grasp. As very young children, our mother sent us to Sunday School, but eventually our attendance dropped off. Saturday was a big drinking day for our father, which meant a hard one for our mother and Sundays followed Saturdays. Whether we went to Sunday School the next day depended on how many times Father hit her, or how loud he yelled and how many bruises were on her body. While in my early years in high school, Sandra and I had gone out on our own and joined a Methodist church; hoping to find some peace and understanding in our secular young lives. We were baptized in a church of strangers, where everyone hopes to feel like family. Perhaps that's why we joined, to find a family. Encouraged by a concerned neighbor and member of the church, who understood what was happening to us in some removed way, we set out to find religion, to find our God. For years from my child's bed at night I prayed for Him to shield us from the violence of my father, to save my mother, to save us all. I prayed for the drinking and the beatings to stop, for the screams and the pain to end. I absorbed The Bible, testament by testament, page by page. As my prayers seemed never to be answered, the pages were left undisturbed. Like little church mice, Sandra and I sat in the rear pew going unnoticed by the congregation and, I thought, perhaps by God.

Mercer was close to home. My mother wanted it that way. And now I had made it through a college education provided by the blood of my father. I was happy for them — the graduating students and their families. The joy in the air was almost contagious, I only wished it was mine. I peered through the crowd looking to see if my sister and mother had arrived. They were nowhere to be seen. It was just as well. Our family wouldn't fit in well with the mood of the day. We weren't used to such outpourings of joy. Public displays of affection were foreign to us all and I felt that void keenly this day.

The chapel bells chimed, signaling the beginning of the ceremonies. As families and friends moved into the church to take their seats for this auspicious day, the excitement carried from the yard into the chapel. The graduating class of the summer of nineteen hundred and seventy-seven now collectedly lined up for that all encompassing momentous walk.

We started up the chapel stairs one by one, the large red doors opened wide for us. I could see the rows of people standing and looking back as the graduates entered the chapel. I looked over my shoulders one last time to see if there was any sign of Mother and Sandra. Maybe I had missed them. For a moment I hoped that perhaps they already had taken their seats. As I sat among my graduating class, I tried to feel a part of it — to finally be a part of something, to belong. But I knew, as I sat there like a ghost, not being seen by those around me I might as well have been a stranger. Although I'd spent the last three years walking the campus and academic halls studying with my fellow graduates, I felt I barely knew any of them. By attending every summer quarter, I was finishing a year early. During that time I didn't make any friends, none at least that would last past this day. Now I was walking the same path with these strangers as we all peered into the future. I had always been a stranger and this day would be no different. They were talking among themselves, to their friends and classmates, but I had no one to talk to. But that was okay, I had made it this far. Remember, I wasn't good enough to have friends. No one would want to be friends with me, so why bother. It was a fluke that Mercer had allowed me in. A mistake that for three years I hoped they wouldn't find out about. Many times while in class, I watched the door waiting for someone from the administration office to walk in and say, "Mr. Chumbley, there was a mix up, you don't belong here...GET OUT!" I just had to make it a few more minutes until I had the diploma in my hands. And then it would all be real...I would have gotten away with fooling them.

One by one the names were called and the audience cheered and applauded each graduate's achievement. "But who would applaud for me?" I wondered.

"James Randall Chumbley," announced the President of the University. I held my breath. I had made it around the field, and now I was crossing the finish line. Thank God, there arose some random cheers and applause — not from anyone I knew, but the audience was kind and I was grateful. I approached the stage trying not to trip over my gown, looking into the rows of people; again searching for my family.

Taking my diploma, I returned to my seat; telling myself I didn't care if they weren't here, that it wasn't important.

An hour later, the last name was called and the President concluded the ceremonies. The graduates stood and off flew caps tossed high into the air. The chapel filled again with cheers and applause. I held my cap to my side. "Just let me out of here. I want to disappear from this crowd," I prayed.

The chapel spilled out into the yard where the celebration continued. I skirted the perimeter of the crowd, dashing across the lawn. The shadow of the chapel covered me as I ran to the steps leading to the street. Desperately wanting the solitude of my car, not knowing where I would go once I reached it. As if a crowd of angry people were chasing me, I continued to hurry. Like a frightened boy running from something alien, I ran from what should have been my celebration and joy.

When I reached the top of the stairs, I saw my mother staggering, trying to master the steep climb. She was drunk, holding onto the railing. Below on the street my sister's car sped off out of sight.

"Mother, what are you doing?" I questioned. "Be careful. Where's Sandra going?"

"She's mad at me," Mother slurred. "We had a fight and she dropped me here. Has the graduation started yet, Randy?"

"Mother, you missed it, but that's okay," I consoled, as always.

I approached her on the stairs, reaching for her arm as she looked up at me.

"Let's go," I urged, guiding her back to the bottom of the stairs.

This will not be the day I'll never forget, I glumly thought, feeling a sense of disappointment. The little excitement I'd felt had left me. My graduating had changed nothing in our lives; there were no epiphanies on graduation day, no divorcing the past as I had hoped and more than a little afraid of the future, I felt alone. Not only for me, but Mother. What would become of her? I was someone for her to believe in. I lived at home while in college, but now I had to move on. She knew that. The sadness in her eyes stared at me as I reached out to steady her arm. It was added reason for her to drink on such a day. I knew she was happy for me, yet fearful of the loneliness she would have to deal with in an empty house. The pain of her life would be closer after I was gone and the ghost of my father more prevalent.

We had all been stunned at Father's funeral when someone noticed the casket was popped open as it was being lowered. Holding the folded flag in her hands, Mother's face was bleach white as she watched the coffin being raised. She carried that image in her mind and saw it as a sign he wasn't ever going to let her be free.

I handed her the diploma. Mother had always dreamed of going to college, but never could. Oh she was smart enough and had the desire, but she'd married young and my father kept her at home; never wanting her to be anything except forever under his dominion. Demanding full control of her, he never let her work. He snuffed out her aspirations one by one. Most of her life she dreamed of a singing career. Ever since she was a young girl, Mother collected sheet music. She sang like a song bird around the house, but mostly when Father wasn't there. She cherished every note and page of music she acquired over the years. Her angelic voice complemented her beauty, and for a short moment, she was living her dreams, hopeful one day those dreams would come true. While in the hospital recuperating from one of her breakdowns, my father collected the stacks of sheet music and threw them out like useless trash. A part of Mother never recovered, with the music went a large part of her soul. She married to get away from the hell of being her parents' daughter, to escape confinement of a small Alabama town and to make her dreams a reality. What she found was a different hell and greater limitations with my father. Three kids later, several nervous breakdowns and a husband dead by his own hand, she never lived those dreams. He took her dreams to his grave.

She owned nothing. Nothing of hers was sacred, not her sheet music, her clothes, not photos of her life before him. He had controlled everything. My mother had a cherished photo of her with Gene Autry, the legendary country singer, standing outside a theater in Alabama. The photo was a symbol of her dream, the dream my father scoffed at. Before going into the hospital another time, she took the photo and taped it to the back of the mirror in her bedroom so it wouldn't be missing when she came home. Her stays in the hospital were long — sometimes weeks or months, always returning for her children and the broken promises from my father that things would be different.

She clutched the diploma to her breasts. I could see the tears build in her eyes. My heart began to break.

"You did it, Son. You're the first to graduate from college," she said, wiping her cheeks. Her tears gently fell on the diploma, each one a lost aspiration.

"No Mother, you did it. It's your diploma, your graduation. I want you to keep it. Congratulations, I love you," I said, wishing she had a better life. Truly longing for her the happiness she had been unable to reach. And hoping the diploma gave her some hope for her own future. After Wilson's suicide, Mother had tried to pull herself together. It could have been a new beginning for her. A chance to find happiness, and possibly, some of it with another man. In her mid-forties, there still was a vibrancy about her. A trickle, that Father hadn't managed to squeeze out. After his death, there were glimpses of the fresh girl with a look of promise on her face, as the one pictured in Mother's high school annuals. That next spring, after the winter's mourning, Mother began singing around the house again. She sang with a voice as crisp as the spring air and as brilliant as the colors of the azaleas blooming in the back yard. After being kept caged for so long by the bird keeper, she flew from the bars of confinement. The rose had come back in her cheeks and her powder white skin was free of any bruises for the first time in years.

She took a waitress job at a donut shop in walking distance from the house. The blue 1967 Galaxy Ford my father drove sat in the back yard still wrecked from the accident he had the night before his suicide. The plan was to get it repaired for Mother to learn to drive, but she was always too nervous. Even her psychiatrist agreed that Mother should wait until her nerves got better. Finally the fender and passenger door were repaired, but the car remained unused. The interior still smelled of Father, as if he had just driven it yesterday. A year later, the Galaxy was sold. There was a small insurance policy that Mother put in the bank, but no insurance on the house. And there was the annuity and benefits due her for being the wife of a career Army man; enough to get by and then some. But no amount of money could repay her for the years she had lived with him. The job was mainly to get out of the house and meet new people. Up until his death, there were no real friends in her life, so she had to go out and make some. Waitressing was the best job she could secure after not working the past twenty-one years. Before marriage, Mother was a secretary at the County Extension Office in Fayette, but her typing skills were rusty. I think she preferred putting on make-up and wearing the tight white uniform that showed off her figure.

But, the song Mother wanted so desperately to sing was never finished. Her voice began to drown in the liquor and was soon choked by the constant smoke of cigarettes. The job lasted long enough for her to meet some men, not much different from my father. She drank on her off time and sometimes went to work drunk until she slipped on the floor at the donut shop. Mother said the floor was wet, but I knew she just fell down drunk on her ass. There were a few other jobs after that, but they all ended up the same.

Where do I go from here? I thought to myself as I helped my mother into the car. College was over. In a way it had been a haven where I could drown myself in studies and forget about my home life, erase the past and most of all not think about the uncertainties of a future for which I felt unprepared. Now that sanctuary was over, the future was here. Where would I go now?

I remember reassuring Mother I was only a phone call away and only thirty minutes by car. That last night in the house, I sat for hours on my bed afraid of what I'd find out there, worrying about her and wondering if I should leave. The same bed I had run to from my father and his belt. It wasn't so long ago I laid there kicking at him, feeling the sting of the belt. Now, I was afraid his ghost would come in the night to keep me from leaving. His ghost was still there, and I was leaving her alone with it.

One might think I would be happy leaving the house I had been a prisoner in for so many years. Now I could walk out of the past and into the future. How I had ached for this day. I'd kept a lot of miserable secrets here and now I was ready to leave them. I closed the door of my room and wept, as Mother walked through the house late into the night. Since his death, she hadn't been able to sleep well, as if she was afraid to close her eyes, uncertain of the dark hours. Instead, she slept during the day and stayed awake at night haunted by his return. I thought I was crying for her, for our parting, but I was crying out of fear. I was afraid of freedom. How could I take mine and leave Mother without hers?

Mother never wanted me to major in art and she was upset when I switched from biology after the second quarter of my freshman year.

"How can you make a living at art, Son?" she would say. "You have brains, use them for something. God knows, Wilson is gone now, you can be something. Your father beat the brains out of me, but it's not too late for you."

I compromised, double majoring in art and psychology. I knew I was different and wanted the freedom I thought being an artist would give me. I craved freedom. Art gave me the chance to express myself, express the feelings and desires I had kept hidden away. Psychology would allow me to help others. How, I didn't really know, but I had a need to help others. I could sense sadness in people, read their faces and look into their souls. It would be easier to help others and not deal with my own demons. Art had always been an escape for me as a child. I went off by myself and drew imaginary places I could escape to away from our house. I'd draw happy families, draw a different kind of life colored in with bright colors, unlike the blackness where we truly lived.

Fielda was a retired school principal. She loved the idea of me returning to study education. It gave her an opportunity to tell endless stories of her "good old days." My mother was happy of this news as well. She wanted my future to be secure, believing teaching would be good for me. Mother's drinking seemed to grow worse after I left home. At first she tried to hide it as in the past with Father, not wanting me to worry about her. But, it reached the point where she was drinking all the time, evidenced by the empty bottles spilling from under the furniture. I loved my mother, but I didn't know what to do for her anymore. Having Fielda next door was a comfort.

I took out a student loan for grad school and changed my hours at Macy's to part-time so I would have enough time for classes and studying. And I started seeing Besty again. I was drawn to her personality, her sense for fun. The guilt was still there, but I was trying to have the kind of life I felt a guy should be living. I still went out dancing with Monica, trying to keep this knowledge from Besty. It lasted another few months until the urge to pull away from Besty fell over me again. This time she was over it and told me in a nice enough way to get lost, that I was too fickle for her. Monica became persistent in wanting more than a dancing partner. Appropriately, Besty took back her love seat, so Monica and I had sex in the television room of her parent's house after our Saturday nights out dancing. And there was still this nagging guilt. Her aggressiveness eventually proved suffocating and my bouts of guilt too disturbing, leaving me no choice except to pull away from her as well. I soon found myself with no girlfriend.

Fielda had a lot of younger male friends who came around to visit fairly regularly. Her favorite was a music minister, Carl, and a school teacher, Dennis, who lived on the ninth floor. Both Carl and Dennis were nearly five years older than me. Dennis was six-two, husky, with thick blond hair and a light beard — a big teddy bear of a guy. He looked like an outdoors man. Carl, on the other hand, was thin, dark and bookish. I met them one evening after coming in from the Library. Fielda heard me and rushed over to invite me in. Of course, I accepted and stayed at Fielda's well after Carl and Dennis had left.

"Randy, you got in later tonight than you usually do. Did you have a lot of studying to do?" Fielda asked.

"No, not really," I responded. "I had to walk to the Library today. My car wouldn't start this morning. I don't know what's wrong with it."

Fielda thought for a moment, and then said, "You should ask Dennis to take a look at it. He is very good with things like that. I see him all the time working on his car in the back."

"Fielda, do you think he would mind?" I asked, not sure if I should call this imposing stranger.

"Not at all," she insisted. "I think you should, perhaps tomorrow after he gets home from work."

Like everyone else, I hated having car problems. But I loved my car as much as a person could love a car. The 1968 white two seater Datsun 2000 roadster with black interior and convertible top gave me my own sense of freedom. I bought it used when I started college, after convincing my mother I wouldn't end up dead in a car accident because of its size. A fun car to drive when it worked, but not knowing much about mechanics it usually cost an "arm and a leg" when it didn't. I was low on cash, so I was hoping maybe Fielda was right and Dennis could fix it at a minimal cost.

I rang Dennis shortly after four o'clock. He sounded a little surprised to hear from me, but was quite willing to help out.

"Dennis, this is Randy from downstairs," I said, hoping he remembered me. "How are you?"

There was a pause on his end of the line.

"Oh. Yes, Randy, fine and you?" he replied in sudden recognition.

"I'll be doing great if you know anything about cars," I detailed.

"What do you mean?" Dennis asked.

"Well," I began to explain.

"Randy, I'll be glad to take a look at it," he responded, to my relief. "Now, if you would like."

"That would be great!" I exclaimed. "I'll meet you in the parking lot. And thanks!"

Dennis approached my car with complete confidence. Brotherly, he examined the engine, touching and pulling at wires and hoses. After a few minutes of looking under the hood, he discovered the problem.

"I think what you need is a new rotor cap," he advised, propping a foot on the front fender. "This one's cracked. Your spark plugs may need some tending to but I don't think you have a big problem on your hands."

We made it to the auto parts store just as it was about to close. After returning to the Massey, Dennis worked on the Datsun until it was almost dark.

"Let's see what a good job I did, Randy," he said, with assurance. "Why don't we take it out for a drive and get something to eat while we're at it."

"Okay. But dinner's on me," I insisted.

The car ran better than ever. It was reassuring knowing Dennis lived in the building, just in case something went wrong again; it was like having a big brother around to look after me. For a moment I thought about Stephen.

We pulled into the restaurant parking lot. Dennis squeezed out of the passenger side, his large frame having stuck snugly in the seat. The restaurant's old southern feel was enhanced by dark wooden walls covered with old photographs of Macon. I came to learn Dennis wasn't only mechanical, but an interesting guy, as we sat for more than an hour in one of the small dining rooms among a mix of locals and college students. He had so many different facets and hobbies, from camping to flying airplanes. A medic in Vietnam, Dennis recounted a few war stories. He seemed to be an all-a-round caring individual and I was glad we were becoming friends. As the weeks passed, I looked forward to seeing Dennis in the building. He always had a comforting smile and something nice to say.

When several days flew by without us running into one another, I found myself looking for him everyday as I came in and out of the building. Finally, I asked Fielda if she had seen him.

"Dennis is on a camping trip with his Boy Scouts. I think he will be back after the weekend," Fielda informed me.

"Boy Scouts?" I inquired, surprised at yet another activity.

"He is a Scout leader," she explained. "He loves working with children."

I always wanted to be a Boy Scout when I was little, but that meant making friends with other boys. And of course, that would be risky with my parents' drinking, especially Father's. The few times I tried to make friends, without fail, he always did something to embarrass me. So I stopped making them.

Several days later, I ran into Dennis in the mail room. I was both nervous and excited, but not sure why.

"Dennis, I heard from Fielda you've been out of town. How was it?" I asked.

"It was great to get away out in the mountains with the scouts," he replied, looking through his mail. "Were you ever a Boy Scout, Randy?"

"No, I never did anything like that growing up," I answered.

"Well, you'll have to come on a camping trip with me sometime," Dennis proposed.

"Okay, that sounds like something I'd like to try. Let me know the next time," I urged. Suddenly, there was an awkward silence.

"I have to go up and study," I said, hastily. "See you later."

Yes, it would be nice to go on a camping trip with Dennis. A new experience, I thought as I climbed the stairs to my second floor apartment, opting not to take the elevator with Dennis. Once in my apartment, I suddenly felt alone and afraid. I couldn't understand why I was feeling this way about Dennis, as if I had a crush on him. He had been on my mind too much. Why was I thinking about this guy? Got to get my head on straight, I thought.

I hadn't talked to Besty or Monica since Dennis fixed my car. Monica had been by to leave a note, but I hadn't gotten back to her. Besty wouldn't call, although she had felt sorry for me and gave me back the love seat. She would wait until I called her first.

For some reason, I momentarily lost interest in Besty and Monica, becoming distracted. There was something going on inside of me. I was feeling funny and it had something to do with Dennis; I knew that much. I want to be more like him, I thought, as I sat down on the love seat in the middle of the room. I reached to the floor for one of my class books and began looking at the pages, trying to concentrate on reading the material for class the next day. But it was no good. The harder I tried to concentrate, the more I thought about Dennis upstairs on the ninth floor in his own apartment and wondered what he was doing. What would it be like to go camping with him? Finally, I gave up and put the book down.

I got up and started pacing the floor. I felt trapped, like a caged animal wanting to run free. My mind was congested, filled with countless, confusing thoughts. I walked out on the balcony. The afternoon air was hot and thick, not helping to clear my clogged mind. I could almost feel the heat scorch my nostrils as I breathed the dense air into my lungs. I watched the sun beginning to set over the trees in the distance burning through the late afternoon haze. I stared at its yellow core, searching for the order to the confusion in my mind, until my eyes began to sting. Finally I had to turn away. I needed someone to hold me. I hungered to feel protected from the loss inside of me. I felt so alone.

The light began to change in the room. I returned to the love seat and sat down with my back to the open French doors. Without thinking, I reached for the phone. I began dialing Besty's number. My finger struggled as I tried to remember if it was six-four or four-six. It rang once. And before it rang again, I hung up the receiver in fear she might answer. The room was dimmer now as I laid my head back on the arm rest and curled up like a baby. I could hear Fielda shuffling at her door and then the noise the bolt in the lock made as she turned the key.

From my infant position, I quietly watched the room continue to change hues, as the sun began disappearing into the tree line behind the Massey. A grayish pink haze moved on the air, filling the efficiency. The light faded and I closed my eyes.

There was a knock at the door. At first I wasn't sure, as I tussled to resume my sleep. Then a louder knock. My trance had been disturbed and I stumbled off the love seat toward the door. Having fallen asleep for an hour or so, the room was almost dark, only lighted from a street lamp outside. At my first try, I missed the knob of the door, grasping it on the second.

"Hello, who is it?" I called out disoriented, as I pulled the door open before the visitor could answer.

"Dennis, oh, it's you. What's up?" I said groggily.

"You look like you were asleep," he said.

"No, no. Come in, I was just reading, I guess I nodded off for a few minutes," I lied.

"I was on my way out to get a beer. You want to come?" Dennis asked.

"Well, yes, but I have a lot of reading to do tonight. I should really stay in and get it done," I explained.

"Sure, Randy, maybe next time," he responded.

"Listen, Dennis, I have a few beers in the fridge," I offered, hoping he would come in. "Well, if I won't keep you from studying," Dennis answered.

"I could use one right about now," I lied again.

Talk about a coincidence, I thought as I slid my hand on the wall feeling for the light switch. This guy must have ESP or something. Here, a few hours ago, I'd been thinking about him, and earlier today I couldn't get him off my mind. Now he's knocking at my door.

I excused myself to the kitchen, maneuvering through the school books on the floor to retrieve the beers. Dennis was standing on the balcony when I returned. His back was to me as I stepped on the metal floor in my bare feet. I noticed again he was a big man, with broad, strong shoulders. As Dennis turned around, I handed him the beer looking up into his face.

As we were talking, I realized I was standing there in two sizes too big boxer shorts and a t-shirt. Dennis was dressed nicely in a plaid button-down and chinos. I found myself feeling a little awkward about my appearance. I felt silly in my boxers with this big man fully dressed. I ran my hand through my hair, trying to comb it, as I took a large gulp of beer. "Man, I must look a mess," I said, trying to start up the conversation.

"So, how's the car running these past few weeks?" Dennis asked.

"I haven't had any trouble with it, thanks to you," I smiled.

"I was glad to help you out. Let me know if you have any more problems," he replied.

There was a long pause of silence as we stood on the balcony drinking our beers. Dennis glanced at me for a second and then looked up into the sky, as if he was thinking to himself.

By now the haze had moved on, leaving the sky lit up with hundreds of stars. I'd lost all concern for my studies. I was experiencing something new. An anticipation of some sort, a different kind of emotion.

"How about another beer?" I asked Dennis.

"What about your reading?" he quizzed.

"It can wait a little longer, besides I'm not in the mood for studying right now," I replied, not ready for him to leave.

"Okay, sure, Randy, I'll have another," Dennis responded, taking the last sip of his beer.

As I began to turn away, I felt Dennis' large hand take a hold of my arm. My bare feet stopped in their tracks. He pulled me back toward him. Something very different is about to happen I thought. The anticipation was almost over. Without a word, Dennis put his lips to mine. I flinched as I felt his beard tickle my face.

A streak of fear ran through me for an instant. Like ice, my manhood melted. Dennis put his arms around me and my fear eased for a moment in his embrace. The kiss was gentle. There was no whiskey on his breath, no rough whiskers against my skin. Just the softness of his lips and the cushion of his beard. This is not my father, I reminded myself as I stood frozen — this is not my father.

"You're beautiful, Randy," Dennis stated.

The apprehension must have shown on my face. My body stiffened, as I looked away not knowing how to respond.

"Is this awkward for you?" Dennis asked.

I stood there without saying a word. Awkward and

strange yes, I thought. Past moments with Besty and Monica came into my head. What would they think knowing I was standing in the arms of a man? For a second I wanted to break from Dennis' arms and run to them — find my manhood again. What was I, a man or a woman? Why was I not fighting this?

"Randy, you're not saying anything," Dennis said, as he stepped back. "Are you okay?"

"No, it's fine," I managed to say, as I pulled away. "This is something new. I didn't know you were like that."

"Like what, Randy?"

"Well, you know, homosexual. Do you think I am? You must think that. Do I look like I am?" I asked, sounding both paranoid and defensive.

"It's not that I am or you look like you are, Randy," Dennis explained. "There's just something about you. I've been thinking about you a lot since I fixed your car, actually ever since I met you at Fielda's. I wanted to do this the night we had dinner."

"So, then you're gay," I asked.

"I don't really know what I am," he replied. "It really doesn't matter. I guess I may be bisexual. Do you want me to leave?"

"No, no, I guess not. Let's sit down. This is too much for me to take standing up," I said, as I walked toward the love seat.

We both sat down, Dennis' size taking up most of the space. I found myself consciously thinking it was Besty's love seat. Dennis and I looked right past each other.

"Damn, I have five chapters to read before class tomorrow," I blurted out, while staring at my watch.

"Listen, Randy, I'll let you get back to studying," Dennis said, as he got up. "We can talk about this later if you're still speaking to me."

"Sure. Of course I'll be talking to you. Maybe I'll see you tomorrow," I said, unable to look at Dennis.

Over the next few days, I only saw a glimpse of Dennis

popping into the elevator as I was entering the lobby of the Massey. He must have seen me coming up the walk through the glass iron doors, while he waited. I had wanted to call him on the phone since the other night but fought the temptation.

I tried not to think about what had happened, about kissing him or the way he made me feel in those few seconds. Even though Dennis was twice my size, I should have hit him. That would have been the manly thing to do. He thought I was a fag. I never really thought he was one. I didn't know what to think. I didn't know what I was. I wasn't like those other guys, those homos. Sure, guys called me sissy in school, my own brother called me that, but I wasn't like that, not like Kenneth Hanes. Any feminine qualities I thought I might have, I tried to correct, tried to change and be more like the fraternity guys at Mercer, more like my brother.

I called Besty the next day after classes and rushed over. We went to the movies and then came back to her apartment. I felt uncomfortable, but hoped she wouldn't notice. And I tried not to notice my own discomfort as well. Besty was cautious, understandably so. We weren't as close anymore, but I tried to act as if the weeks of not seeing one another hadn't occurred. I wondered if somehow she knew, after all it was her love seat Dennis and I were sitting on.

I spent the night. We made out but stopped before making love. Restless, I laid awake most of the night. It was strange being in her bed again; it wasn't the same anymore — I wasn't the same. The next morning driving away from Besty's apartment, I knew last night was the last time I would sleep beside her.

Later that day, I found myself standing outside Dennis' apartment door. I was driven by an inner force to find out what were these feelings going on inside of me. I was nervous all the way up in the elevator. It stopped on the ninth floor and I held the doors open while staring into the hall. The doors began trying to close. The alarm went off, while I decided whether to continue or go back down. Startled by an elderly couple coming around the corner to get on, I stepped out into the hallway to face an unknown part of myself; to come to grips with another side that would begin to change my world.

For the next six months, Dennis became my teacher. He introduced me to new strange experiences, brought out sensations in me I had never felt with a woman. The sex with Besty and Monica was fine, but something had been missing. I was going through the motions trying to be a man in that way. But with Dennis, I felt a brotherhood. A connection with an inner part of me that surpassed the flesh. If it was wrong, why did I still want to be with Dennis? I tried not to fight my confusion. Like a little boy who was up to mischief, I visited Dennis' apartment. Always careful not to be noticed in the elevator and hallways–sometimes taking the stairs. All the while hoping Fielda or anyone else wouldn't find out. If they had, I would have been devastated. Still, around Dennis, I felt safe and sheltered. With him, something was opening up. But I wasn't completely sure I truly wanted to understand what it was. He seemed to care about me, like I had some worth as a person, that my existence in the world mattered. Perhaps my life wasn't a mistake after all. Being around Dennis gave me a chance to stop feeling so lonely. He was a reprieve from being bogged down in the sadness of the past. He would be a friend, something I had never really had up until now. And in exchange for that friendship, I awkwardly stood naked before him. Like a little boy removing himself from the present by placing his being somewhere else in his mind, and playing a different game. And Dennis was experienced. I was sensing his actions in a man-to-man encounter were as natural to him as that of a man sharing with a women. And, for me, what I was experiencing through him was akin to watching a foreign movie.

We took a trip to Florida in his parents' motor home. Dennis' parents knew nothing of his interest in men. This would be my second trip to the Sunshine State, the first being at the end of my senior year of high school. For that trip, I had saved the one hundred and fifty dollars required. The senior class met in the parking lot of Warner Robins High at ten o'clock in the evening for the twelve-hour Greyhound bus trip to Miami, where we would later board a ship for the Bahamas. It didn't matter I was easily one of the least popular kids on the bus. High school was almost over, my father was dead and the world was out there for me to explore. I was going to make myself popular somehow. As the bus drove over the Georgia-Florida state line at two o'clock in the darkness, I felt a sense of liberty. I'd finally made it out of Georgia to a new world. Almost everyone was still awake, wired that they were on their own, except for the adult chaperons: Two teachers and two parents, who'd given up on trying to keep order two hours ago. I looked out the window at the brightly lit, "Welcome to Florida, The Sunshine State" sign, which seemed to pop up out of nowhere.

Getting out of Georgia wasn't enough to make me popular with the other kids though. I mostly hung around with a few who were considered on the same low scale as myself, while the other kids tolerated us. Five days went by and I was back at home. Miles of land and ocean couldn't free me from where I came from or make me any more popular.

So now Dennis and I made our way down the Atlantic coast of Florida in the blue and white six-sleeper motor home with all its comforts. There were stops in St. Augustine and Daytona, where the hotel on wheels broke down on Atlantic Boulevard. With minor repairs, we headed on to Cocoa Beach, crossed the state to Orlando and the Parliament House. My first experience of being in a gay bar, the Parliament House was more like an amusement park, more like a mini Disney World for gay men complete with hotel accommodations. The establishment sat back from a busy four-lane street divided by a median lined with palm trees. Bright flashing lights of topless clubs and fast food places scattered the strip.

Two fake palm trees greeted us as we entered the front

door, their green fronds draped in white mini lights. A large man in long, blond curls and a low-cut red dress exposing his ample hairy chest took our money. Dennis guided me through the dim entrance leading into a huge warehouse of people as colored lights flashed in the distance. The place was full and men were looking at me, bumping into me. Some looked back smiling with more than a casual "excuse me" look. Somehow I knew it was a communication without words — a communication of acceptance. Their lips were smiling and their eyes were doing the talking. For the first time I felt I had something to offer. I was back in Florida, but this time not with my senior class, and not feeling on the lower end of the popularity chart. I watched the cornucopia of men. Many of the guys were good looking, athletic, like the varsity football team at Warner Robins High, like my older brother, and they were all looking back at me. They were mixed in among the guys easily singled out in high school as sissies, and the guys who looked like your average Joe. But there was no name calling, no bullying and no one being shoved into their lockers. Still, there was a sense of uneasiness surrounding the sense of kinship, as if I was in a place I shouldn't be. I tried to ignore my growing anxiety. I was with Dennis and I knew he would watch over me. We danced like I had danced with Monica, but not for hours. It was odd dancing with another man. Before it was just Dennis and me with no one else around, no other soul knowing the things we were doing. But now, in this place, it was like everyone knew and the secret was out.

Adjacent to the bar was a motel much like the Holiday Inn where we were staying. I'd had enough of the motor home and wanted to sleep in a real bed. Dennis explained it was part of the Parliament House, where men checked in for a night, a weekend or a week. It's square architectural two story structure stood by a triangular swimming pool surrounded by a chain link fence. Many of the doors to the rooms were open. Some wide, as far as their hinges allowed, letting the room's light spill out into the night. Tacky green shag carpet covered the floor and cheaply framed shell prints hung on the walls. Unmade beds from the day before — or from moments ago — were in clear sight, their sheets rumpled and draping the floor. Articles of clothing were strewn on simple wooden chairs with yellow vinyl seat covers. Other doors were slightly ajar with the light teasing out, not revealing much of the contents of their rooms.

As Dennis and I walked along the fence, my eyes were drawn to two men quietly laughing as they sat closely on a lounge chair. A man stood off in the corner watching them intently. Another couple sat on the cement edge surrounding the pool, one with his shirt off, both dangling their feet in the water. As my eyes were drawn back to the lighted rooms of the motel, I observed men lingering about in the exposed rooms watching the activity outside. They appeared to be waiting for someone to walk by so they could snatch them in and close the door. Some occupants were shirtless, exposing their skin to the warm night air. Others were sitting on the beds in shorts or underwear, and some stood clothed in the doorways. A number of men walked around the pool, casually checking out their possible encounters in the rooms. All looking for the same things: Companionship to fill the few hours left in the night, sexual fulfillment and validation that they were desired. Some waited patiently and others paced, appearing in the doorway of their room and disappearing for a second, then reappearing again in the light.

We continued walking slowly to the motor home, eyeing the activity with little discussion between ourselves. Dennis wanted to go to bed. I wanted to stay and watch the men of the night. But Dennis was the Scout Leader, the teacher, so I did as he said. My eyes and mind absorbed these new sights; there was a lot to digest. My response was one of confusion accompanied with desire to investigate the lighted doorways, the open curtains, and the men associated with them. The night was steamy, the bar had been crowded and hot. The smell of strong cologne loomed in the air as two men passed talking softly, holding hands. I looked up at Dennis for a second, contemplating the activity of two men in one of the rooms that caught my immediate attention. A man walked through the lighted door from the outside, stopping for a brief moment as its reassuring occupant motioned the guest in. The door closed, retracting the light shining out into the night and then the room went dark.

The things that happened between Dennis and me were kept between ourselves. He didn't want anyone to know, and neither did I. He would be fired if the School Board found out he was having a relationship with another man. Sometimes I felt ashamed for being with him, yet there wasn't anything I could do about it. I wanted to be around him, to feel the brotherhood. At the time, I was drawn to Dennis and finally, I stopped questioning it. Besides, I was used to feeling ashamed. When you're raised by alcoholics, your life, especially as a young child, becomes nothing but shame. You grow into it until the feeling fits like a glove. I was used to the feeling, used to seeing the face of shame as my reflection in the mirror. Now, I was afraid people could automatically tell I was engaging in homosexual activities just by looking at me. Becoming more self conscious about my mannerisms, I tried to act manly to compensate for my "friendship" with Dennis. I used him as a model — no one would think he was gay. Although, because of that involvement, I felt less than a man. Like the old tale: If you masturbate, you will grow hair on the palms of your hands. I wondered if my effeminate traits were becoming more obvious now that I was with Dennis.

The landlady's son at the Massey was obviously gay. And a constant reminder of what I didn't want to become. Since he had his own apartment on the fourth floor, I saw him often. When I first met Maxwell in the lobby, I was taken back — almost repulsed — by his "queerness." He swayed as he walked up to were I was talking with his mother. Maxwell stood with his hands loosely riding on his hips. His voice was soft and demure, tilting his head back and ending many of his words with a lisp. His colorful shirts fit his slight body like a blouse, the top buttons opened, exposing his hairless chest. His jeans were tight, accentuating his thin legs. I noticed the hint of red nail polish around his cuticles, wondering what his mother thought about her son, wondering if it was indeed nail polish or merely paint he had gotten on his fingers and hastily wiped off. Hoping for his mother's sake, that the latter was the case. I didn't want to step far into this kind of life or be unable to back out. Dennis had been a fine example, always manly. But the fear was always with me that I would slip and become like Maxwell or like Kenneth in high school. I just couldn't allow myself to be laughed at, rejected, or alienated anymore. Would I not know it before everyone else did? Would I be the last to notice the hair growing on my palms?

It wasn't the sex I wanted with Dennis. In fact, I didn't get very involved in the act. I usually laid there and let him do whatever he wanted. He was always gentle. He seemed to be satisfied with my lack of participation, playing with my body and exploring it with his tongue, licking me for hours as his beard continuously brushed against my skin. I wasn't comfortable with reciprocating Dennis' actions. I guess I figured if I didn't, then I wasn't doing anything wrong. We kissed and he sucked my dick. I beat Dennis off, but wouldn't take him in my mouth. I told myself I would grow out of this, that I'd eventually have a normal life by society's standards. Sandra had kissed the Tailor girl in the ditch by our fort plenty of times and she grew out of it. I was sure this was a temporary situation. I would come to my senses soon enough.

For two years previously, Dennis had been dating a fellow teacher, Donna. She stood a foot shorter than him. Donna's wavy black hair, almost blue, fell to the collar of her blouse. She had a tomboy quality that suited her cute face. Although they made a nice looking couple, they'd recently cooled things about the time I moved into the Massey. He cared a great deal for her, even confiding to me that he loved her, but that he was more satisfied in the intimate company of men. She knew nothing of his other life and Dennis wanted to keep it that way. There wasn't an official break up. They still talked at school and Dennis saw her occasionally, just not with the same intensity as before. Donna thought they were taking a break, rethinking the relationship, slowing down perhaps to pick things up at a later time.

After more time with Dennis, I became growingly dependent on him like a parent. He knew it and played the role well, nurturing me while I gave him the pleasures of my body. He looked after me, showing me the attention I had never received. Dennis had a way of making me feel special. He said he was falling in love with me, but love was a term I didn't understand very well. It was a confusing word with contradictions. Mother had said, she loved me, but she kept going back to my father. Sometimes I saw that as her siding with him. How could she love me if she was with him? Father, on occasion tried to show love, but I never remember the word being spoken by him. So, I learned not to trust anyone who said those words, or tried to imply them. Every time something bad happened — a fight, a drunken binge, a beating — my father asked for forgiveness, promising it would never happen again. He could never keep his promises of love, so the word "love" meant trouble over the horizon.

Several months into our association, Dennis and I moved into an apartment not far from the Massey. Everyone thought we had just become good buddies and were moving in together to save money. What a facade.

My time with him had given me some sense of security. And a part of me began to feel the need to move on. I was slowly becoming bored with graduate studies and living in Macon. I wanted to see the world, to see what, if anything, existed out there. I dreamed of moving to a large city and being an artist, though I'd done little with my art while with Dennis. I realized finishing grad school and landing a nice, safe job as a teacher wasn't for me. My heart was never in teaching, I knew I would be doing the profession and myself a great injustice if I continued in something for such poor reasons. My constant search for safety, stemming from the first time my father laid a hand on me was easing; allowing me to think about following my dreams. But regardless of how safe it felt with Dennis, I couldn't see me staying with him. With my new sense of confidence, I thought about Besty and Monica, thought about being a man again.

Dennis didn't like the idea of me quitting school or leaving town.

"Randy, you should wait until you finish school," he insisted. "Everyone needs as much education as they can get today. Besides, I don't want you to leave. I love you. I think you're what I've been looking for. We can make things work."

"I don't know what I want to do. I just don't think this is going to be forever," I pleaded.

The more Dennis talked about me giving up the idea of moving, the more I thought about it and the more I was determined to leave. The shame I felt about our relationship loitered. A change would be good. It was time to get back on course with that "new life." Dennis had made me feel good about myself; he had built some confidence in me. For once, I had hope for the future. My future, I felt might be more than just a dream.

Atlanta was ninety miles north of Macon. I had visited there a few times with Besty and liked the feel of it. My first reaction driving into the city was of Dorothy coming into view of the Emerald City at the end of the yellow brick road. And Dennis had taken me to some gay bars there, but that wasn't why I was going. As the days passed, I thought more and more about making the move. My mother would see this relocation as a move farther away from her. I hoped it wouldn't cause her any pain. After all, it was just one and a half hours away, instead of a half hour now. Her drinking hadn't stopped, and I feared my initial move to Macon had encouraged it. But, I couldn't move back in with her and end up like the landlady's son. Although Maxwell had his own apartment, it was evident he had never moved away from his mother. I had to break away — break away from Dennis, Besty, Monica, the landlady's son, from my mother, Kenneth and from what I was fearing I might be turning into. Everything I knew told me to run.

My persistence in making plans deepened the rift with Dennis. We began to argue about little things. Dennis wasn't willing to either give his blessings or continue a friendship.

"Once you move to Atlanta, it'll be all over between us. That town is full of good looking guys. You'll find someone else and forget about me," Dennis would lament.

"Look, this will be good for both of us. I need to see what's out there. Atlanta is only an hour's drive, for God's sake. Besides, how can two guys stay together? I'm planning to get married one day and have a family, like you should. What about Donna? I don't think this is right," I responded, still trying to deny my deepest needs.

I decided to wait until the end of the quarter of school before making the move. During that time period, Dennis and I continued to argue on and off. When he realized I was determined to leave, he started dating Donna regularly again. He rationalized that if I was going to leave, then he was better off with her. I hoped Donna would be good for him and that one day I would meet the right woman and settle down. In a strange way, I felt like I was a child leaving home again. Soon Dennis and Donna were together almost everyday and I found myself oddly jealous of their relationship. I started feeling lost again, like the day I graduated from college and like the day I left home. It seemed as if I would never shake that feeling, that would keep cropping up and consuming me.

After convincing myself to move on, there were a few intimacies between Dennis and me. Sometimes I felt insecure, unsure of what to do and gave in to him. But at all cost I had to stick to my plan. Perhaps, for the most part, they were instigated by me. I needed to test his love even though he was back with Donna, to see if he still wanted me. I seduced Dennis, it was a terrible game to play with him. One I knew was based in years of loneliness and rejection. I craved to be loved and Dennis was always willing to comfort me, even as Donna eased back into the picture. I became the seducer, perhaps I had always been.

I quickly found an apartment on Euclid Avenue in the young, trendy Little Five Points section and would be moving in less than a mouth. I was given a transfer to the downtown Atlanta Macy's in the Visual Merchandizing department; my art background helping me get the job. A week after telling Dennis, he broke the news that Donna was taking a teaching job in Florida. He would soon follow her there and they would marry. If I wanted him to stay, I would have to stay, too. While making my plans, I had presumed Dennis would stay in Macon and be there if I needed him. Their moving to Florida was upsetting. I knew this meant Dennis wouldn't be around for me anymore if I told him to go. I realized this was a chance for him to get married to a nice woman and have a family. He was that kind of guy; he would make a great husband and father, I thought. I couldn't be selfish anymore. It was time for the game to end and let Dennis go.

"Randy, I know in my heart I love you," Dennis explained. "It's hard for one man to love another. Many people see it as wrong, but I only know my heart. I think I could spend the rest of my life with you if you were willing to try, but if you say no, I'm going to get married. Maybe it will work with Donna and maybe it won't, but I think it's better for me to be married and divorced if things don't work out, than never to be married at all in our society. You need someone to look after you, I wanted to be that person, but I can't seem to break through to you."

"Dennis, you have a chance at something that I don't want to mess up. I don't know what I want, but I can't stand in the way of this," I said. "I may need you today, but I have to grow up sooner or later. It may as well be sooner."

The day the U-Haul truck sat in the driveway of our apartment was a dreary one. It rained on and off as we loaded up Dennis' belongings. I fought back the tears, trying not to be too emotional around Donna. I didn't want her to suspect a thing. For all she knew, Dennis and I were just good friends. She didn't know I'd shared the comforts of his body against mine or that his arms had held me as many long nights turned into mornings. She would never know of the times his lips had kissed my body and I would never know his touch again.

In another few weeks classes would be over and I would be leaving as well. My "new life" looked very sad as they pulled away. He was hers now. I envied Donna as the truck turned the corner and disappeared down the street. The rain began to fall hard out of the dark sky. As each raindrop hit my face, it felt like bullets shooting for my heart, and I realized, sooner had come a little too soon.

roberto

Over the years, Todd had gathered a tremendous number of friends. So it was no surprise the waiting room was getting crammed. In fact, the hospital operator informing: Todd had more calls coming through the switchboard than the Governor of Georgia had when he was a patient. His three brothers, two older, the other a twin, stayed close to their mother's side, spending the afternoon crisscrossing from the hospital room to the waiting area. The moment I saw Mrs. Weaver, I knew instantly, that she was Todd's mother. This was our first meeting. The preppiest woman I had ever met. Mrs. Weaver and Todd were very much alike. Over the years, I had always joked with Todd that he was too preppy and he always denied it. Even though Mrs. Weaver knew Todd was gay, she had never met many of his gay friends before now. The Weavers were from a small town like myself; homosexuals were never talked about, at least not in a pleasant manner. Mrs. Weaver was touched by the pouring out of love for her son and she quickly took to Todd's close friends. Occasionally, as our friendship grew, Todd had invited me to come with him to visit his family. But, because of my family background, I never took up his offers. It pained me to be around other friends' families who had a good history. Even though I was happy for their amicable upbringing, it was too much of a reminder of the failings within my own family.

Marie got off the elevator and stopped several feet from

where I was standing. "How long have you been here?" she asked. She had been the one who called me that Todd was in the hospital. I had introduced them during a charity fund raiser that we had all worked on together. They hit it off from the beginning. Marie and Todd were like soul mates reunited from a previous life. Her smile was comforting, as I watched her tall, statuesque body walk toward me. Marie's blond hair brushed the tops of her shoulders as she moved. Besides being beautiful, Marie had the heart of an angel. It was no wonder why Todd and her became close so quickly. A doctor carrying a folder made note of her attractiveness, throwing a glance of appreciation her way as he passed. Marie had the qualities of several women I had known over the years. She was the best of them. Tall like Besty, she carried herself well. And when Marie walked into a room, her presence didn't go unnoticed. As well, she had the quiet flirtation that had once attracted me to Monica.

After six months at the apartment on Euclid, I moved to Marietta, just north of Atlanta, in with Archer, Monica's ex brother-in-law. Atlanta was more expense than I had expected and I needed to save money. Shortly after getting settled in, Todd and I finally met one night at a party I had been reluctant to attend. A sharp looking guy had handed me an invitation the weekend before, during a brief visit to a gay bar. I made myself go, practically sneaking out, so as to avoid any explanation to Archer of my plans for the evening. I followed the directions printed on the invitation; several times wanting to turn around. But I was determined not to give into my insecurities; at the time, that was a huge feat.

I turned the corner on Stillwood Street as indicated on the invitation. For a mile, both sides of the street were lined with cars, where manicured homes stood positioned on large lots among an abundance of seasoned trees. I approached the brick walk of the Tutor house displaying a crowd of silhouettes moving in its lighted windows. I told myself, there was no turning back. A few feet in front of me, four well dressed men neared the door. I followed them in.

Todd approached me as I stood in a corner near the buffet table gulping down my second beer. I was feeling especially nervous, wondering what would happen if my very straight new roommate ever found out I was at a gay party.

"Don't I know you?" he asked. "I'm Todd."

"Randy," I answered, surprised at his introduction.

"Where do I know you from?" Todd questioned.

"We've said hello at some of the bars around town. I saw you last week at the Pharr Library," I explained.

"That's right. You're always by yourself. Are you new to Atlanta?" Todd asked, reaching for an hors d'oeuvre.

"I moved here from Macon less than a year ago," I answered.

"Well, I just moved here about the same time from Athens. I went to school at the UG," Todd said.

"So, you're a BullDog!" I commented.

"That's right and proud of it," Todd responded. "Where did you go?"

"Mercer. You've heard of it?" I asked.

"Yes, I know a few people that went there. Do you know....," Todd started to ask before I stopped him.

"I didn't know many people there, Todd," I interrupted. "What was your major at Georgia?"

"Art." he replied.

"Me too," I answered, happy we had something in common.

Todd could tell I was shy, where other people might think I was stuck on myself. I somehow hoped by spending time around him I would learn something. Mostly how to be like him. I wanted to have an outgoing personality like Todd and I wanted people to flock to me the way his friends congregated around him. I later learned you have to be a special person; those qualities can't easily be learned.

After five years of marriage, Archer's wife had come to the realization that she was a lesbian. When I first moved in, I decided to forget about any experiences that anyone might determine as gay. This decision was faithful to a history of always attempting to erase painful and confusing situations. But my curiosity occasionally sent me to the other side, and eight months later, I wasn't so sure anymore. The feelings were too strong again, making it harder and harder to keep my mind off men.

At all cost, I didn't want Archer to suspect anything. Because of his ex-wife, sexuality was a sensitive subject around the apartment; his manhood had been injured. He was an ex-football jock, often having his college buddies and their girlfriends over. I was not sure how he, or they, might respond to the months I spent with Dennis, or my sporadic visits to gay bars. They joked about having their dicks sucked by other guys, like it was okay as long as you didn't touch the other guy. Bantering among themselves, Archer said to one of his friends, "Suck my dick," and always got the response, "You only wish I would." Practically every Saturday, they rough-housed while watching college football on television. Grabbing each other, joking, wrestling and hugging were spectator sports, but I felt aroused by their innocent show of comradeship. Archer and his friends weren't bad guys and they had adopted me into their group, the kind of situation I'd longed for since grade school. They were like the guys in Phys Ed class who'd grown up and, in the process, stopped being such complete jerks. I feared losing their acceptance if they knew I'd ever been with another man. Monica and I still kept in touch, mostly to avoid suspicion on my part. She eagerly made the short commute to visit, always spending the night in my bed. I would do anything to fit in, and that meant continuing to sleep with Monica. She was a beautiful women. Sex with her wasn't difficult, but as before, it lacked something I couldn't quite put my finger on. Perhaps something in me was lacking. It was hard being on my guard all the time, trying to act like "one of the guys." Always afraid of that flashing neon sign on my forehead giving me away, spelling out my past. I wanted to be totally straight, like Archer and his friends, but I had no one to talk with to help me make sense out of these feelings. Nevertheless, I could play the game. As difficult as it was, I could pretend there was nothing missing.

Maybe that's the way sex is for me, I thought. Perhaps that's the way it is for everyone; the hint of something missing, something incomplete. But, I wanted more, needed more, maybe too much more. I found myself fantasizing about one of Archer's buddies, Gavin. Even with Monica in the bed with me, I dreamed about him. In the morning I would be hard, almost sore from my erection ready to explode. Monica thinking my condition was because of her, woke me with her mouth on my cock. But it was his lips — Gavin's — I wanted on me. He was the nicest one of their group, sweet but still manly. Occasionally, when Gavin had a few too many beers, he would throw me over his shoulder and toss me around. It excited me. I had to concentrate on not allowing any physical response that would reveal how much I enjoyed his muscular arms around me, wrestling me to the ground. If he only knew I'd been with another guy; and what would Gavin think if he knew I'd slept with him in my dreams? I thought, while his body pinned me down. And what would Monica? His horse play was, I guess after all, some gesture of brotherhood to the smaller guy in the group, but it meant more to me.

I had to endure a fag joke here and there around the apartment, many times the result of a recent conversation Archer might have had with his ex-wife. But I wasn't one of "them." I'd only experimented, I had an open mind, which meant the confusion would end soon and everything would be fine. Archer and his friends were accepting me, not having done so if they thought I was a fag. Monica and I were getting along fine; she had been coming up to Atlanta more and more, and maybe, just maybe, things would work out.

An incident after one of Archer's parties at our apartment unnerved me. At least fifty people attended, most of whom were his friends. I'd invited a few friends from work, mostly women, but no gay guys. An associate of Archer's left a note on my bed while the party began winding down.

A white sheet of paper folded four times stating: Randy, call me for lunch at my office, 876... Gary. Why not just ask me? Why leave a note on the pillow of my bed? Such a personal place to leave a note. During the course of the evening, we'd been talking in the kitchen while his wife socialized in the living room. As far as I was aware, we discussed nothing of real interest, nothing of an intimate nature. Gary and Archer had gone to graduate school together, but Gary knew few people at the party. I imagined that was why he spent so much time talking with me. After the few friends I'd invited had left, I appreciated his company. A charming person, with analyzing eyes, Gary was very controlled. He paused his breathing as he listened to me talk, and then exhaling slowing with interest, his eyes reacting to what I was saying. He stood close, sometimes touching my shoulder as he laughed after amusing himself by something he said; causing me at times, to feel the need to step back and regain my space. After awhile, I got the feeling he had other things in mind. I'd sensed it before — the way his eyes watched me like Dennis'. My discovering the note confirmed it, and as far as I was concerned, the feelings weren't mutual. Not as mutual as they would have been had it been Gavin talking close with me, his large stature less than a foot from me. He was occupied by a new girlfriend. How I wished the note was from Gavin. Still to say, the note excited me. It was from a man, left in the most intimate of places. But how could Gary tell about me, about my short history with Dennis. Was some inner sign flashing? How could I unplug the sign so it would stop. Was there a scent left on me from being with another man that could be picked up, like a dog sniffing out a bitch in heat? It was a good thing Monica wasn't in town for the party. It would have been tough pretending to get excited over her.

I made the mistake of showing Archer the note after the party, and he had apparently had one too many beers.

"I always thought Gary was a little different," Archer said. "Though I don't think Susie has a clue."

"Well, I can't believe he left this note on my bed," I said, trying to be totally surprised by the situation.

"You never know about a person, even if you've lived with them for years," Archer said. "I never knew about Liz until the day she told me. It takes all kinds. Maybe I should try it," Archer said, as he grabbed at my shirt, pulling the tail out of my pants.

"Try what?" I replied, as I stepped away from him, a little concerned with what was on his mind.

"Doing guys, and I think I'll start with you," he answered with a laugh.

He started chasing me around the apartment, continuing pulling at my clothes.

"Archer, you've had too much to drink and besides, you've got the wrong guy," I said, not happy with myself that I was really wishing he was Gavin.

"I don't think so, Randy. Don't worry, your secret is safe with me," Archer said, as he threw his weight against me, causing us to fall to the floor.

"Are you telling me that you're gay, Archer?"

"No, just that I'm horny and feeling open minded at the moment," he insisted.

"Well, I'm not interested, so get the hell off me," I said adamantly.

Archer got the message and stumbled to his feet, cautiously holding his right knee he had permanently injured playing ball. Now standing, he offered his hand to help me up.

"No thanks, I can manage just fine," I asserted.

"Okay," Archer said. "Suit yourself."

"Look Archer, what makes you think I'm gay?" I asked.

"You never talk about girls and you don't even seem to be interested in them," Archer explained. "Monica mentioned she had an idea since you've shown little interest in her at times. You know, she's a great girl, we talk about Liz, about you...you know relationship stuff. Monica says you're not aggressive, she has to almost always instigate things between the two of you. You never go to Macon to see her; she always has to come here. If you're not interested in a girl who looks like that, then you have to be gay!"

"Is that a problem with you, Archer? I mean, if it were so?"

"I don't care what you are Randy, but I don't think you want to let the guys know. I was just kidding with you to see what you'd say. I saw Gary talking to you most of the night. I like girls and only girls, so don't worry I'm not fucking around with any guys. I'm strictly into pussy, if you know what I mean; Monica's sister Liz is the funny one. Maybe if I were on a deserted island, but he would have to be awful pretty. I won't be coming into your bedroom in the middle of the night to get any, and don't worry, I won't tell anyone. It looks like Gary is the one you need to worry about."

"Archer, HELL man... I'm not interested in men, and besides Gary's married. He's as straight as you are," I affirmed.

"Yea, he's married alright...and so was Liz to me, but now she's doing the muff diving. Man, we've been living together for almost a year. I been watching you...you're not like regular guys, but that doesn't mean something is wrong with you. Believe me, this thing with Liz has really changed the way I look at things," Archer reacted.

"Well, that doesn't have anything to do with me," I responded. "Just keep yourself out of my room if you're sleepwalking, thinking you're on some island somewhere without any women, if you know what I mean Archer."

As much as I wanted to, I wasn't about to admit anything to Archer about my feelings. I wasn't going to trust anyone, at least for now. But, since I couldn't seem to shake my feelings from the past regarding my sexuality, I was a little relieved Archer didn't seem to be bothered by my questionable state. After all, he'd been taking Liz's situation pretty well, after the initial impact, from what I could tell. Until I knew where my head was, or at least the vicinity it was in, I would keep quiet. And if Archer knew for sure, maybe he was telling me it was alright. I thought we respected each other's privacy up till now. Maybe I wouldn't have to be as uneasy around him, but I was surprised he accepted it or that he wouldn't tell anyone about our conversation. At least I hoped he wouldn't. All the more reason to get out on my own again. We had less than four months left on our lease. And, as far as Monica was concerned, Archer was right. I was just letting things happen, not instigating anything. Which could just mean I was passive, not homosexual.

Since I'd moved in with Archer, it was taking longer to get to and from work. The commute home, especially on Friday afternoons was a bear. Normally a twenty minute drive in moderate traffic. As I sat in traffic, I often wondered why had I moved all the way out to suburbia. Regardless of what time I left, it seemed everyone in the city was on my schedule. There was always a hint of anxiety as I walked to the parking lot, wondering if I was going to beat the bulk of the traffic. If I could get on the interstate — only a few blocks from work — by four-thirty, then I would stand a pretty keen chance of beating the brunt of it. If I was really lucky, I would pull into the apartment complex by five-fifteen. My anxiety was magnified by the deteriorating condition of my car; it didn't have another commute left in it. Driving Atlanta's interstates compared, at times, to entering a battle my car wasn't equipped to engage in. The congestion at rush hour was enough to blow the thermostat which always ran hot. If it rained, then I was wet by the time I arrived at my destination, since the rag top leaked and the window on the driver's side often refused to roll all the way up. Now that Dennis was out of the picture, and my salary wasn't enough to keep it in good shape, the car was barely working. The only things holding it together were: Prayers, duct tape and the loving hands of an understanding mechanic. Bob was recommended by Nelson, my boss. Apparently, Nelson and Bob were an item some ten years ago. Everyone referred to Nelson as "mother." Why, I'm not sure. In his mid 40s, and as gay as they came, he took great pride in sharing stories of his weekend visits to various truck stops and rest areas along Interstate 75 south between Atlanta and Valdosta. He was explicit in giving the details of crawling in the back of a trucker's cab and engaging in sex. And if a trucker wasn't available, there were others like him hanging around to walk back in the woods behind a rest area and go at it. All day long he talked about men and sex, and men and sex. It was "girl this and girl that... girl all you need is the right man to make you see the light." It wasn't the best working environment if you're a gay man fooling yourself in trying to be straight. Everything and everybody associated in visual merchandizing — or "display" — it seemed was gay. And, if you weren't gay, everyone thought you were once you told them what you did for a living. It was everything I was trying to get away from. My first year in Atlanta wasn't putting very many miles between me and Macon. I hadn't met any women to make me stop thinking about men. I hadn't found a cure for what ailed me. And Nelson's persistence in his storytelling sickened me such that I felt more ashamed.

The fact that Bob was gay and his garage was next to a gay bar, in a predominately gay section of town, may or may not have had anything to do with the good rates he gave me. He may have been tuned in to what was going on under my hood, as well as the condition of my car's motor.

I was ready to move closer to downtown, into the Midtown area. Not far from the part of town I first moved into. I'd received a nice raise that would compensate living alone again. My interests were in the Midtown area because of its proximity to work and the charm of the old Victorian homes. Many of which were divided into apartments, reminding me of Macon. The fact it was known for its large gay population was of little consequence. So what if anyone thought I was gay, I'd made several straight friends who lived in Midtown; female, but straight all the same. But as with the somewhat false perception of working in display, the same was true of living in Midtown. I could act as straight as I wanted, but that, and actively suppressing my gay thoughts wasn't enough to quell the desiring interest which occasionally continued to surface. So what did I have to lose?

Almost two months had passed since my conversation with Archer after his party. I'd managed to stay out of the gay bars. Todd and I kept in touch over the phone. For that short period, he was my only contact to that world; he was understanding of my torn feelings. Then I met Roberto.

He was tall and dark, you can take the handsome part for granted. I saw him coming like a bull released in a spring pasture, as I tussled with a mannequin's torso in men's IZOD.

"Excuse me," he said with a Latin accent, "Do you work here?"

No, I thought to myself. I just hang out in department stores and rearrange the displays. What does he mean do I work here?

"Yes," I answered, finding it hard not to fall into those big, dark eyes.

He was potent. When he spoke, the strength in his voice required attention. I would like to have such an effect on people, I thought to myself. I found myself collecting qualities in men I wanted for myself, thinking maybe all along that was my attraction to them. I wasn't gay, I just wanted to be another man other than the one God made me, more than the one my father had made — the inferior one. There were periods when I felt very gay, which meant weak and vulnerable, like Kenneth and the landlady's son at the Massey. Other times, I felt strong and untouchable by the desires related to forbidden encounters and dreams of a man's lips on mine. All the time, struggling to be a man and remake myself with those qualities I coveted in others I viewed from a distance, like this Latin stranger.

"Can you tell me where I can find the children's clothes?" he inquired, in his broken English.

"One floor up to the left," I replied, still holding the half mannequin.

"Thank you," he said, pausing for a moment as if he was going to ask another question. He turned, heading off in the direction I'd instructed.

I watched him walk away. My eyes were fixed to his shiny, thick black hair and the way it laid against his head, touching the collar of his cobalt shirt. With the imposing presence of a robust prince, he carried himself. I continued to watch him make his way to the base of the escalator. Stepping up, he turned around scanning the store. His head moved in my direction, catching my eyes on him. Quickly, I looked down pretending to be busy, hoping he was unaware of my gaze. With a quick glance back, I could see his shoes stepping onto the second floor. Just like that, he was gone. I put the torso down to regain my composure.

I had a lot to do in the store. Too bad, I thought, I didn't have anything to do in the Children's Department. It would be pointless anyway, this man was straight, like I should be. I needed to get my mind back on work. But, it wasn't him I wanted, I convinced myself, I just wanted to be him. To have his life and discard mine. This man was a prince and I a peasant.

Finally, I finished putting the IZOD mannequins back together with their new dress. My next project was in men's dress shirts, pinning shirts on the bust forms; ten of them. When I got out of college, this wasn't what I thought I would be doing. Graduation was supposed to be like a rebirth for me, filled with freedom and new experiences, not pinning shirts on bust forms in a Macy's department store where the management thought the world revolved around the next One Day Sale. Working in retail made me feel like a servant to the public which most of the time blended with my low self-esteem. Everyone was better than me, so my place was to serve the better people. "We're a part of your life," was Macy's slogan. To me it was more like you're a pain in my butt. But I was happy to have a job, and some days I felt it was the only thing I would do for the rest of my

life. On better days, I dreamed I would free myself of
Macy's as well. I preferred to be working on the painting I
had started two days ago, but it would have to wait until I
got home. Hopefully, I wouldn't be too tired to work at what
I really loved. The late nights were catching up with me,
having been up until two o'clock the past several mornings.
I was managing on only four or five hours sleep a night, but
I knew it was worth it. I disliked my job, hated everyone
assuming I was gay because I worked in display, but mostly
because I longed for the day I would be free to be a painter. I
wouldn't have to serve anyone; it would be my turn to be a
prince.

By the time I'd finished the sixth shirt, I saw him again
walking across from where I was working. He was carrying
a shopping bag as he looked over the racks of clothing. I
coveted him as he came into clear sight, heading for the door
to the parking lot. He glanced my way and our eyes met for a
second. He nodded his head at me. Then he was out the door.

I thought about the stranger several times during the
remainder of the afternoon, and later at home that evening.
There was an enveloping air about him. Perhaps it was just
the fact he was foreign. I'd seen good looking guys before
and not always thought so much about them. But there was
definitely something about this guy making me stir more
than usual. The next day upon returning from lunch I saw
the prince again in Fine China. My heart skipped as I tried to
keep my composure. I walked over to the register pretending
to use the phone, so as to watch him without seeming too
conspicuous.

He picked up a crystal wine glass, scrutinizing the delicate etched cuts. I stood watching every part of his being,
examining his stature and wishing I was as fine. Our eyes
met again, but this time, I dared myself not to turn them
away. There was a slight smile on his lips as he looked at me
and then at the glass and back to me again. The nervousness
grew inside me. At that moment, thoughts of my straight
future, as questionable as they were, crumbled and I could-

n't control its demise. It was like an earthquake and he was at the epicenter. I kept telling myself to walk away, but my feet stood frozen. The internal fight was going on again inside of me. Dennis, my crush on Gavin, and now this stranger, had taken hold of me.

He put the goblet back on the shelf and slowly turned in my direction. It was obvious my eyes were glued to him. Too late to conceal my interest as he approached me.

"Hello, you are the one who directed me yesterday. My name is Roberto."

"I'm Randy," I replied, feeling awkward and shy, afraid of being scolded for staring.

"You're not from here, are you?"

"No, I am from Argentina."

"So Roberto, what brings you to Atlanta?" I searched for something more to say.

"Well, I work for my government in promoting trade with the United States."

"That sounds like a very exciting job, much more so than what I do here."

"I am sure you must enjoy your work."

"No, not really. I'm an artist, I just do this to pay the bills, if you know what I mean."

"Yes, I do Randy. That is important. What kind of art do you do?"

"I'm a painter. I'm not really sure how I would describe my work. I'm still trying to understand it myself. I've only been out of school for a short time."

"Well perhaps you can show me sometime and I can judge it for myself."

"Sure, why not?" I answered in astonishment at the outcome.

"We should have dinner and you can show me around Atlanta. I will be here for another two weeks."

Later that night, I picked Roberto up for dinner at his hotel not far from my apartment. On the way over, I wondered what was on his mind. I still wasn't sure if he had the same feelings I did. Maybe he was just lonely and wanted someone to show him around. Maybe he thought I was just a regular friendly guy. I had been trying to fool myself I was straight for so long and I guess it was working; at least on everyone else.

Upon arriving, Roberto informed me he had an early morning appointment. It had been scheduled after we had talked in the store. He asked if it was alright that we eat in the hotel restaurant. Whatever he wanted was fine. He could take charge of the evening; I was certainly not in control.

Like a school boy, I sat across the table listening to stories about his native country. My mind filled with romantic ideas and I hesitantly wanted to go there. My daydreaming brought me in and out of the conversation as Roberto talked. Good thing he was a talker. I just wanted to listen to him.

My heterosexuality was again sliding away, my desires too slippery to hold onto it. I'd been so good keeping my distance, but now I felt like I was being pulled out of a layer of skin that had been suffocating me with confusion. I couldn't take my eyes off him during dinner. I still didn't understand why I was there. "What was I supposed to do?" I kept wondering.

His knee brushed mine under the table as Roberto moved to a more comfortable position in his chair. I was startled.

"Excuse me, Randy."

"No problem," I replied, looking away from him for a moment.

So it was an accident, I thought. He really didn't mean to do that. I felt silly and wished I were at home where I wouldn't have to deal with this uncertainty. Maybe I'd made a wrong call, Roberto was straight. I didn't have enough experience to be able to tell. I needed something to calm me and the first beer wasn't enough. I ordered another, drinking it quickly. The infusion of alcohol into my system calmed me. But I reminded myself, as I often did, not to drink too much. Careful not to become dependent, as my parents had. Sometimes my body wanted it like a medicine for forgetting. It was easier to talk to people with a few beers in me, easier to pretend I was someone else.

By the third beer, I was feeling much better. It didn't matter how foolish I felt with the situation, dinner would be over soon and I would be back at my apartment. This would be the last time I looked at a stranger in the store or anywhere else for that matter. I will get over these feelings and the right woman is going to come along. I reminded myself, I was going to be a real man.

"Randy, are you with me?" Roberto asked, leaning over the table.

"Yes, I'm sorry. This beer is getting to me a little. I tend to be a lightweight when it comes to drinking," I confessed, excusing my wandering mind.

By now Roberto was finishing the bottle of wine he'd ordered when we first sat down. I didn't drink any of it because wine gives me such a headache and a nasty hangover, but it didn't seem to affect him at all.

"Well, Randy, I would really like to see your art sometime," Roberto said, as he reached for the check the waiter had just left on the table. "I seem to have monopolized the entire conversation and not allowed you to get a word in. Maybe later this week we can get together if you would like. It is getting late and I must get to bed."

"That would be great, I've enjoyed this," I answered, wondering if he could detect the disappointment in my voice in the outcome of the evening. "How much damage did we do?"

"Please, let me get this, Randy."

"Are you sure?"

"Very much so. It's the least I can do for you sitting here listening to me going on about myself."

I had enjoyed it more than he knew and more than I wanted to admit. Roberto walked me to my car. Suddenly there was a slight chill in the air. My knees began to shake as we stood in the parking lot. I was nervous not knowing what he thought of me and I was nervous he was probably not like me. Ashamed, to the point of mortification I had been such a fool. I reached out my hand to shake his. Roberto extended his and pulled me close to him. I was totally taken by surprise.

"You have the prettiest green eyes, Randy. Latins love light colored eyes."

I held my breath as Roberto leaned his face to mine and our lips touched. He was like me, I thought. My heart began to jump in my chest. He pulled slowly away and let go of my hand.

"I will call you tomorrow, Randy," Roberto said, as he walked toward the entrance of the hotel.

I stood in the parking lot long after Roberto was out of sight. The chill had suddenly left me and there was an unsettling, but warm awareness filling my gut. Excited, I drove home sourly savoring the sweetness of what I'd just experienced. But Roberto's kiss wasn't enough to halt the voices tossing the sexual debate around inside my head. I told them to let go and let me be free from the familiar rising guilt. For a short time, I was finally beginning to think I had come a long way from Macon to Atlanta, but this night had somehow taught me otherwise.

All I thought of the next day was Roberto. My mind had lost all control over any reality concerning a slight kiss by a stranger from another part of this world. I felt weak, like the kiss had sucked some energy out of me, but the man who took it appeared anything but weak. Of course, I called Todd to tell him I'd slipped. All along, he'd been telling me to follow the will of my soul. Todd seemed not as enthusiastic by my news, even though his words were still those of support. But if I was to slip again, I think he wanted me to do so with him.

I couldn't wait to get home from work, and of course, the traffic seemed slower than ever. I sat by the phone from five-thirty until nine, hoping it would ring. Every time it rang, I lunged for the receiver and then I held my hand over it, daring not to pick it up until the second ring. Three times it rang for Archer, Gavin being one of the callers. I sat watching the hands of the clock on the mantel move under the glass, slowly making their way in a circle. The tape playing on the stereo had stopped one hour and fifteen minutes ago, and still no call from Roberto. Then the phone suddenly rang, alarming me. Instinctively I looked up to the clock, it was nine-twenty. This had better be the call, I thought. Yes, it was Roberto.

He came over. There was an awkward excitement about the evening. Roberto insisted we go to my room shortly after he arrived, worried that Archer might come home while we were in the living room. He wasn't as talkative as the night before at dinner. We sat on the bed a few feet apart with little conversation. My mind wondered what his thoughts were; wondering why his eyes were examining me. They stared into mine as if looking for something and then moved on to scrutinize my face. Reaching out, he rubbed his hand over my shirt stopping for a brief second at each button from my neck to my waist. He proceeded to unbutton my shirt. As I reached over to unbutton his, he gently stopped me, grasping my hand and placing it back to my side. I surrendered to his unspoken wish as he slowly pulled the shirt away from my skin, letting it lay around me on the bed, still tucked in my pants. Now, his hand rubbed against my bare skin, as his eyes examined what he had unwrapped. Roberto's warm tongue tasted my flesh, brushing over my excited nipples as it moved down the trunk of my body.

After he had finished taking off my clothes, Roberto got up from the bed and began to undress himself, exposing his bare, dark skin. His body hair filled in the strength of his chest. He was what I had imagined an unclothed prince looked like. There were certain things I wouldn't do; things that would make me feel like a real homosexual: No dick sucking — if a guy wanted to go down on me, that was fine, and no anal sex, at least not where I was the recipient.

The next morning I overslept. I was awakened by the

sound of the landscaper's blower outside the window. I looked at the clock radio by the bed, it was eight forty-seven and I was alone. Roberto had left sometime after I fell asleep.

I rushed to get ready for work. The only good thing about being late was that I would miss the traffic into the city. I had to come up with a good excuse for the boss, but I would worry about it on the way in. Now I was more concerned as to why Roberto had left me in the middle of the night.

Roberto didn't call until the following evening just before seven. I was out the door seconds after hanging up the phone. We went to The Pleasant Peasant for dinner; a favorite restaurant in an old bare-brick building with a green stripped canopy, and a flower box in the front window. The candles, on the tables that were covered in crisp white linens, gave a sense of intimacy and romance to the dimly lighted room. The moon's light filtered in ever so softly through a large skylight in the middle of the high ceiling. Starched waiters moved between the tables seated with people engaged in private conversations; the candlelight reflecting off their faces as the quiet hum of voices filled the room.

I was content to sit and watch Roberto again wondering if the other patrons thought we were gay. It was Midtown after all, and several of the tables were seated with same gender couples. I wanted to know everything about him and I mostly wanted to be in his company. There was a mystery about him mirrored by the dimness of the restaurant. Unlike before, he seemed to be turning my questions at dinner back to me. I wanted to know more about Argentina and in my mind I thought of how it would be to be there with him. Strangely I had the feeling, though, he was holding something back,

"Randy, you would love it there, and the people would love you. It is a country that has a great history full of beauty as well as tragedy."

Against my better judgment, I drank several glasses of

wine, but the atmosphere commanded it. Now, I wanted the same liquid passing through Roberto's lips to pass mine. I wanted to taste what he was tasting, to fill my stomach with it. I needed to relax, how I felt in the morning was of little importance to me now. The waiter brought our entree and the conversation slowed. We watched one another eat.

I spent the night in his hotel room. Roberto was aggressive. Our love making consisted of touching and tasting, and unlike before, with Dennis, I wanted to participate, to eat Roberto, to drink him. Like the wine at dinner, I wanted to fill my gut with Roberto until I couldn't drink or eat anymore of him. My world was changing fast. I perceived Roberto as a messenger, holding me to the past I had forsaken, while somehow leading me into the future.

A marathon, I saw him each night through the weekend and into the following week. I knew so little about him, but all I cared about was the way he made me feel. The days came and went, but the nights seemed to last forever. I had stopped worrying about Archer and his friends, about Monica, about what they were thinking about me. But it was easier to meet Roberto at his hotel than risk too many inquiries. Archer asked questions, which I responded simply, "Nothing's going on." I wasn't ready to think about anything I had been doing these past days. My mind was preoccupied. Monica called a few times, but I didn't return her calls.

It was Thursday morning. A week and a half had passed in what seemed like the blink of an eye. I left Roberto's room as the sun was barely breaking through the early morning darkness. The lack of sleep from night after night forced me to hold my head down as I slowly walked to my car. I wouldn't see him until Friday night at eight. Roberto was leaving for an overnight business trip to Washington, D.C. That was good, I needed the rest. Hoping to get a few hours sleep before getting ready for work, I raced the sun back to my apartment. Roberto must like me, I kept thinking as I drove. Maybe I'll go back with him to Argentina. I knew he would be leaving the following Wednesday, and I didn't want us to be separated by all that geography — not yet — my stomach wasn't full.

Friday afternoon, I was anxious to get home as early as possible, in order to relax from the long week and enjoy the freedom from work for two whole days. My anxiety was higher than usual as I sat through the rush hour, trying my best to weave in and out of the traffic to make some time. Normally, I would have planned to spend the evening and most of the weekend painting. But, since I had met Roberto, I had little interest in painting. Luckily, Archer was out of town, so I wouldn't need to worry about him being around. I turned the corner into the entrance of the apartment complex and checked my watch. It was five-fifteen, right on schedule. Maybe Roberto will be a little late. Making a good impression tonight was my goal. I wanted to give him a reason to return, or at least ask me to visit him there.

I began finding out about myself I was becoming more and more concerned how I looked around men. I spent hours getting ready now instead of just rolling out of bed, taking a quick shower and running a comb through my hair. I had exactly two hours and forty-five minutes to get ready for this date. I needed enough time to take a nice soak in the tub for at least thirty minutes. It had been a bitch of a day, which had started at six that morning. Hoping it wouldn't be a "bad hair" night, another fifteen to twenty minutes was needed to comb my hair in just the right way so it would dry the way I liked it. There was always the possibility it wouldn't dry correctly and I would need another fifteen to wet and blow dry it if the first attempt wasn't successful. I needed another thirty to forty-five minutes to decide what I was going to wear, usually having to try on several combinations before I got just the right look. Like Cinderella, I knew I had a limited time frame before I turned back into a pumpkin. Anyhow, I could clean myself up and feel good about myself for only a short time. The bath helped wash the same old filth away, but it wouldn't be long before it rose to the surface again and the reflection in the mirror would be one from the past. I had been trying to develop a new look for myself other than my usual khakis and button downs. I needed the remaining forty minutes to straighten the apartment and make sure everything was neat and in its place. With whatever time was left, I spent worrying about how the evening would turn out.

The car came to a halt in its usual spot. To my surprise, Roberto was sitting on the stairs in front of my door. He couldn't wait until eight, he wanted to see me now, I thought.

"Roberto, you weren't supposed to be here until eight. How was your trip to D.C.?" I said, walking up to him, smiling from ear to ear.

"I could not wait, there is something I have to tell you, Randy."

"What is it?" I asked, my spirits were still high as I unlocked the door. Roberto followed me into the apartment.

"I will be going back earlier than planned."

"When?" My body filled with disappointment.

"Sunday night."

"So, when will you be coming back?"

"It will be a long time from now, I cannot say."

"That's okay, I'll come to visit you."

"No, Randy you can't. I should have told you from the beginning."

"You have a lover in Argentina?" I asked in knowing disbelief.

"No, I have a wife and a little girl. We are expecting our second child in another month, but I must return now. There are problems with the pregnancy. I must go to her."

My eyes filled with tears. I should have known it was too good to last. Selfishly, my concern wasn't for Roberto or for his pregnant wife, only for me and what I was about to lose. What a fool I was. I had been consumed with this exotic, exciting man. He was a half dream, part real, and part fantasy. I thought he gave justification to my sexual feelings and now I felt foolish. I was falling for him, falling for a man

I knew nothing about. I was only sharing him, he never was mine. Was this the way it would be for me? I thought about Gary for a moment and about the note on my bed so nicely folded four times. This was a new breed.

"You're married?" I blurted. "What...are you bisexual...What are you?" I questioned, confused, stripped bare and feeling alone again all at once. Wondering what did this make me?

"I love my wife," Roberto answered. "She does not know about me this way. I was just a long way from home... maybe I should have told you. Can we just leave it at that?"

I ran upstairs leaving Roberto standing in the foyer. A minute later I heard the front door close. It hurt. The anguish inside of me powered with confusion was intense. I realized Roberto would always remain an illusion. If I ever visited Argentina, it wouldn't be with him. I wasn't good enough...he was ashamed of me, ashamed of what I was and what he was.

I wanted the phone to ring after he had left, but it didn't. Part of me wanted to understand what had taken place the past two weeks and the other just wanted to forget. I was scared — as scared as if I were a little boy again with my father standing over me, and I needed someone to tell me who and what I was. I needed for Roberto to explain what it was all supposed to mean. I called him Saturday evening and went to his hotel room. He greeted me at the door, his eyes looked at the floor and not into mine as they had before.

"I am glad you called, Randy," Roberto said, as he gave me a hug. "I hope I did not hurt you, I did not mean to."

"It's okay," I assured him, but not really thinking it was. We both knew it was a lie.

I went over with a lot of questions in my mind, questions about his family, about him and his sexuality and about mine. Could Roberto answer a few and shed some light on my inner confusion? But once I was in the room, I couldn't pull them from my head. I sat in a chair by the bed as Roberto carefully packed his suitcase with baby clothes, the ones he had bought the first day we met.

He asked me to stay one more night, his plane was leaving in the morning. I knew it was probably wrong to stay; it would be selfish and just prolong the inevitable. Suddenly, the fact he had a pregnant wife and child seemed to matter too much at the moment. The news of their existence only took a second for Roberto to divulge, but I had spent days and nights with him. I had cast aside my sexual identity for him — an identity I'd fought to gain and fought to lose again. Maybe another night might help me understand. But I feared it would make things even harder. I went home and sat on the sofa watching the clock's hands making their circles under the glass, but this time I knew the phone wouldn't ring. Roberto had a family at home who knew nothing of me and I knew nothing of them. I pictured a little Latin girl with dark hair and eyes like her father, and a pregnant wife waiting at the airport in Argentina for Roberto. In my mind, I was standing across from them as Roberto reached down to lift up his daughter and then lean over and kiss his wife. I was a stranger in the picture — alone. Why would one man take another if he had a wife and children? At one point in my life, I thought I, too, wanted a family, to have children, to be a better father than the one I had, to be a husband, but you had to be straight to have that, or did you? How does anyone know whether they want something until they have it? What was I supposed to want now? Was I bisexual and didn't know it? That could explain my confusion. My sexuality had been so screwed up from the past, and now I didn't know what was what or who was what.

ted

How desperate I am for you in this one moment of passion.
It has been long since I felt the fire which your presence
tonight has
brought into my flesh.

I hear the call from the wild side as I hold your bullness in
my hand. How
strong that bull is, my grip cannot hold back its desire for
long.

Nor do I truly wish to curtail its journey into me, for I know
it will be a
wild and pleasurable voyage into the jungles where passion
lives.

But I must wait and resist with every energy left to my
sensible side.

Although the moment has caught us in this position, I do not
know you well.
The animal in me wants you to plunge forward and thrust
into me; it begs for it.

But the reality of me tells me not, for after we are through
and the animal
sleeps, we may have taken a dangerous step, unable to ever be
the same
again.

Dr. Griffin, Todd's doctor, walked into the waiting area where Mrs. Weaver was surrounded by her sons, her sister Virginia, a first cousin, Margaret, Marie and a few friends of Todd's who had just arrived moments ago. The room went silent as Mrs. Weaver stood up. The expression on her face yearning for good news — but it was crytococcal meningitis.

"Mrs. Weaver, we're going to operate on Todd to relieve the fluid building up and placing pressure on his spine and head," Dr. Griffin informed, as his hand rested on her petite shoulder.

Three more of Todd's friends: John, Bill and Shannon had arrived. Shannon's older brother, Richard, had AIDS, a battle he had been fighting for ten years. Todd and Shannon had been close for years. The dread in Shannon's face was obvious. His brother, and now another friend...when would it all stop. The visitors despairingly looked at one another and then at Mrs. Weaver. Virginia stood up next to her sister and took her hand. A foot taller, she offered her body as a column to lean against if needed.

"Will he be okay?" Mrs. Weaver asked. "I mean...is Todd in any pain? It's hard to tell you know. He never complains."

Todd was acting bravely. Mrs. Weaver was right, he wouldn't complain. Rather, he kept asking me if his family and friends were okay even though he was the sick one.

"This procedure will make him more comfortable...and then we'll see," Dr. Griffin answered.

While everyone was listening to the doctor, I took the opportunity to peek in on Todd. Cautiously, I slipped into the room so as not to disturb his sleep.

I went out with Todd two months after we'd met at the party in the Tutor house. It took me that long to get over Roberto; the experience had me in a quandary. After that, Todd coaxed me out a few more times. My desires had a bitter taste now and I saw it as a sign to shy away from men. We danced together; I felt honored to be seen with him again. Todd was sweet, innocent and fun. And he was safe; there was no chance for any sexual involvement, or at least I thought so. I decided to be a spectator instead of a participant in the gay life, as if that was a decision so easily made. He was definitely of the "A" list crowd and I still hoped everyone was watching. He introduced me around, I was the new guy in town. But I kept my distance not ready to fully step into the circle. We hung out together most of the evening until it was time to go home. Out of the blue, Todd asked me to go home with him.

"I'm not like those other guys, Randy," Todd said, in an attempt to sway me. His request caught me off guard.

"Ah, it's late, I need to get home. And besides, Archer asks a lot of questions. I just want to keep things cool. I like being around you Todd, you're a great guy, but...I got to go," I said, sensing disappointment on his face.

Even though Todd was very cute, I wasn't aroused by him. The goal was to become good friends with Todd, not have sex. And not just friends because he was gay, but because he was a good guy.

Todd knew the struggle I was facing. He'd been a good ear for me, many nights listening on the phone until late. And that's what Todd did: Listen. He made no judgments, maybe a few jokes, but that was his nature: A jokester. "Just let me know when you're ready, I'll ease you into things," he would say.

But I had already been eased in and the results hadn't met my expectations.

Still, being stung and left dazed wasn't enough to kill the thoughts of being with men. Monica could keep my mind clear for short periods, but I soon found myself with the thoughts again. I would see a man, like Roberto and something would click in me. Regular guys, or even good looking ones didn't have that kind of effect on me, but if they emitted a quality of forcefulness and power, then I heard the click in my gut.

It would take someone like Marshall. A Goliath whom I'd admired from afar when out with Todd. Marshall was the first guy I met as a result of being in a gay bar, and when I saw him, I heard the click. And maybe, I thought, the fact he was out in the bar would make a difference. Dennis and Roberto were found in the mainstream of life, where Marshall was out where men go to meet other men. Perhaps this situation would be different.

Marshall had the qualities of the others: A forcefulness, well over six-feet tall with dark blond, slightly receding hair. His clothes took shape to his muscular frame. With Todd at my side and usually aware of my game, I tried to position myself in the bar were Marshall could see me. Making numerous trips past him as he talked with his friends, I had little success and very little confidence of being acknowledged. Going up to him would have been out of the question. In fact, if Todd hadn't introduced himself at the party, we may have never become friends. A few times before I had watched Marshall leave with another guy. What should that matter to me, I was just a spectator now. But for how long? On one occasion I stood and watched him walk toward the door. I feared I had spent another night only failing again to catch his eye. As Marshall got closer to the door I found a moment of courage. Putting down my beer I followed him. Todd was on the dance floor with a friend. By the time I made it to the parking lot he was getting into his Volvo. I raced to my car not sure what I was doing. Catching up to him at the exit of the lot I rolled down my window and finally caught his eye.

I followed Marshall back to his house where we eagerly messed around. It was easier to have sex with someone than to think of something to talk about. And that became a standard practice in the future. I was ecstatic, he must like me, I thought. We made plans to have dinner a few days later.

I arrived at Marshall's on time for our dinner date, catching him still getting dressed. I was excited about seeing him again, imagining a wonderful candlelight dinner at a quaint in-town restaurant and then, a night of just being with him. He wasn't married and I hoped there wouldn't be any surprises as with Roberto.

Marshall got us beer while I sat on the sofa taking in the beauty of his polished home and admiring his collection of art from his travels around the world. He was a professor at Georgia State. He had the body of a football player and he was smart. What more could I ask for?

"You know, I'm not really that hungry, but I'll go along if you are," Marshall blurted out.

The dinner was obviously not going to happen. I told him I could pass on eating. For a few minutes, at my encouragement, he talked about his teaching and travels. Then we were in his bed.

I wanted to find out how he felt about being gay and how he got this way. But it was obvious Marshall didn't. No dinner. No conversation. No intimacy. I realized I was nothing but a fuck. There was no substance to the evening. Sure sex was something on my mind, that's what got me there in the first place, but I needed more information on why. I was disappointed, feeling like a kid from a small town getting screwed in the big city of Atlanta. Marshall eagerly climbed on top of me. His hand moved over my ass trying to push his finger in me. I repeatedly pushed it away until he got the message. I still wasn't ready to go there, not ready to be a full fledged homosexual. The next morning it was worse. My car wouldn't start. I had to ask Marshall for a ride home, unlike the ride he tried to give me the night before. When he dropped me off, he said those fatal three words — "keep in touch." Which meant, call me if you want to get fucked. I knew that was the end of that romance.

From the arms of Marshall I ran into Todd's. Tuesdays, Thursdays and Friday nights were Pharr Library night, where all the more conservative professional homosexuals — "preppies"— converged. Todd had explained to me Atlanta had its share of gay establishments which each night of the week drew a crowd. Saturday night, it was the Armory — a place known for its rougher crowd, although everyone eventually showed up there. Around midnight, everyone migrated to Backstreet, a more mainstream dance bar frequented by all types of people, ranging from the leather types, to drag queens to the all-American football players. Interracial straight couples went to Backstreet because they wouldn't have to worry about being hassled. Also, a number of accepting straights frequented the dance bar as well because it was known that Backstreet's deejays played the best music in the city. If you were really desperate for companionship and hadn't scored, or you were drunk or on drugs, or just wanted to stay out all night, you went to the Cove after Backstreet closed where the soles of your shoes stuck to the floor. On Saturday and Sunday mornings the parking lot would still be filled with cars until noon. There were several other cheesy bars around town one didn't frequent on a regular basis if one wanted to keep a good reputation.

Todd and I danced until almost closing. After leaving the bar we went to Todd's apartment where I didn't leave until late morning the following day. Why? I guess he caught me on a good night or maybe because I was tired of the big guys trying to screw me. I put my desires to be in the company of huskier men like Marshall aside and took Todd. At first it felt awkward but it was very much like being with Besty and Monica. In comparison to Todd I was the bigger guy, outweighing him by thirty pounds and standing several inches taller. For a night I had played the aggressive role of Marshall, and Todd, the role of me. I blamed the night on too much drink.

Todd was very direct; one of the things I liked about him. After our one night together, he wanted to continue seeing me intimately. I broke down trying to explain my confusion and desire for men like Marshall. Todd was great from then on. He sat and talked with me about his feelings and his emotions. Relating them to mine, he explained that emotions are the sensors which send us out into the world to find fulfillment in life. "If we are true to them we will find peace within ourselves, but if we deny them or have others deny them for us, an eternal restlessness results," I remember him saying. He continued to illuminate me by expressing that these emotions live in everyone directing us. He said, "They are visceral feelings stirring from our very individual cores, steering us in one direction, when society or our own mind tell us to take a different road. If we stay true to ourselves we will know the right road to take. Take your time, Randy. Listen to your heart," Todd lovingly advised. Because of Todd's friendship and understanding, I was beginning to understand the emotions raging inside of me.

Albert and Roger, two friends of Todd's I had become close to, came into the room. "Hello Randy, Mrs. Weaver said you were here," Albert whispered. "How's the little guy doing?" Roger asked.

"He has been sleeping on and off most of the afternoon. I'll let you two visit...he should be awake soon," I said, stepping out of the room. I walked back to the window in the waiting area.

Albert and Roger were handsome men. Albert, a social worker, was twenty-seven and four years younger than Roger, a big corporate attorney. Both had brown hair and athletic bodies; Roger had a nicely trimmed mustache and a larger build. In happier days, my new friends, including Todd, were showing me what their lives were like. At the time, years ago, I thought that perhaps I might find out how different their world was from mine, and in that way, I could find relief. I could justify my separation and feel more like the ones whose characteristics I had coveted. Show me I was normal. Or, on the other hand, show me how much our lives were alike.

My second year in Atlanta, for Thanksgiving, I went on vacation with Albert and Roger. Todd spent the holiday with his family. It became a trip that would change a big part of me.

As I remember, the late afternoon sun lit a path through the pale blue room. From the window, it skipped across the bed and settled on a wicker chair against the far wall. Shadows from the panes, tall and opening into the room, were elongated and distorted on the walls and floor. The room felt fresh, as it was washed by the cool breezes from the sea. In the distance, I could hear the water crashing against the rocks and cleansing them, mixed with faint noises of traffic and voices from the street below on the other side of the hotel.

The air in the room was warm and I could feel perspiration beading on my forehead and behind my neck. I stood there quietly trying to absorb the moment. Every few seconds the breeze came through the window, sending a slight chill through me.

I was in a strange place, but not afraid. The clean white sheets and pillows on the bed reflected the sunlight, illuminating the room. The whiteness of the surroundings was calming; it was a soft feeling. The bed looked inviting and it made me a little anxious. I knew I would be on it soon and I was trying to imagine if it was as soft and comforting as it looked.

"Randy, the shower's ready, let's get cleaned up," a voice called from a small hallway around the corner of the room.

I looked away from the window in his direction. Everything felt like slow motion; I was being awakened from a trance. There he stood a few feet from me. The sunlight through the window reflected off his muscular frame covered in suntan oil from the day on the beach. As I looked down I could see a trail of sand made by his feet where he walked. He moved his large hands from his sides to brush particles of sand from his barrel chest and then reached down to regain control of the white towel slowly slipping from around his waist.

I'd just met Ted six hours ago on the steep sloped beaches in Acapulco, Mexico. Still shy, yet not so wet behind the ears, the door to my sexuality was opening wider.

After three days, we'd fallen into the usual vacation mode: Eating, basking in the sun, shopping and sightseeing. Albert and Roger had holidayed here several times before and knew their way around. The hotel was on the beach and the days were relaxed under our palapa (an open air hut with a thatched roof made of palm fronds). The area was openly gay, palapa after palapa of gay men. They were out in the open, not hidden in a dark bar in some obscure part of town. I was still flirting with the idea I could go one way or the other with my sexual orientation, not making a commitment either way. And shamefully, still stringing Monica along. She had no idea I was off frolicking in the sun with two gay men. I lied, telling her I was in Alabama with my mother and grandparents. Archer and I were on a month to month lease at the apartment.

I needed time to stall, so as to face the fact there were serious contradictions inside me that needed to be addressed. And in the meantime, there was nothing wrong with having gay friends. Though, emotionally, I kept them at a distance. I'd put myself in another category, separate from Kenneth, the landlady's son, the gay men I worked with, and my new friends who were rather more like Stephen — Archer and Gavin. My only sexual experiences had been with Dennis, Roberto, Marshall and Todd. Roberto had left me wanting more of what I almost thought I had with him and, as always, not entirely without guilt. It was desire that was fulfilled behind the backs of others, covered by the darkness of night, never to be seen in the light of day, secrets to be kept close to the confines of the soul. I knew how to hide but didn't want to anymore — I'd left home to stop hiding. If I was gay, I feared I would have to continue to hide, continue to stay buried in the grave with my father. Roberto was gone now, back somewhere in Argentina, but the taste he left in my mouth had lingered. He had the sanctuary of a family to protect and disguise him from the judgment of others. I wondered if it was right to want more. Religion and society told me I was a sinner in finding pleasure in the flesh of the same as me. I had come to know the statement of how "God made Adam and Eve, not Adam and Steve." And I was deeply concerned of what God thought of me, even though I'd reached out to Him as a small child and felt He had abandoned me. I didn't know if I should follow the desires of my heart or the god that society had instructed me to.

I reasoned: God didn't speak to me in my mother's womb and say, "Listen Randy — that's the name they're going to give you, Son — you're going to be a boy, and normally as a rule, boys grow up to like girls. Actually they hate them first, but once puberty sets in it's every boy for himself and they become girl crazy. But, Randy, you're going to be different. You're going to be boy crazy. Now that's a sin. You'll have to fight it all your life and be miserable and unfulfilled in love. It's a test. GOOD LUCK! I'll see you in heaven, if you make it."

Gays were joked about, looked down on, legally stripped of all rights, especially the right to be different. Was this what I wanted for myself?

It was Monday mid-morning, we'd just gotten to the beach, although it was already crowded with sun worshipers. The surf rolled up the sloped beach several feet from our palapa, making it the perfect vantage point to sit in the shade, courtesy of the large palm fronds, and people-watch.

I took a short walk down the shore to get my feet wet. The water felt refreshing lapping against my legs as I looked at all the people. I stood amazed by the vast collection of men — hard to believe they were all gay. The sun beat against my back as I walked. They were so out in the open here. Nothing to hide behind, and certainly not much to hide in, from what many of the men were wearing. Right under God's blazing sun, their bodies being washed by His water. Like a baptism, they had come to share their likeness out in the open, fearing no one, fearless of no one's judgment. Doctors, bartenders, lawyers, priests, teachers, students, policemen and CEOs, they were all here on the beach together in their boxers and bikinis. They came from different backgrounds, different lives, with different dreams and desires, yet they were all looking for acceptance and happiness, to be able to live their lives without ridicule. They came to shut out attitudes and laws made out of fear and ignorance that would prevent or slow them down from finding inner fulfillment. And somehow, after seeing all these men, I understood the intricacies of their lives. They were different as I had been different all my life, but many of them were ready to stand up and be counted. Still, I wasn't so sure if I was — at least not yet. In some way, I felt a breakthrough that would perhaps help free me.

Most of the men at the beach were in couples, like Albert and Roger. And like my friends, I was learning, were as good as married, just without the ceremony or piece of paper that would serve to make their marriage legal under the law. Their nuptials weren't spoken in a church or a town hall, but in their daily lives. They shared a bed, a house and paid taxes — lots of taxes, had two dogs, gave dinner parties, and were respected professionals. Few of their many co-workers knew they were gay and, so what if they did, was their attitude. Albert and Roger were adults, in control of their faculties, both had served their country in the military, well before the lame "Don't ask, Don't tell policy." I was learning by being around them that their love was special, committed and the hell with anyone who said anything against it. What did they care? They were living the way they wanted to, the way they had to in order to be happy and fulfilled. Any other life wouldn't be for them. At first I saw it as strange. It's one thing to have sex with another man, but it's another to commit your life to someone of your same sex. And their love didn't make them perfect. They had the same problems everyone in love had. Whether gay or straight, the important thing was they cared about each other; their separate hearts beat for the other. They wanted the same things from a relationship as everyone else: To love and be loved and share their lives with someone they deem special. And not unlike heterosexuals, there was something inside of them bridging their emotions, making them the way they are, and as far as they were concerned, it was natural. And because of this, they couldn't live by the so called moral laws set forth by a society that refused to understand their differences. A society that birthed them, but couldn't accept there were biological and psychological factors that would give them emotions that made them gay. Many, like Albert and Roger were forced to make a choice. They could suppress their true selves and face the likelihood of an unfulfilled life; they could conceal that truth for the sake of not losing the love and respect of family and friends, and to protect their careers — by doing so, separating themselves from society and living a lie while fulfilling their desires in locked rooms and dark bars. Or they could take a stand as repressed groups had throughout history and stand up for their human birthright to find completion in every aspect of life, and find their true authenticity. To them it would be a struggle, but one worth making in order to find their own way and not someone else's or some other group's way.

Not sure I was strong enough to fight the antiquated pressure and lack of acceptance by society, I still could see many of the men were meant to be together. Like a convention, these men came to Acapulco year after year. They gathered to soak up the sun and congregate in a yearly migration like a particular species of mammal to watch one another walk the beach. They ranged in age from seventy, with lots of gold jewelry, to guys of my own age. The code seemed to be: The older you were, the more gold you wore. The beach was covered with gold shimmering off very tanned bodies.

After stopping to speak with some of the people I'd met over the past few days, I decided to head back to our palapa. Albert was playing cards with one of the guys. Not much of a card player, I sat down beside them to watch the game and take in the beauty of the ocean. Occasionally, someone made a comment about a man on the beach. By now, over the course of the past week, or from the yearly migrations, many people had met one another. Gossip carried back and forth between the palapas, as the Acapulco sun squeezed its way through the palm fronds. Everyone was very chummy. This was definitely a new experience for me. The vacation seemed like something out of a novel, this totally different world I had stepped into.

Albert dropped his cards and motioned for us to look towards the water.

"Look at that one... my, my, my," he said, lowering his sunglasses down the bridge of his red nose. "Where did that come from?"

Everyone looked in the direction where Albert's eyes were focused. There, walking on the beach in front of us was a huge man. With short light brown hair, he was at least six feet three inches, 240 pounds of solid muscle, all nicely tucked into a pair of black Speedos. By now everyone in the surrounding palapas had noticed. "Oohs" and "ahs" filled the sun-washed air as heads popped out from under the palm fronds to see where the attention was directed. Even the guys in the water stopped to watch him walk by.

"What a fine specimen," called someone from behind us. "Girl...who is he with...anyone know him?"

"I'd like to," remarked another admirer.

This Adonis had the complete attention of everyone at the beach.

Albert looked at me and said, "I bet you'd like to get hold of that."

I responded with a big smile, too shy to say anything. He interpreted my smile as a yes and offered a little laugh. Albert and Roger, like Todd, knew about me, about my awkwardness to gay life, having shared stories about Dennis and Roberto. They made no judgments, pushed nothing on me. But Albert was right. It was true. Like a reflex, one look at this man made my entire body come alive. Within seconds, my mind was racing with images. It still wasn't clear to me how masculine men could be interested in other men, but the evidence was all around me. Like at the Parliament House, here there were brawny types, sitting under the palapas, walking the beach — and they were all gay. And there were the not so masculine ones, too. A tall lean man with dark hair sat in the palapa next to ours. He reminded me of Kenneth, who sadly died in a single car accident on his way home from college in his senior year. He looked like what I thought Kenneth would look like ten years out of junior high. But, here, the big guys were laughing and talking with the "sissies," not at them.

The man of men, much more impressive than others who'd awed me, whose characteristics I had wanted to be a part of my makeup, stopped and turned toward the water as everyone continued to look on. My heart raced as his body descended into the warm tropical surf. I had to do something, even if in vain. But what? I got up from my chair and slowly began heading in his direction. My eyes glued to his massive back. Albert called out in the background, "Good luck," as if he knew what was on my mind. His possible understanding embarrassed me and I felt flush. I didn't believe I would get his attention, but I had to try without getting the attention of the whole beach as well. Casually, I continued. As my feet stepped into the surf, I stopped. The water eased my rush of heat. By now Adonis was waist deep into the ocean as he scanned the beach. Was he looking at me? "No way," I thought. I waded in the water for a moment, still facing him. Fearing everyone was watching my silly display, I began walking slowly down the beach, wishing he was looking at me.

After several feet I turned slightly to see where he was, trying to appear cool and unaffected by this man. Truth is, I was affected, things were stirring inside of me. These feelings seemed to come from nowhere.

Now it appeared he was looking in my direction, but he could be looking at anyone. There were a lot of guys around me. Hell, he could be straight for all I knew and had wandered off by mistake onto the gay beach. I decided to move further to where there were fewer people, but stay in his eyesight. Yes, he was still looking my way. What to do now? I laid down in the surf on my stomach. It felt funny but, if it worked in "From Here To Eternity," with a little adaptation it might work for me. The sand was warm on my stomach as the surf rushed up between my legs. The feeling was sensual, except for the gritty sand being forced into my red and white boxer shorts by the rush of the waves. I should put up with the discomfort of the sand, I thought to myself; it was a good pose and might pay off, even if it was a long shot. I really didn't know what I wanted to happen, delirious at the very thought of this man.

It was all I could do to keep from being tossed around as I lay in the shallow surf. The waves were strong against the steep slope of the beach, but I held my ground like a soldier digging my toes and fingers into the wet sand to help steady me. For a brief second, I imagined the warm sand against my upper body was his chest pressing against me. The pounding surf between my legs became his strength repeatedly thrusting on me and the heat of the sun on my back became the warmth of his body on mine. Soon, I forgot about the other people on the beach.

I looked back to see him swimming in my direction, hoping he was coming for me. The sound of the surf mixed with voices around me, as I feared he was going to swim past me and my fantasy would come crashing down. I couldn't look anymore.

"Excuse me, has anyone ever told you that you have a

great ass?" Came a voice from the water behind me.

I turned my head and saw him, the water splashing just below his knees. He was incredible. My eyes were nearly blinded by the reflection of the sun off his wet body as he waded toward me in those black Speedos. Was I still fantasizing? How was I going to answer?

"You're the first," I responded shyly, although it hadn't been the first time someone said those words to me.

"Well, those shorts make it look very inviting. Need someone to brush the sand out of them?"

I was embarrassed now, certain my shyness was apparent. His directness was piercing. He was reading my mind even before I knew what I was thinking.

"I'm sorry, my name is Ted. I don't mean to sound disgusting, but you do have a great butt."

I turned over, sliding back up the beach out of the surf. Squirming in discomfort as I moved, the sand was well up between the cheeks of my butt. But, I soon forgot about it looking up at him. There wasn't anything disgusting about this guy, his comment about my butt notwithstanding. In fact, I couldn't see a damn thing wrong with him.

He sat down beside me, our feet just brushed by the surf. We continued to talk for awhile, exchanging brief information, exclaiming how beautiful the day was. I kept thinking what a magnificent guy he seemed to be and amazed that he was talking to me.

The local catamaran rentals were further up the beach and Ted asked if I wanted to join him sailing. Of course, I said yes. Like an excited boy, I took my catch back to our palapa and introduced Ted to Albert, Roger and the others. Their eyes were as big as golf balls.

I'd never sailed before, but he was doing a good job explaining how things worked. Too engrossed in looking, I found it difficult to pay attention to what Ted was saying. I looked at him as if I understood the entire workings of the boat. All the while, trying not to stare at the bulge in his Speedos. As the catamaran cut through the water my entire body became covered in goose bumps resulting from the wind and nervous excitement. I began to shake and hoped, Ted wouldn't notice. Watching him, I thought how it would feel for him to lean over and kiss me. I felt like a child looking at this massive man. I wanted him to hold me; I wanted to become lost in his arms. The people on shore grew smaller as the boat moved across the blue water under the hot sun. The landscape was a mixture: Brown mountains in the distance, rolling green hills covered with tiny houses and high-rise hotels appearing to be standing on the water. Like a moving photo for a travel guide, I watched the landscape change, all a backdrop for Ted's magnificence. I tried to imagine this beach before the hotels were built, before Acapulco became a tourist attraction. I imagined us alone without the people and high-rises.

After sailing for an hour, Ted suggested we go parasailing. I'd already promised to have a late lunch with Albert, Roger and a new friend, Cody, but Ted didn't want to join us. We made plans to meet back at the beach in a few hours where the parasailing boat took off. I didn't want to leave Ted, afraid he would take interest in someone else while I was gone. But I'd promised Cody, who was returning home that evening. He'd taken an interest in me earlier in the week. I liked Cody, but Ted was occupying my thoughts now.

I rushed through lunch, fearing Ted would be gone when I returned to the beach. My body was covered in suntan oil, and I was still trying to shake out the sand from my shorts. Fearing I looked my worst, I ran to the hotel for a quick shower. I wanted to look good upon returning to the beach, hopefully to find Ted waiting for me. I hastily washed and blow dried my hair as well, although telling myself, because of such vanity, I was going to miss him. Besides, it was senseless to wash my hair at the beach. Ted had seen me already. What did it matter? I just had to clean up a little. I ran out of the room and down the hall to the elevator. Impatiently, I repeatedly pressed the elevator button, my heart beating like I had been in a marathon.

My eyes searched for Ted. Not to appear too eager, as I raced passed the palapas, I slowed my pace once I had the parasail boats in my sight. One had just taken someone up. I watched the parachute sail over the water as the boat pulled it along, not really sure if I wanted to try it. Roger had told me at lunch that the driver of one of the boats overran the beach a few years ago, sending some poor guy crashing into the side of a hotel.

Then I saw Ted waiting by the boats like he had said. Relief swept over me, no longer concerned with Roger's story. There was a long wait, so Ted and I spent the next hour or so soaking up the sun. Ted went up first since he'd been waiting. Then, as the parachute scooped me up, I looked back at Ted as the wind rushed around me. By now, the afternoon sun rode low in the blue sky of Acapulco as its rays danced on the water below. The beach was thinning of tan bodies running in and out of the turquoise water. The breeze coming in across the water was cooler, as the horizon pulled the sun from the sky. If it wasn't for the fact Ted was waiting below, I would have preferred to stay floating over the beach until the sun had disappeared. It was exciting, but an encounter with Ted, once I got down, would be more like it.

Ted ran over to assist me out of the parachute. I was light-headed from the experience of flying next to the sun. Walking back to the palapa with Ted, I knew if something was going to happen, it had to be soon. I became anxious, not wanting the day to be over with him. My mind raced trying to think of something to say. I would be leaving paradise in a few days. If I didn't do something soon, it would be a handshake and paradise would just keep walking away.

The distance to the palapa was growing short. Most of them by now were deserted. Their occupants were back in their hotel rooms getting ready for happy hour parties before going to dinner. I prayed Ted would ask me what I was doing later in the evening.

"I'm starved, how about you?" Ted asked.

"I'm pretty hungry myself." I replied.

"Well." Ted said. "Lets go back to my motel, get cleaned up and then we can get a bite."

Hotel was the key word. Still in the running, for what I wasn't sure, but I didn't want to let this real man out of my sight. The anticipation of where this invitation might lead was unnerving. Just hours ago, I was sitting with Albert and the others watching a card game and this god of a man walked by. Now I was walking off with him.

I definitely felt like a school boy now. There was something I wanted to experience with this man and the desire had been growing all afternoon. Like a thirst that needed to be quenched. I wanted him to expand my world. Maybe it was the sun and the beach, the freedom of being out in the open, but I had never been with a man like Ted. Not even Roberto could compare. Somehow, I knew this man could take me to a place not many had journeyed. A guide to a new awareness of myself, and when the journey was over, I would no longer be an innocent boy spoiled by his father's touch.

"My hotel is just up from the beach," Ted said.

I was actually going to his hotel room. Almost every gay man on the beach wanted to be in Ted's hotel room, but I was the one making the journey. I felt this was an important walk in my life. My feet dug deep into the sun baked sand moving between my toes, as I maneuvered the slope. Ted's feet made larger impressions in the sand than mine. There was a force behind his walk, taking control of every step. He was conquering the beach, making his way, retrieving his spoils, like a knight returning to his castle after a victorious battle.

"It's that small white building over there to the left," Ted said, as he pointed with his hand.

Somehow, I knew I would walk out of it feeling much differently than the way I was feeling now.

The nearby large hotels spread along the beach front

dwarfed Ted's; a block in from the sand and water, it looked like a haven, a cool shelter from the beating rays of the sun. It would soon become my world for a short time, one I might not want to leave too soon. I felt grateful for a moment Ted was going to share it with me.

It was obvious this wasn't a five-star hotel. But that didn't matter. Whitewashed many times over, inside and out, the lobby was stark. A few old, nondescript pieces of furniture sat on the scuffed white-and-black tile floor. A man behind the counter nodded as we entered the elevator. Ted hit the button for the fifth floor and the doors began to slowly close. The motor groaned as if in need of major repair. I looked over at Ted. He smiled, shrugging his shoulders.

"It sounds bad, but I think it'll get us to where we're going."

I sure hope so, I thought, thinking back to the moments on the catamaran. I wanted that kiss now in the elevator, and if we got stuck in this outdated replacement for stairs, then that would be fine with me. The longer I got to spend with him the better.

The doors opened with the same reluctance as they had closed. With a hissing sound of relief the motor of the elevator quit and I followed Ted into the dim hallway.

"To the right," Ted directed as he searched through a gym bag looking for the room key.

The door opened with a creak and sunlight from the room flooded the hallway. Surveying the scene, I entered the room a few steps behind Ted as he tossed the bag in a chair by the door.

"Do you want something to drink, Randy?" Ted asked, as he headed for the small refrigerator under the bar.

"Just some bottled water," I answered.

Ted pulled out a bottle and proceeded to take a gulp from it. He then turned and offered it to me.

I took a sip as he watched. Some water dribbled down my chin as I nervously pulled the bottle from my lips. I was

shaking on the inside, wondering if Ted detected my anxiety.
"Let me help you." Ted said, as he leaned toward me.

His tongue licked the drops from my chin and lower lip.
"That tasted good, how about some more," Ted smilingly said, as he leaned back.

I was speechless. Before I could take another breath, my lips were surrounded by his. He drank from them, sucking out the water I'd just taken. The moment had finally arrived. A moment I once thought might never happen was here. Ted gently put his arms around my body. His biceps tightened and engulfed me. I was finally in his arms, lost in his strength. So much larger than I. I was a child in the arms of a man. For an instant, I felt a connection I had with Dennis and the others, but this was deeper, much deeper. And it was raw. Something animalistic, pulling from the deepest part of my being as Ted held me close.

Ted's embrace tightened. Still kissing me, he opened my lips and filled my mouth with his liquid and warm tongue. My mouth became filled with his wetness, my thirst was being quenched by his kiss. For a moment, I thought Ted would break me in half with his strength. His caress became tighter and tighter, as his tongue plunged deeper into my mouth. Just when I thought I might suffocate, Ted slowly pulled away.

"Wait here, I'll start the shower so we can get cleaned up," he said.

He left me standing in a trance. I nodded and watched him walk down the hall. Turning, I looked out the window hoping to see the ocean. The breeze felt good coming through the open window as I closed my eyes and took a deep breath. The water began running in the shower. Was I really here, or was I dreaming? Did this day really happen?

The water rushed over my body cooling my sunburned skin. Ted rubbed my stomach with the soap with one hand and massaged my torso with the other. He stood behind me, my back tight against his massive chest. I closed my eyes as his hands slowly ran up and down my water drenched body.

The soap fell to the shower floor. Now, with both hands on my hips, Ted pressed my ass against his pelvis and I could feel his excitement growing. Mine was obvious.

In total possession of my body, I felt him biting into the back of my neck and then kissing where he bit. Ted moved to his knees, kissing my back on the way down. Still holding my thighs steady with his giant hands, he began biting my ass, thrusting it into his face and licking in between my cheeks. The cold water could no longer keep my body cool. Foreign to this kind of pleasure, I was burning from the inside as Ted slid up against me. He retrieved the soap, rubbing it between the cheeks of my ass. I was totally relaxed until his finger moved into me. My rectum tightened, first resisting as I experienced a jolt of discomfort. Then I submitted.

Eyes still closed, I felt his body slide down against mine again. The bar of soap drop to the shower floor for a second time. Ted's lips began rubbing against my buttocks. Spreading my cheeks with his hands, he began licking me, pushing his face into me again and again and again.

Under his spell, Ted turned me around and rubbed his head against my hardness, up to my stomach and then on my chest, kissing my flesh until he made it to my lips. Ted's arms tightened around me, as the water rushed over our heads and round our locked lips. I could barely breathe. I felt as if I might drown.

Suddenly, his arms loosened. Ted slid his left hand down my waist until it rested on my butt. He caressed it while turning off the water with his free hand. The plumbing knocked in the wall as the water drained under our feet.

"Well, I think we're clean enough." Ted said, reaching for a towel.

"I don't think I've ever been this clean in my whole life," I replied.

With the white towel, Ted dried me off. I took it from him and returned the favor; the skimpy towel hardly thick enough to dry him, much less both of us. The bathroom floor was flooded. Ted took the water-soaked towel from me, letting it drop to the floor. The breeze from the open window hit my nude body. A chill ran through me as he led me to the neatly made double bed. Ted sat me down on the cool white sheets and leaned me back onto the pillows. The bed was soft like I had imagined. Suddenly I felt vulnerable, as the Adonis stood over me.

Without a word, Ted leaned over and placed one knee on the bed between my legs, pushing them apart. He brought his face to my chest and began to kiss my nipples, his lips surrounding them, sucking on them as my hands held tight against the bed by his. Now with both knees, Ted spread my legs even further apart, crouching over me. He slid his body closer, coaxing my legs around his waist. I could feel his size against me, touching mine; he was heavy. Ted released my hands, freeing them to touch him and feel the strength in his body. Feeling the power in every muscle, I massaged them over him. Ted began to rock himself against me.

I touched his throbbing erection. His cock was powerful and I was overwhelmed by it. Ted unwrapped my legs from around his waist and flipped me around. He began licking my stomach, licking further down until he took me in his mouth.

His hardness now against my face, I felt the weight of his testicles on my lips. The smell of Ted's manhood filled my nostrils. Its soapy clean scent was warm, powerful and sensuous; I was drowning in him.

Ted's cock kept brushing against my lips. The breezes from the open window could no longer cool the room, as sweat rolled in my eyes. Ted was all over me, the heat from his body consuming. At that point I could no longer resist. I wanted it like I'd never wanted another man's dick in my mouth. It would be the first. I took him in my mouth. He was more than I could handle, only able to take a portion of it. I choked. Like a thirsty dog lapping water, I began to lick him instead. Hoping, this was giving him as much pleasure as he was giving me.

The sheets pulled out from the bed as Ted rolled over me and his face found its way to my butt. His tongue pushed between my cheeks. Ted's saliva was fluid as his mouth ate into my ass. Suddenly, in a rush of excitement, Ted turned around on me, spreading my legs again with his knees. Pressing hard against me, his eyes watched the bliss on my face. I could feel the wetness he had left between my legs. Ted had made me ready for him, he was about to take his prize.

My legs were once again tightly wrapped around his massive body; my knees practically touching my shoulders. Again, I could feel his hardness laying against me. He began to rock on me sliding himself over my buttocks. Ted kept rocking as he feverishly kissed me on the mouth, pressing his penis harder against me trying to enter me. I felt intense pain unable to keep from yelling out. Ted stopped his movement on me.

"Are you okay? Randy, am I hurting you?"

Yes he was, but I was willing to take the pain to enjoy the pleasure of his manhood in me. I hoped it would pass in a moment.

"No, I'm fine," I said, concealing my pain as well as my virginity.

Ted got up and walked to the bathroom, returning with a bottle, which he laid on the floor by the bed. After squeezing out a generous dollop of lubricant in his hand, he rubbed it into my ass, moving his finger in and out of me. My legs spread as he had left them, he moved himself between them again, slower now. He began penetrating me, slowly filling me up. I concentrated on relaxing and gradually the pain dulled. I had never experienced anything like this before, never had a man inside of me until now. I felt nourished as he entered me. Ted filled a mental void in me, as well as a physical one.

He consumed me, filling me with the passion of his manhood and it felt wonderful to be surrounded by his body, to be locked together in this brilliant close moment. He was responding to my sighs. The bed began to knock against the wall, slowly at first and then faster, much faster. I felt it moving on the floor under us. Our breathing quickened. Our bodies now covered in sweat as they slid against one another. Faster and faster Ted moved into me.

At the very moment I thought my body couldn't take another second, I felt him explode. Still pressed against me, Ted expelled a deep moan. There was one last deep thrust and then his body jerked. The bed quieted. In a reflex, my penis spilled cum out on my stomach. I felt it roll down my side onto the white rumpled sheets. Ted's lips slid from my mouth down my cheek to my neck. His body became limp on me; I felt his weight against me again.

Ted lifted his head, gently kissing me on the lips as he rolled off me. As we both tried to catch our breath, we lay quietly together. Laying on his side, Ted reached over pulling my body to his, my back to his chest. The warmth of his comforting breath exhaled on my neck.

The filtered sunlight had almost left the room. Shadows on the walls were softer and the whiteness of the room became pink as the sun set on the water. An orange tint filtered into the room and the air became quiet. I could hear Ted drift off to sleep as my mind wondered over the past moments with him. Night was coming, but I wanted to stay awake as long as possible to relish being in his arms. Unlike the endless nights of childhood, where I fought off sleep to prolong peace from the violence of a father, I now had found a sanctuary this night in the arms of a stranger.

Like forbidden fruit from the tree of life, he had picked me. He filled my body with pleasure, riding on pain, it had never experienced and gave me a new sense of myself and the world. With him, I had encountered who I was. The desires I had suppressed could no longer remain caged. Yes, I had fleeting sex with Ted — very physical, hot sweaty sex. But it was more, it was a connection that helped define me. It wasn't just the act of sex but, more, the emotion I just experienced that brought an understanding of myself.

gilbert

Todd came through the first operation with little discomfort, or so he said. The following day, a problem developed with the drainage tube that had been inserted to relieve the fluid buildup caused by the meningitis. This meant going back to the operating room for a replacement and some adjustments. Mrs. Weaver and Todd's brothers, along with a steady stream of other relatives and friends continued to congregate in the waiting area. It quickly began to look like a campsite. Bags and baskets of food, along with books, magazines, pillows and blankets covered the floor and a few unoccupied chairs.

Marie took Mrs. Weaver and the brothers across the street to Mick's for lunch. Except to shower and change, Todd's mother hadn't left his side for the past three days. Marie wanted to get her away from the hospital for a change of scenery. I agreed to sit with him until they returned.

"I'm so worried about the tremendous strain this is on my mother. Do you think she's going to be okay?" Todd asked, as Mrs. Weaver left the room.

"She seems to be holding up really well. How about you?" I questioned.

"I'm okay," Todd answered, in a whisper. "I guess I need to get my affairs in order. Don't want my mother to be burdened with anything after...after it's over."

"Todd, you're going to pull through this," I responded, my tone of voice demanding it was true.

"I want you to speak at my funeral," Todd busted out.

"What funeral? There's not going to be any funeral...you're going to be fine," I rebutted. Todd knew my extreme shyness and fear of public speaking. But that wasn't the reason I objected to talking about the subject. At that moment, the flood gates opened. My eyes filled up. I fought like hell to keep the tears from leaving my sockets, insisting the funeral was a long way off and that he didn't have to worry about anything like that. We would both be old and gray before having to worry about anyone's funeral. "You will be up and around in no time," I told him. Todd just smiled and asked again.

"When the time comes, I'll be there for you," I surrendered.

I could tell Todd was getting tired. He slowly raised his arm to rub his eyes. I studied the IV tube and the bruises made by earlier, failed attempts with the needle. His skin was transparent. Blue veins ran like lines of ink up and down the underside of his forearm.

"Mother said Jennifer called last night at the house. Did you call her to let her know I was here?" Todd asked.

"Yes, she's flying in tomorrow."

Even though I recognized my deep desire for men and had acted on it many times, a beautiful woman could still turn my head. I held onto that and flirted with the women I met, not really thinking, at that point in my life a real relationship with either sex would surface. Well, one did briefly. I flirted a bit too much and she called my bluff.

I met her through Todd and his gang of friends. Jennifer was on her second marriage, with a seven year old son from her first. At the time of our meeting, her present husband of two years had been seeing another woman for the past three months. Jennifer found the standard issue note of betrayal in his laundry. In it, the other woman expressed her fondness for the weekend they'd spent together when he was supposed to be away fishing with some friends. Jennifer confronted him and he promised to break things off. His pledge was good for only two weeks when Jennifer found he'd lunched at the other woman's apartment. She had hired a private detective to tail him.

While Jennifer spent time away from home deciding what to do about her husband, and how much to make him suffer, our friendship grew. It began with dinners at cozy restaurants and drinks after work at neighborhood pubs. It was a mixed group, some artists and actors, a few young hip business successes, a few gays and the rest straight. Soon, Jennifer and I began innocently having lunch together and meeting away from the group, catching a few art openings and movies and, afterwards, sipping coffee at an in-town coffee house.

Time spent with her made me begin to wonder again about how I should spend the rest of my life, especially my sexual life. I didn't know if I wanted to be walking the streets of Paris at eighty years old with another man. The memory of Ted was crystal clear and my experience with him couldn't be ignored. But I would need to find another Ted, and I wasn't sure how to go about that. I sent him a card after returning from vacation, but never received a response; as far as I knew he was in Miami. In the meantime, I looked forward to just being around Jennifer. She was sophisticated and she was smart. Jennifer cared about people and she seemed to care about my world. Everyone gravitated toward her strong beauty, which helped make Jennifer's small avant-garde art gallery a success. It wasn't exactly my style of work, but art was our common interest. She was a mentally strong woman, often times mistaken for a lesbian because of her non-traditional manner. Perhaps that's why I was attracted to her: She was forceful like a man, but anything but a lesbian.

Our relationship progressed to casually sleeping together. But I knew from the beginning, she was just a diversion until the next man came along. She wasn't concerned that I'd been with men, rather I think to her it made me more attractive. It started as a result of us being out at a gay bar. I had joined Todd and his friends there one evening. Jennifer and I started dancing and pretty much stayed together most of that night. We had lost Todd and the others as the night grew late. Later in the evening as the bar was closing, Jennifer said everyone had planned to go over to her condo. Jennifer suggested I follow her in my car and that we would meet up with everyone there. Her husband was out of town on business, or so she thought. Her private detective would fill her in on Monday. Her young son was visiting his father so she had the weekend to herself. Upon arriving at her place, I discovered there was no party. I didn't leave until five o'clock the next afternoon. So obviously, my sexuality simply wasn't an issue, for Jennifer was not looking for love. And money was no object. She made plenty from the art gallery in addition to the settlement from her first husband, a doctor. They'd divorced because he wanted to move from Atlanta and set up a family practice in a rural town an hour west of Birmingham. Jennifer tried it for awhile, but there just wasn't enough love in the marriage to keep her there. For a year, Jennifer commuted from the sweet little town in Alabama to Atlanta until they finally decided to end it. The doctor later married a local woman with two children, and Jennifer married a banker, who was soon to be her ex.

Sexually, the relationship brought with it the incomplete feeling I had experienced with Besty and Monica, I felt like I was performing instead of connecting. Being with Ted had made that more apparent. Jennifer liked the fact I was young and struggling — something she'd never experienced. And for me, she was my last holdout on heterosexuality. Perhaps in her mind she wanted to guide me along in my art and out of the company of men, or rather, she just liked the drama. But I knew she cared. In my twenties, I was a boy in her bed of thirty-six years. It was something to talk about at lunch with her friends. Jennifer took me to a few dinner parties in Buckhead, where many of Atlanta's rich and famous call home. Once in awhile, she would stumble across a conversation where she was the topic, "Did you know Jennifer is sleeping with that younger man? I understand he's gay or bisexual or something." During that time it was trendy for straight people, mostly women to have gay friends other than their hairdressers. Our friendship was a good arrangement: She let me into her world, introducing me to people who might buy my art and I kept her entertained.

At the time of our fling, I was living in a high rise condominium in Buckhead. The large two bedroom condo on the twenty-seventh floor with its spectacular view of downtown Atlanta was owned by Paul, an eccentric designer. I was happy to finally leave Archer and his friends in Marietta and move in with Paul. He didn't want to live in the condo alone, so I paid a small amount of rent each month and in exchange, got the view, a doorman and an impressive address. After three months, the designer met a skinny eighteen-year-old boy who viewed me as a threat. It came down to either sleeping with the designer to keep the address or packing my bags. I moved two days later.

In the meantime, Jennifer began dating a doctor from California and spent a lot of time in Los Angeles. I missed our talks over coffee and the comments she shared with me of what people were saying about us at parties, but it was for the best. It was back to square one — no girlfriend and no apartment.

I pulled up in front of the building, hoping it wasn't the right address as listed in the Sunday paper. Checking the small print in the folded newspaper laying on the dashboard of my car, I reread the ad: "Midtown, large 1 bedroom, hardwood floors, big windows. References and security deposit required. Call..." The address, 146 Eleventh Street was scribbled where I'd written it by the listing circled in black magic marker in the middle of the page. It was a little rundown, but I quickly convinced myself that once inside it might prove charming. Inside, I found a nice, large one-bedroom unit like the ad described. Three hundred and fifty dollars a month plus utilities, worth of charm. To me, the trash strewn on the street was added texture, and the graffiti on the vacant building next door, an artistic expression of visitors to the neighborhood.

The address bordered on a seedy section of town, but I could see the skyscrapers of Midtown from the street as I stepped from the car. I would be at work during the day, well away from the disorder of the street. At night, the lights of the taller buildings shining down on the apartment would soften the harshness and disguise its shabbiness.

The living room doubled as a painting studio. Furnished with three white overstuffed sofa chairs casually positioned in the middle of the room — all three, with their backs to two large windows, faced an easel positioned on the far wall that ran the height and length of the room. The hardwood floors were covered in drop cloths to keep them free of stray paint splatters. Eventually, the areas of the floor left uncovered became blanketed with paint anyway. I had a habit of walking around the room carrying my brushes, unconsciously letting them drip as I studied my creations. Over time, the floor became a canvas of its own. Sometimes, I used the floor as a model for the canvas on the easel, trying to recreate the colors as innovatively as the accident on my floor.

At night, the street noises made their way to the third floor and into my studio. Eleventh Street intersected with two busy streets, Piedmont and Peachtree. It became such, that I could tell time by the traffic flow and horn honking. There were several clubs and bars in the area. One was behind the apartment building and I could see its parking lot and roof from my windows. The music from inside escaped its walls, vibrating out into the night, as cars drove by and the neighborhood hookers yelled out to their drivers. Every once in awhile a car came to a shrieking stop, and, after a brief negotiation, I heard the door shut. Police cars rushing to a crime scene raced down the street, bathing the room in colors of red, then blue, and then red and blue again. Things rarely quieted down until four in the morning, or until I put

gilbert

my brushes down in the bucket of mud-colored water by the easel and went to bed. By then, after a long day at work and a night of painting, the noises outside slowly quieted as I fell asleep with my hands and arms covered in paint. As I left for work in the mornings, I navigated my steps as to avoid the used condoms — tools of the night, scattered on the sidewalk.

The four-story apartment building was secured by a five foot iron fence with a swinging gate. Each tenant had a key, and the building manager, Rip, lived on the premises. Rip suited the neighborhood. I had little contact with him other than dropping off of my monthly rent check. He answered the door in his leather chaps, t-shirt and black cowboy boots. He was quite a contrast from my Levis, button down shirts and loafers.

Most nights during the summer, at around ten thirty, I could hear him leaving. The sound of Rip's large-heeled boots hit the pavement and bounced off the red brick U-shaped building. I recognized the distinctive gait as his steps echoed through the open windows: Three hard footsteps and then a skip of the metal taps on his boots scraping the cement as he walked to the gate. It squeaked being pulled open, and then made a loud bang as metal hit metal upon closing. It served as a door bell.

Night after night, the sounds of the city called out to anyone who was listening. A whole different culture was just awaking, as another was going to sleep. I'd just crawled into bed and the nightly sounds told me it was close to three in the morning. It was Friday night so I would probably sleep in late the next morning. As cars moved in and out of the parking lot below, I watched the shadows from their lights crossing the walls of my bedroom. It had been a busy night on the street. The air conditioner had been broken for two days, so the windows were wide open, letting the night rise and creep into the room, accompanied by random voices. I left a message on Rip's machine asking him to please take a look at it, but I didn't think he would get to it this weekend, since his habit was to stay out until the sun came up and sleep the day away. It wouldn't be fixed until Tuesday, at the earliest.

Just before falling asleep, a voice from below clearly made its way through the window.

"Hey, up here," the voice instructed. "Let's go on the roof."

"Are you crazy?" the other voice responded.

"Come on, we can be alone up here," he answered.

This conversation caught my curiosity, pulling me out of bed. I walked over to the window and watched, concealed by the darkness of the room.

Behind the bar next door, the two guys kicked through spilled trash around the dumpster making a path in order to climb up on it. They then leaped a short distance and stepped up on the roof. One of them called the other Buddy. The white towel in Buddy's back jeans' pocket led me to believe he must be a bartender there. They quickly began fondling one another, moving to the center of the roof so as not to be noticed by anyone in the parking lot. However, I was in clear sight of them.

"I only have a few minutes before they know I'm gone," Buddy said, as his friend slipped his hands up the bartender's t-shirt.

They began hungrily kissing one another, pulling at each others' clothing. Buddy moved his friend over a few feet to a low support wall running across the length of the roof. As the guy began unbuttoning his jeans, Buddy turned him around facing the wall. I continued to watch in amazement as Buddy assisted his partner of the moment in pulling them down around his ankles. Rapidly, Buddy unbuttoned his jeans to release his erection. They began screwing; Buddy's white towel flapping until the force of his movement caused it to fall from the pocket. Their lustful silhouettes humped under the lights of the tall buildings surrounding them. The traffic of people in and out of the bar continued, unaware of the sexual tryst on the rooftop as the two men's faint moans carried a short distance in the air. After a few minutes they were done. Fixed, I watched as they scaled down the dumpster, Buddy unaware the white towel had fallen out of his pocket. Their black outlines returned to the noise of the bar through the back door, and I went back to bed surprised at what I'd just witnessed.

The heat riding on the summer air carried in the room with the music still ringing out into the night. Sweating from the eighty degree temperature, I plugged in a fan and set it in the opened window. My nude body stuck to the sheets of the bed as I tossed and turned as a result of the escapade that just happened outside on the roof. The fan helped, but I was hard and ready to explode. I rolled over on my stomach to let the warm air generated through the fan brush over me. My hair was dripping wet as I wiped it out of my eyes while feeling a pool of liquid forming at the curve of my back just above my butt. Biting into my pillow I began humping the bed, imagining Ted was behind me, his sweat mixing with mine. I felt the pool of sweat run down my crack. I continued to hump the bed faster and faster as the sheets became twisted and wetter and wetter, until the cum spilled out of me.

The tenants in the apartment tended to keep to themselves, coming and going without much notice. Only a few seemed as out of place as I did. The majority appeared as colorful and as lawless as the graffiti on the walls. Malcolm, a short, attractive preppy guy around my age lived one floor below in the end unit. Over several weekends, I had noticed him with a tall, somewhat athletic, well-groomed gentleman who drove an expensive black German car. Malcolm's friend caught my eye immediately. Older by about ten years, he was very Ivy League. His size led me to think he had perhaps played football in his college days. His voice was strong and commanding whenever we exchanged greetings in passing on the common stairs and yard. The Muscogee County sticker on his Georgia license plates told me this frequent visitor lived in Columbus. I'd lived there as a small child; it was the city where my search started, where my torment began, and where I thought it had been put to rest. My first recollection — Mother in the hospital for two months and us left alone with *him*. When we visited on the weekends, she stood in an enclosed wire balcony high off the hospital and waved down to us. Dressed in hospital clothing and a white robe, she stood there with her delicate hands wrapped around the fencing of the cage. I could see her mouth moving and hear the faint sound of her voice being carried down from the floors above. My little arms stretched out to her fragile frame, but she was too far away in the wire cage for them to reach.

One Friday, I arrived home early from work. Within minutes, there was a knock and the Columbus visitor was standing at the door.

"Hello, I'm Gilbert," the tall man with thick dark slicked back hair greeted, holding a silver ice bucket.

"You're Malcolm's friend," I said, extending my hand, noticing ,the wedding ring on his finger as he swung the bucket to his left hand to shake mine.

"Would you happen to have any ice? It's been a long week and I'm in desperate need of a scotch," he said, advancing the ice bucket through the door.

"I believe I do," I responded to the request, taking the bucket and motioning Gilbert into the studio.

I went into the kitchen and emptied two ice trays into the bucket, returning to find Gilbert looking through some in-progress canvases leaning against the easel. He was dressed in a brown, light-weight wool suit tailored perfectly for his six-foot-four frame. I was sure it wasn't purchased in Columbus. Gilbert's dress and manner was that of someone used to the good life and judging from the tasteful gold crested cuff links peeking out of his coat sleeves, he was born to it. Money can buy a lot of things, but it can't buy style.

"Ah, very nice," he said, as he looked around the room. "You're an artist."

"It's that obvious?" I questioned, handing him the filled

bucket.

"Listen, Randy would you like to join me for a drink? Malcolm is going to be late and I'd appreciate the company."

I followed Gilbert down to Malcolm's apartment. It was furnished as if someone very southern and proper lived there. The antique sofa and chairs were layered with white doilies turning yellow with age. Most of the knickknacks must have been from his grandmother, I imagined, taking a seat. Quite a difference from Rip's apartment directly below with its erotic male posters, thrift store furniture and leather accessories scattered about.

Gilbert drank his scotch while we sat and talked. I slowly sipped on a soda with lime since there was no beer in Malcolm's refrigerator. I discovered they were both from Columbus, meeting years ago at the church their families had attended for generations, while Malcolm was a freshmen in college. Gilbert, twelve years older, to be exact, was a senior partner in a well-respected, successful law firm that had been founded by his great-great grandfather after the Civil War. And Gilbert was married with two teenaged children. His wife, with her charitable and society organizations, lunched with his mother at the country club. They lived in a grand Georgian mansion, complete with pool, guest house and live-in help: A maid, a cook and a nanny.

His law firm handled a big client in Atlanta, so he was able to come to the city in the disguise of business as often as possible. Gilbert had his secretary make reservations at the Peachtree Westin Hotel downtown, but seldom went there except to check in. He preferred to stay with Malcolm in the heart of Midtown where he could be close to the gay bars and the men. They had a sexual relationship in the beginning, but it later slowed into a friendship. During the height of their relationship, Gilbert saw to all of Malcolm's financial needs and continued to pay rent on the apartment after the sex fizzled, a modest sum to a man of such means. It was Gilbert's way of keeping Malcolm's loyalty and silence.

The afternoon was growing late and I realized I needed to go upstairs and continue my work. As I was trying to find the right moment to interrupt Gilbert and excuse myself, he encouraged me to stay until Malcolm arrived so we could go to dinner. I would have liked to hear more about Gilbert, but I was uncomfortable being in Malcolm's apartment without him there. Sure, Gilbert had said they were just friends, but "just friends" could mean a lot of things.

"Are you sure you won't stay and dine with us?" Gilbert asked, putting down his glass.

"Thanks, but I really must go and paint," I replied, using work as a valid excuse to leave.

"Well, maybe we'll see you over the weekend," Gilbert said, as he got up from his chair and walked over blocking my exit.

The moment was awkward as I stood there waiting for him to move away from the door. Gilbert ignored the extension of my hand and moved closer to hug me.

"I do hope we have a chance to visit again," he said, his embrace bringing my head into his chest.

I could feel the heavy starch of his white shirt against my face. The expansion of his hands gripped the flesh of my back through my clothes as he squeezed tighter. I was amazed at the information he had divulged to a total stranger over a mere few glasses of scotch. There was something interesting about this man. He was handsome, but not in the usual way. It was the combination of his size and the scent of his success that was good-looking about him. He lived in two worlds and loved the diversity of each. Such a pillar of Columbus society, with a dark life in Atlanta, close to home. Something told me he liked it that way, having danger and the best of both worlds. Gilbert had the money to pull it off. No one would ever believe it anyway — except for me. Walking back up to my apartment, I had a feeling I would come to learn more about this man.

I saw them the next day in the yard of the apartment as I

was leaving for the gym, but this time instead of the usual friendly "hello" in passing, we stopped and chatted for a few minutes. I could tell from their armful of Brooks Brothers and Saks' bags that they'd been shopping. They were headed upstairs for a few cocktails and then off to dinner, Gilbert insisted again I should join them.

Like most gay men of that era, I'd become increasingly concerned about my body. Shyly, I joined a gym and began studying books on body building. Maybe working out would help my self confidence, so I diligently stuck to a workout schedule. After several months, I began to notice a change in my body, as well as the way I carried myself. The physical exercise did a lot for my mental state as well. My aspirations were not to become a muscle man, but to tone up and hope people noticed. The combination of eating right and sticking to my workout program began to transform my body, adding size. As other people began to notice, I continued the workouts. If I was going to find someone to love me, then I thought I had to have the right package. After cleaning up from my workout, I met them at Dailey's, a downtown restaurant not far from the Peachtree Westin Hotel where Gilbert was supposedly staying. Over dinner, I could see why Gilbert had been interested in Malcolm at one time. He was pretty and there was a sweetness about him, as was characteristic of many southern gay men. I hadn't picked up on that before during our brief "hellos," but after more exposure I could see Malcolm was proper and well-mannered, as I'm sure he must have been raised. Talking to him and listening to his accent was like stepping back to a time of lazy Sunday afternoons after church services. Pitchers filled with iced tea and lemonade and chocolate cake being eaten on white verandahs as the June breeze carried the smell of honeysuckle. I could just hear Malcolm's mother calling to him, "Sweetheart, pour your Granddaddy another glass." He had the "Scarlet Complex" — prim and proper, but with an underlying mischief about him, brought about, I supposed, by the opposition of his southern culture and the minister's sermons preached in the Baptist Church up the hill, and the unexplained desires beating in certain young southern boys, who would end up looking for love in the likeness of their daddies. I could also see why Gilbert had lost interest. The sweetness wasn't enough for a man like Gilbert, after awhile, going to bed with Malcolm was the same as sleeping with his wife. Malcolm was very much like the apartment he lived in: Antique and southern, the very things Gilbert, unknowingly was running from. He had moved on, and with each new encounter the men became tougher and less like Malcolm. I was sure, regardless of his testimony the afternoon before in Malcolm's apartment, they were having sex when Gilbert felt the need for it, when he required the qualities of a woman in the body of a man. He was looking at me over dinner like I was the next stepping stone.

Gilbert picked up the check. "A business expense," he joked.

We went back to my apartment. Malcolm left us alone in the studio while he went to retrieve a bottle of scotch from his apartment. He surely ran down the stairs, because he was back before the door barely closed. They both had doubles, while I had a beer. Malcolm and Gilbert amused themselves by watching the men from the window as the traffic outside the bar started to pick up. They commented on the various styles of dress and personal presentation, giving points to the men as if they were contestants in a beauty pageant. Malcolm and I compared our knowledge of the tenants in the building, exchanging information and personal observations of them. Gilbert continued to stand at the window, like a house pet, scratching at the pane to get out with the rest of the tomcats.

"Lets go out," Gilbert said, still peering out the window. "The bar is getting packed next door."

"I'm up for it," Malcolm responded to his suggestion. "What about you?" he said, looking at me.

Todd and I had gone out the weekend before, where he had met a really cool guy from New York. I left them dancing at three o'clock in the morning. Todd called on Sunday evening, telling me they hadn't gotten out of bed for two days. He sounded crazy about this guy named Zack, and I was glad for him.

"I get enough of it living next door, but I'll go for awhile. Don't want to be out too late," I answered.

As we approached the bar, a string of men rushed in the door as if they were afraid of missing "Mr. Right." Looking up at the apartment building, I noticed I had left the easel light on, clearly illuminating the top portion of a large painting. Before that observation, I hadn't realized one could have such a clear view into the studio. This prompted me to think about the many nights I had worked late, walking around the room painting in nothing but boxer shorts. Suddenly, I realized the possible meaning of a note taped to my door a few weeks before, on which was written: "I want to see more, show me more!" It was probably from someone living in my building who frequented the bar, I thought, as I followed Gilbert and Malcolm through the door.

The hard-core surroundings were not for me. It must be leather night, I said to myself, as I made my way through a sea of men wearing tight fitting clothes, ripped in all the right places: At the crotch of jeans to tease a prospective trick for the night; in t-shirts, complete with erect nipples, some pierced, peaking through the holes. The dim lighting made them all look the same. Gilbert pointed out a group of men dressed in leather vests and chaps without anything on underneath.

"Unfortunately, they have the worst looking bodies," he remarked with a snicker. "I guess the idea is for their ass to hang out, but, look, they don't have any to show, none that I would be interested in seeing. But you would look good."

"Yea, right, I don't think so," I answered.

I turned around to make note of the men he was referring to, but in a second, Malcolm and Gilbert were swallowed up by the crowd. A choking fog of cigarette smoke hung in the bar making it difficult to see. As I continued on looking for them, a hand grab my arm. I turned around to see Rip leaning against the bar.

"I can't believe my eyes," he said, squinting. "What's a nice boy like you doing in a place like this?"

"I came with Malcolm from the second floor and a friend of his," I explained, over the loud music. The music was deafening.

"I have never seen you in here before, let me buy you a drink," Rip offered, turning around to the bar.

"Thanks, but that's okay," I said, trying to sound appreciative. "I need to catch up with them."

The large warehouse bar was filling up by the minute. By now, I had to turn sideways, brushing against the bodies to get through the crowd. Someone grabbed my butt, I turned around thinking it was Gilbert or Malcolm, but it wasn't. I continued pushing my way through the men, deciding if I didn't find them soon, I would leave. It was too uncomfortable for me to stand around and wait for them to appear out of the masses. Feeling awkward with some of the looks I was getting, I headed for the door. I was too concerned someone might think I was here to pick someone up. But, that was the point, that was why most of the men were here.

"I think you are in the wrong bar," Gilbert called out, standing off to the right. His shirt was unbuttoned, exposing his meaty chest with a concentration of black hair on the skin over his sternum bone sprinkling down to his navel.

"You look a little uptight," he added.

"Where have you been?" I asked impatiently.

"We've been on the dance floor. Malcolm's around here somewhere," Gilbert answered.

With a closer look, I saw that Gilbert's shirt was soaked with sweat, exposing his strong well developed biceps. I watched them flex with the slightest move of his arm, as he wiped perspiration from his face with a napkin. I knew then I might be in trouble.

"What about yourself? Have you been held up with

someone in one of these dark corners?" he asked grinning.

"Hardly Gilbert!" I replied.

"Well, why don't we head back over to your place for awhile?" he suggested, taking a step toward me.

"What about Malcolm?" I questioned.

"He'll be fine by himself, besides, I would rather just the two of us go. We can talk about your art or something," Gilbert said, as he placed his arm around my waist.

Malcolm walked up just in time. "So there you are," he said, holding two drinks in his hands. "I got you a scotch, Gilbert."

I took this opportunity to excuse myself. I knew what Gilbert had on his mind and it wasn't to talk. A part of me may have wanted him, but I was trying to convince myself the last thing I needed was to get involved with another married man, especially one with children. He was looking for excitement and I was sure I would get the short end of the stick, or worse. I didn't want to share anyone, especially someone with a family. Even if he was in the same category as Ted.

As I walked the short distance back to my apartment, I thought about Gilbert: His deep voice with just a slight detection of southerness, about his tall frame, his large hands and manly mannerisms. Safely in the bed, I closed my eyes only to see his dark eyes looking at me and those hands pushing his thick black hair off his forehead. "Go to sleep, you know this is not right," I told myself. Somehow, he was like a magnet pulling me in. I kept telling myself, he's married, he has children, over and over in my head until it hurt. I told myself, "been there — done that."

An hour hadn't even passed and I was still wrestling with sleep when Gilbert knocked at the door. The music from the bar still escaping into the night.

"Did you forget which apartment Malcolm lives in?" I said, half jokingly, as he stood in the door holding two bottles of beer.

"No. I gave the door man a twenty to let me carry these

out," Gilbert said, holding one out to me. "I got this one for you."

"It's a little late for me, but thanks. I'm going back to bed now. May I suggest you do the same," I said, as I started to push the door closed.

"That sounds like a good idea," Gilbert responded. "What side of the bed do you like to sleep on?"

"Both sides, so good night."

I closed the door leaving Gilbert standing in the hall still holding the beers. I stopped a few feet from the bedroom to listen for his footsteps leading away from the door and then continue down the stairs. For a second, I thought of going to catch him, but if it was going to happen, I wasn't going to be that easy. Besides, I needed more time to think and put distance between the desire and the opportunity. I knew then there was some attraction between us, and now I was certain it had started the first time we saw each other passing in the courtyard. I felt a familiar sense of danger coming over me about Gilbert, there was a sense of power in having the attention of a man like him. I had a choice, go back and get him for one night, or wait and have him longer. I decided to wait.

I walked to the bathroom and stood in front of the mirror. My visitor had excited me and my hard penis pushing out my shorts made that truth obvious. I stared at my reflection and asked myself, "Who am I?" not knowing if I should be ashamed of the answer.

The following Wednesday, Gilbert showed up at my door. It was six-thirty. He had just left a meeting with a client and decided to stop by to see if I was in. Without hesitation, I invited Gilbert in. Four hours later he left. He called the next week from his office. His wife and children were going to the family beach house on Sea Island for a long weekend. Gilbert was staying in Columbus and thought I might like to take the hour drive to visit while they were away. I could stay in the guest house to keep up appearances for the staff. I had told him earlier of my living in Columbus as a young child and that my father was buried at the Army base, Fort Benning. His invitation stirred up recollections: Mother standing behind the cage-like enclosure, her hands gripping the wire, Patsy's Playhouse — a children's television show, and being left alone listening for my father, wondering when my mother was coming home.

I didn't take Gilbert up on his offer. There was something not right about it. I dare not go to that place again, nor could I infect the home of his family with what we might do, but mostly, it was too close to my father. I thought if I never set foot on that ground again I could leave the past in the grave with him.

Malcolm started working weekends at an oriental rug store, leaving Gilbert to fend for himself on his visits. He spent that time with me. If I saw his car parked in front of the apartment on Friday afternoons, I could be sure he would be up to see me later. So, I waited for his knock at the door.

He took a fancy to my work, or so he said, and after many months of coming to the studio to watch me paint on the canvases, he bought one. Instead of selecting from the dozen or so in the studio, Gilbert asked me which was my favorite. I was still working at Macy's, not sure how to really make it as an artist, not sure I had any talent. So the canvases piled up; I'd sold a few here and there. But that was okay, each painting became a friend, and I found, good friends are hard to let go of. Jennifer placed some for me, convincing her friends I would one day be a hot new artist. Todd did his part too, sending clients over, so I sold a few that way as well. He even wanted to buy a piece for himself, but instead, I gave one good friend to another.

I think in his mind, Gilbert was purchasing a piece of me, and paying for the time he took away from my painting. How could he take it with him back to Columbus though? There was no place for it in that life. He knew the painting wouldn't fit in anywhere in the home where he lived with his wife and children or at the office founded by his ancestor, but he wanted to own it, like he wanted to own me. Gilbert asked me to keep it in the studio, but separate from the other canvases leaning on the walls.

"Hang it over the bed so I'll know where it is when I'm not with you and I'll know it's mine. If I could, I would take it and hang it over the bed I sleep in with her, but I...," Gilbert stopped, without completing his sentence.

Actually, I don't believe he wanted his two worlds to touch, lest a collision occur. Taking that painting into his world in Columbus meant they had crossed. And if that were to happen, he would have to acknowledge how separate the two worlds were and how potentially dangerous that would be; disrupting the order, control and separation he now held over them. I never knew exactly when I would see him, a weekend here and a weekend there. He might call me in the middle of the week to see if I was free for dinner, knowing the answer in advance. His favorite restaurant, Gene and Gabe's, was known for its spectacular Italian cuisine and colorful patrons. As he recounted his life, I looked out to the street staged by the heavy red draperies on the windows. Even with me he couldn't leave it behind. By nine o'clock, before the restaurant began to crowd with people and smoke, we left for my studio. Gilbert usually stayed until eleven or twelve. For those few hours, the studio filled with the music he loved. Tapes he'd brought on his visits — Franz Liszt, Frederic Chopin, Wagner and Grieg — filled the dark rooms, uninterrupted except for the brief sigh or moan of pleasure that washed out into the night as we laid under his painting, as he gave me the passion he said he no longer desired to give his wife.

There was no love left between them, or so he said. But that was a story I put little merit in. He wanted me to believe the marriage was only a convenience now for the sake of generations of families and money. There was the community, the club, the firm, the social standing of the family, and more importantly, his children — the generation to follow. Somehow I sensed it was more than a convenience. Maybe I was the convenience. It was just a story to tell a gay man, or a woman, for that matter, in order to get them into bed; a story that allowed Gilbert to sleep around. And I bought part of it, making it easier for me to lose my guilt in his story.

Gilbert's calls became more frequent as did his brief visits into the city. He phoned from the house on Sea Island while his family was on the beach or while out to dinner with his wife and friends at the club.

"Just wanted to call," he would say. "I only have a minute, but I wanted to know what you were doing. I was thinking about you Randy, and I had to call."

His wife, Nancy, began to question the growing number of late nights, coming home past one o'clock in the morning, and the increased number of weekends away from the family. Gilbert told me she'd spoken to his father about her concerns and in turn, Gilbert Sr. brought it up one afternoon while they were playing golf. Gilbert said he ignored the topic and told his father not to be concerned, which didn't sit well.

Gilbert verbally fantasized about us going away for a month to Greece. He said he wanted to lay with me on the beaches as far away as he could possibly get from his other life. Our bodies would bake in the sun, turning brown as we lost track of time. Our nights would be spent wandering in one another's arms.

"Maybe I'll just run away," he said, as he drifted with the music. "I'll take what we need, and we'll just go. I wish we could just go. I'll call you one day and we'll go. You can paint anywhere...can't you?"

I wasn't sure how to feel about Gilbert or his dreams. I had bought two bottles of Dewar's to keep around the studio for him. I knew now I was with him because, like the other men I had laid with, I needed a part of him — a part to fit a puzzle. Maybe it was the experience of being wanted by him and that I wouldn't have him forever. I would be there for him as long as he needed me. And I hoped he wouldn't move on until I felt his contribution to the puzzle fit tightly in place. I expected nothing from him except the experience of being with him. He was my connection to a straight world that I finally had realized I couldn't be a part of. I was gay. I would have to accept the truth and of course, deal with my self imposed shame and that awarded by society. I knew by now I would never marry a woman and probably never father children. There was no need to fall in love with Gilbert. A mistress shouldn't fall in love with someone not attainable, for I was Gilbert's mistress.

The more Gilbert came to Atlanta, the more things began to slip with his work. Gilbert Sr. became increasingly unhappy in what he perceived was his son's lack of interest in the firm and his family. They had almost lost a major client due to Gilbert's inattention and his father had to step in. Gilbert Sr. told Gilbert to straighten up, he didn't like what he saw. He began to question Gilbert about every detail of his time away from home and office. Nancy kept Gilbert Sr. informed of her husband's growing number of absences.

"If you're having an affair, Son, I hope you are keeping a very low profile. I hope it isn't anyone we know and, for God's sake, it isn't anyone associated with the club. That's all I'll say about it. Buy something nice for Nancy."

"If only my father really knew," Gilbert said to me while Liszt's *Liebestraume* was filling the apartment. "It's better he thinks I'm having an affair with one of the secretaries. God knows, he has had his share of the women in the firm and then some."

As the weeks passed, Gilbert Sr.'s cracking down on Gilbert's activities was getting to him. The phone calls as well as his visits began to taper off. It had been a month of little contact with Gilbert when he called me one Tuesday afternoon. I was beginning to feel withdrawal symptoms, playing his music in his absence. Possibly falling in love with him.

"I want to see you," Gilbert requested. "Can you see me tonight at seven?"

I'd been waiting for this call, as I had done many nights.

Chopin's piano *Polonaise in C sharp minor* was playing when he arrived at the studio thirty minutes after seven. I didn't mind his tardiness. There was a nervousness about his manner as if he was excited to see me, but at the same time in a hurry to go. Gilbert preferred to stay in and order Chinese take-out, as we'd done many times in the past.

He began commenting on the new painting on the easel as he sat in the center white sofa chair loosening his tie and unbuttoning his shirt collar.

"I like this one, Randy," Gilbert said, as he stood and walked over to the closet, opening the door exposing the stereo. "What were you thinking about as you were painting it? I feel like I could walk right into the painting and become lost in its quietness."

"I don't think about anything when I paint. I try to close my conscious mind and go for a feeling. I try not to think, but rather, I try to feel," I answered, not sure if he understood my meaning.

The music abruptly stopped as he ejected the tape.

"Have I played this one for you?" Gilbert asked, as he put in another tape. "This piece is called *Liebestod* from Wagner's opera, *Tristan Und Isolde*, his greatest musical drama, translated "Love Death.""

The studio slowly swelled with the intensity of the orchestra until it filled every corner. Gilbert turned the volume down and returned to the chair, as he quietly looked into the painting in discussion. I handed him his glass of scotch, hoping he would only need one, because he had finished the second bottle. Perhaps tomorrow I would get some more. The ice cubes clanged as he took it from my hand.

"I wish I could take this one, Randy. I wish I could take them all," Gilbert said, without blinking his eyes. Without any expression. "I can't see you anymore," he blurted out looking over at me. "I want you, but I can't give up what I have. It's destroying me and my life. If we had met years ago, before I married, things might be different. I didn't know then what these feelings were I had toward men. I thought I could handle it at first and by the time I had slept with the first man, I'd been married four years and we had two young children."

"I understand Gilbert. You don't have to say anymore," I said, trying to let him know I grasped his meaning, not sure myself if I really did. "When you were my age, Gilbert, it was harder to be gay. Times have changed. I don't have the same pressures as you did. But, it's still hard to be gay, even for me sometimes."

"I thought I could have both worlds," Gilbert said, as he got up and went to the window looking down at the bar. "I didn't think there would be a chance of me falling in love with one of the men I slept with. There only have been a few others, you must know that, Randy, and then I met you. Until you, it was just some kind of sexual desire I had to fill. It became addicting, but I never fell in love with any of the men. There were no attachments, no deep emotions, not even with Malcolm. He was convenience, our families knew one another. He kept me out of trouble."

I sat down in the chair to the right of him, looking up at his face, listening without interrupting. "He is so handsome, and he is going to get away," I found myself thinking. I held my breath at that thought. Gilbert looked away from me for a moment as his voice slightly cracked and then he walked back over and sat down. The music stopped, neither one of us got up to change the tape. In a few minutes, it would automatically start again.

"How will you feel if we never see one another again, Randy," Gilbert asked, his eyes to the floor.

I remained quiet for a moment. Thinking to myself, if this is our last time together, then the sum of my experience with Gilbert was two empty bottles of scotch. There would be no need to stop at the liquor store tomorrow.

"I will be fine," I answered, with a sigh of sad relief, as I fitted Gilbert's puzzle piece into place in my head.

"I think about you all the time," he said. "I think about how creative you are and how simple your ambitions are, about how I feel when I'm driving the hour or so to see you, about how it feels to hold your body in my arms and the way your skin feels on my lips, and I think about your face. When I leave you at night and drive back to Columbus, I think a hundred times of turning back and taking you away. And when I realize I can never let go of what I have, I realize I can never have you. It's too painful."

Gilbert stood up from the chair and walked over to me. Reaching out his hand, he pulled me to my feet and lead me into the bedroom. Gilbert stopped for a second just inside the doorway, smiling as he looked at his painting. I sat down on the bed looking up at him trying to imprint his face in my head. Gilbert then leaned over me and pulled off my shirt. He sat down beside me. The music began to play again and the smile left his face.

"Love Death," Gilbert said, as he leaned over to kiss me. His eyes were wet.

I laid back, quietly not wanting to say anything, not knowing what to say. My heart pounded. He began to rub my torso until I feel asleep.

mills

After the second operation, Todd had made little improvement. His days in the hospital ran into weeks; desperately he wanted to go home. The doctors tried everything they knew and even used combinations of new experimental drugs. The outlook was a wait-and-see situation. Arrangements were made for Todd to have home nursing care. He was happy to be back home and in his own bed.

His petite frame grew smaller as the virus ate at him, making Todd weaker as the days passed. Eventfully he was too weak to walk. Mrs. Weaver asked me to help carry Todd to his doctor's appointment. It was the last appointment of the day on a Thursday afternoon. I arrived at Todd's house early to ensure we would make it on time. Mrs. Weaver greeted me at the door. "Randy, Todd doesn't want to go but we have to make him," she urged. "The doctor needs to see him and I think he's afraid to hear they can't do anything for him."

I went into his bedroom and motioned "hello" to the nurse standing by his bed. It was heartbreaking to see Todd helplessly lying there. He had deteriorated so much, his weight had dropped considerably, and I knew his dreams had also. I spoke to him as I walked into the room. "Todd, I know you don't want to go to the doctor, but you have to," I begged. "You'll be back in your bed before you know it, and besides, it'll be good for you to get outside."

I hated feeling I was talking to him like trying to reassure a child. I knew I had no idea of what was good for him. Although I could see the physical results of the illness on Todd's body and the pain in his face, I had no idea of the hell he was going through. I just wanted to say the right things to make him feel at ease. Todd had been such a stronghold for me over the years, I wanted to be that for him now.

He just looked up and nodded his head. I reached out to hold his hand.

"We'll get through this together, Todd," I promised.

I picked up his frail frame and carried him to the car. All I could think about was the horrible virus running rampant through his body as I felt the sharpness of his bones against me. Once so full of life and joy, he was limp, looking off in a blank stare. I think it was at that moment, the reality of it all hit me like a bus. My dear friend Todd, in my arms, wasn't going to be around much longer and there was nothing any-one could do to change his fate. This wasn't some little something we could just talk about over dinner or laugh off while we spoke on the phone, like we'd done so many times over the years. This was serious. The fun was over. They were only memories now.

I sat in the office's waiting area while Mrs. Weaver paced outside the examining room. Her arms folded, she looked at the floor and then the closed door. A receptionist behind the desk asked if she wanted a cup of coffee. Mrs. Weaver raised her hand in a jester of no thanks and contin-ued her walking ritual. Several male patients moved in and out of the chairs as the doctor's assistants called them in. A few of their faces looked familiar, but I tried not to make eye contact. Instead, I flipped through a *New Yorker* magazine.

The day before, Todd had been talking about Zack. They had kept a long distance thing going for about eight months until Todd met Eric and his interests diminished. Todd's business required a lot of time, which resulted in less trips to New York as well, adding to the separation of the relation-ship. Eric was already in Atlanta and an easy distraction from New York. It wasn't a bad break up for Zack, he soon found someone else and there were no hard feelings. They both knew in the beginning, the long distance relationship would pose some problems sooner or later. Zack died eighteen months ago; Todd believing he contracted the virus from him. But he didn't hold a grudge, saying, "I should have been more careful, but I thought I was in love." We were a lot alike in that respect. Todd and I were both looking for love. But love couldn't keep him safe from AIDS. Maybe a condom and some safer practices could have prevented his outcome. But I had been guilty of not always being safe. We didn't know at the time there was anything to worry about. How could intimacy kill you? It might break your heart, but it wouldn't kill you, or would it? Regardless of the outcome, I believe Todd's search was a healthier one, where mine was polluted. It didn't seem right that he was the one dying. My search had taken me to New York as well.

From my seat in the middle of the plane, I could hear the flaps of the wings slowly extract as we started to circle over New York City. My body followed the turn to the right, leaning in the same direction of the plane.

The Delta captain's voice came over the intercom.

"We're beginning our descent, ladies and gentlemen. The skies are cloudy, chance of light snow tonight in the area and the temperature is 30 degrees. We should be landing in approximately twenty minutes. There will be agents at the gate to help you with any connecting flight information. Thanks again for flying with us and have a good night."

Sitting by the window, I put the magazine back in the seat pocket. Below, I could see a city filled with millions of lights beckoning up to the heavens. As far as the eye could see, lights, lights and more lights were scattered as high as they were wide. The city looked like it had been lit by a billion candles in the night. This was my first trip to the city called the "Big Apple." Naively, I found myself wondering why people referred to New York that way. From up here I could see nothing red, as in apple about it. The big was right, but red I didn't know. Maybe tomorrow I would discover why, but tonight, I saw it as the city of endless lights.

The "fasten seat belt" sign began flashing. I reached for the cardigan sweater I'd shoved under my seat earlier in the flight, putting it on before buckling up. The captain came on the intercom again, announcing this time that we were cleared for landing. I could hear the engines slow and feel the plane descending as my ears popped. Looking back out the window, I watched the head and tail lights of cars moving through this city of lights I was about to embark. They were little toys moving in a toy city.

After landing at LaGuardia, I was still a little high-strung coming off the plane. I hadn't seen Mills since meeting him a month ago at a party while vacationing in Mexico, two years after my memorable encounter with Ted. After our introduction, it seemed every time I turned around, Mills appeared. He pursued me, inviting me out several times during the remainder of my vacation, even though I politely turned him down repeatedly, explaining I was already committed. But Mills continued to ask me to join him and his friends. He clearly didn't know how to or wouldn't take no for an answer. I could tell right away that Mills had an intense demeanor about him. Finally, I gave in to the pressure of his persistence, only to stand him up. In fact, I stood him up more than once and he still came back for more rejection. My no-shows weren't really intentional, on some occasions earlier commitments ran late, preventing me from getting together with him. In those instances when I didn't show up, Mills never appeared upset, and if he was, it never showed.

Early one evening, Pierce, a friend of Mills', saw me walking to my hotel while they were leaving a party at a nearby hotel. Stopping me, he commented, coming across as forceful as Mills, "Don't you know what Mills could do for you? You should pay him more attention."

"I'm not interested in anyone doing anything for me," I tersely replied.

From the elegant clothes and tasteful gold jewelry Mills

and his group sported, I assumed Pierce was referring to money, or the things that come with having money. It seemed all too pretentious for me and it wasn't the first time someone dangled dollar bills in my face. I always hated it when people referred to how much money they had. Maybe it was because I'd never had any growing up and it made me uncomfortable. Maybe it was that they threw it around like it is a substitute for good looks, good manners or something else.

After coming out, I thought my friends had unjustly decided I only dated men with money. It was never my intention to seek out rich men and I'm not sure how it started. But once, Todd told me a story about when he was in the Pharr Library, one Friday night. The place was packed, as it always was on weekends. He was with a group of people when I walked in the bar alone. A man in the group commented he liked the way I looked. Another man then freely stated, "You don't have enough money to get him. Besides, he's too aloof."

It's infuriating to be misunderstood. People assume things about you and spread rumors with no concern or interest in the truth. Most don't take the time to find out what you're really about. The truth was my shyness made me appear aloof. Plus, I was looking for big, strong men and that left a lot of guys out of the running. So the only men who approached me were the older ones and many of them happened to have money. Money gave them an edge, made their balls feel bigger. At least that was my experience. I would have gone out with a truck driver if I liked him, if he was big enough. It didn't matter to me, but no truck drivers ever asked me out. I guess Pierce thought implying Mills had money would impress me. He was wrong. While listening to him go on, Mills walked up. I couldn't quite put my finger on it, but there was a creepiness about Mills; something bad hovered over him.

"Hello Randy, how are you?" he said.

"Hi. Fine. How about yourself?" I responded, afraid he

had overheard Pierce.

"I'm great," Mills answered, looking at Pierce knowingly. "But I'd be better if you joined us for dinner tonight, Randy...maybe you can make some time for me. You can't be that popular."

"I'm not," I answered.

My response was to say no, but with the both of them ganging up insisting, I gave in to the request.

"We'll pick you up at eight o'clock in front of your hotel," Mills commanded. "Don't disappoint me."

As before, I never showed, staying in my room the whole evening, not answering the phone when it rang. Instead, I stood on the balcony looking out over the water now turned black, shimmering under the moonlight, thinking about Ted, wondering if I would ever see him again.

The next morning, while walking the beach alone, hoping I would run into Ted but sure he was on another beach somewhere telling another guy what a great ass he had, Mills came up from behind out of nowhere. I apologized for the previous evening. Mills shrugged it off without requiring an explanation.

Not grasping my disinterest, he walked along with me. Either because my guard began to come down, or I was just too tired of telling Mills, no, I reluctantly engaged in conversation with him, talking about our histories and various interests. This resulted in my discovering he was from New York. Mills told me his lover, Jimmy, had committed suicide a month earlier. He found him in their apartment shot in the head, having lost a long battle with drug addiction and depression. The connection was too close to my own history. His loss touched me.

The beach was empty at that time of the morning. Only a few true sun worshipers were scattered on the sand. Mills' personality exuded pressure and I suddenly felt persuaded to socialize with him, fighting my shyness and uncertainty about him. Although for a second, I tried to think of a reason to excuse myself, but none came to mind. He seemed to want to reach out to someone and, for whatever reason, I was the one.

"You must come and visit me in New York, Randy," invited Mills. "I love showing people my city."

During our conversation under the morning sun, I told Mills I'd been considering a trip there and maybe even moving to New York for a short time.

"Being an artist not long out of college, I'm thinking I should spend some time there. New York is the place to be if you're an artist," I told him assertively.

"I know a lot of people in the business," Mills insisted. "I'll introduce you."

I knew Mills was most likely interested in more than showing me New York, but I thought my earlier no-shows made it clear there was only a potential for a friendship. I had grown up a lot since Ted and Gilbert. My naiveté was being squeezed out by new experiences. Most of the gay men I met didn't want to be just friends. Not wanting to assume things about him, as others had about me, I told myself he didn't seem to be such a bad guy. Although, the sinister air cloaked his presence as I had first noticed.

Not long after I was back in Atlanta, Mills called from New York.

"You've got to come and see the city," he urged. "When are you coming? Can't believe you haven't been here yet, Randy. Don't worry, like I said in Mexico, no strings attached," he promised. "You are welcome to stay with me. It'll be fun."

After several phone conversations over the following weeks, I decided to take Mills up on his "no strings attached" offer and make the trip. I made plans to go around the Christmas holidays.

One afternoon, a week before I was scheduled to leave, I called Mills and left a message on his answering machine, relieved he wasn't in.

"Sorry, hate to tell you, something came up and I'll have to postpone the trip," I said nervously. "Call you back later."

I hung up quickly.

I found it hard to say "no" to people, and the more aggressive the person, the shyer I became and that's where the trouble started. Over our phone conversations, Mills continued to come across as very pushy. But, some unexpected financial problems did develop — again that damn car of mine. I needed to spend the money I'd saved for the trip to New York on the old clunker. Besides, I was still a little uncomfortable with the whole idea. Mills was probably harmless, but I didn't know him very well. I took my financial situation as an omen not to go.

Later that evening, the phone rang. It was Mills, of course.

"What do you mean you can't come?" he questioned. "I've made all these great plans for you to see the city. You have to come, I've gotten tickets to 'Cats,' and there's a big party Saturday night I want to take you to, you're not going to want to miss it!"

"Mills, this is just not a good time... I appreciate you going to so much trouble, but I'll come another time. I promise," I said, wanting to keep my New York connection open for later when I was more comfortable.

"Randy, is it the money?" he pried. "I'll be glad to pay for your plane ticket... it's nothing to me. You won't have to worry about a thing while you're here, so come," Mills said firmly.

"Mills, I can't let you do that. I have some financial concerns I need to take care of," I said proudly. "I'll make plans to come at a later date when I get caught up with things."

"Listen, why wait, Randy? I told you money wasn't a problem. Come! You'll have a great time," he said, practically demanding. "No strings attached."

There was that phrase again, I thought. Did he really mean it?

"Well, Mills, let me think about it," I said, responding to his proposal, wanting to get off the phone with him. "I'll call you later, in a day or two."

The next day, Mills phoned again. I hadn't expected him to call back so soon. In fact, I remembered saying I would call him.

"Well, what did you decide, Randy?" he questioned. "You're coming, right?"

"I haven't had time to think about it, Mills," I said, sounding like I was putting him off.

"I'll overnight you the ticket tomorrow," Mills said. "I won't take 'no' for an answer."

"Are you sure, Mills?"

"Yes, Randy. No more discussion."

During my short walk from the gate to the baggage claim I thought how crazy I was for coming. I didn't know this man and yet he was going to pay for everything. What kind of situation was I getting myself into? My body felt hot and I could feel my face begin to redden as my mind reeled off questions. Trying to calm down, I decided to make the best of it and hoped everything worked out; I was here now and there was no turning back. It would be a long run back to Atlanta.

It was Thursday night and the airport was crowded with travelers. Sweat was running down my forehead. My mind went blank for a moment, unable to picture exactly what Mills looked like. I tried to envision his face and blond wavy hair, hoping I wouldn't walk right past him.

There he was in a crowd of people. I was relieved and scared at the same time. How could I miss that hair — pretty sure it wasn't real. Mills had a slight frame, about 5' 8" and he was in his middle to late fifties. I was twenty-five then. Yes, that was him. What was I getting myself into, my mind flashed again. I hope he just wants to be friends, I thought; there is no way I'm going to like this man any other way.

"Randy, welcome to New York!" Mills said, greeting me with a handshake. "How was the flight?"

"The flight was fine, thanks." I responded nervously.

"Let's get your bags and be on our way," Mills said, as

he motioned me to follow him. "How many did you bring?"

"Just two. I tried to bring only one bag, but I guess I brought too much stuff," I said, hating I sounded so naive. My first time in New York, I wanted to be prepared.

"Let's wait over there until your bags come off the belt," Mills said, smiling as he led me to the baggage area. "I never check any luggage unless I'm traveling out of the country... I hate to wait for it to come off the plane, but this shouldn't take too long," he commented.

Luckily the bags came around within a few minutes. Until then, few words were exchanged.

"Lets go outside to the car, Randy," Mills instructed. "Boy, it's busy tonight."

We made our way through the crowd of people to the outside of the airport. I'd never seen so many taxi cabs. I found myself suddenly excited to be in the city and not nearly so nervous anymore. All the commotion at the airport: People hurrying to make their planes, cars and taxies loading and unloading, took my mind off of being unsure of the situation.

"I don't see the car," Mills said, as he stood on his toes to heighten his shortness to look over the crowd. "Marcus probably had to drive around. The police don't like you to park in front of the airport here even if the car is occupied."

"Who's Marcus?" I thought to myself, reasoning he must be a friend of Mills' who had come along so Mills wouldn't have to park the car. I tried to think who I had told about my coming to New York. Not wanting to explain the situation of visiting a strange man I knew very little about, in a city I had never been to before, I realized I'd said very little about the trip and failed to leave Mills' phone number with anyone in Atlanta. The thought of something happening to me in New York and no one knowing where I was concerned me all of a sudden. While Mills was busy looking for the car, I noticed the man from New Jersey who had sat next to me on the plane. I looked at him and smiled as he meagerly smirked back. We had a brief conversation during the flight. I think he thought I was a little dumb. Making conversation, I told him this was my first visit to New York.

"Where are you staying in New York?" he asked.

"I'm not really sure," I responded.

"Well, are you staying in New York proper," he clarified.

"What do you mean?" I questioned, not familiar with the term New York proper.

"Are you staying in the city or outside?" he quizzed.

"Oh," I responded. "The friend I'm visiting lives in the city, but I don't remember the address."

He looked at me a little puzzled. I went back to reading the magazine in my lap realizing again how little I knew about Mills. We didn't talk the rest of the flight.

"Randy, here's Marcus with the car," Mills said, as he motioned to me.

I looked to the direction of the street to see a yellow and cream Rolls Royce pull up in front of us. A tall, large older man in a chauffeur's uniform walked around to the curb.

"I'm sorry, Mr. Gunn," the chauffeur apologized. "The traffic around the airport is unbelievable tonight. I had to circle the terminal a few times, you know, the police."

"That's okay, Marcus. Please put the bags in the car," Mills instructed.

Shit, I thought, as I looked back at the man from the plane. His mouth had dropped open as much as mine. Marcus nodded "hello" to me as he opened the rear car door. As we pulled away from the curb, I looked back and gave a slight wave to my traveling companion from New Jersey. As he nodded back, I thought, "Is this proper enough for you?"

Well, things were looking up after all, I told myself. The car was a surprise. He said money was not a problem. But I had never dreamed Mills had a Rolls Royce. But, maybe he rented it, or it's borrowed from a friend in an effort to impress me. I thought about Pierce and the conversation of the things Mills could do for me if I was nice to him. So this is what Pierce was talking about. I tried not to act too impressed. After all, it's just a car.

"Nice car, Mills," slipped out of my mouth before I realized it.

Riding into New York City for the first time in the back of a chauffeur-driven Rolls Royce was quite exciting. Especially for a poor, small town boy like me. The view coming over the bridge from LaGuardia was spectacular from the deep leather seats — the intense smell of leather filled my lungs as I watched the lighted skyline, appearing more beautiful than any pictures I'd ever seen. I soon forgot about being nervous.

As we arrived at Mills' Park Avenue address, the street was alive with Christmas festivities. Trees, lining the street, blazed with tiny white twinkling lights. Groups of people walked around, appearing to be on their way to or coming from grand holiday parties. I could hear their voices engaged in conversation as they passed by the car. Only a few looked back at the Rolls Royce, casually checking out the car and its occupants. I had a sense limousines were a common occurrence in this neighborhood. I stepped out of the car as Marcus opened the door. Standing on the sidewalk, I looked up at my new surroundings and took a deep breath, inhaling all the city had to offer my senses this crisp, cold night.

The evening was growing late and I was bushed. The chill in the air felt good, the coldness was invigorating, helping to revive me. In my eyes sparkled the lights of the city, as my ears were serenaded by sounds of cars whipping by, of voices bouncing along the avenue, and footsteps hitting the street — like music in the making — echoed off the tall buildings. I could feel the life of the city around me. I wanted to feel a part of it.

"Mr. Gunn, how was your evening?" a doorman greeted.

"Fine, Tony, we just came from the airport," Mills informed. "This is my friend, Randy, he'll be staying for a few days."

"Welcome, let me know if there is anything you need while you're here with Mr. Gunn," he offered.

"Thank you, Tony, I will," I graciously responded.

Tony took my bags from Marcus and lead us into the building. The lobby was spacious. Our footsteps echoed, as we walked across the marble floor. I caught my reflection in the mirrored walls as Tony guided us to the elevator. I could tell it was late by the redness of my eyes. I was ready to go to bed. Alone I hoped.

"The place is in a bit of a mess, Randy," Mills said apologetically. "Its been under renovation for the past few months. I was hoping it would be finished before you arrived, but the workmen are behind schedule."

Mills' apartment had two floors. Everything on the first floor was decorated in white. The second was still under renovation, so much of the furniture was covered in plastic to protect against paint and construction dust.

"Well, you must be pretty tired, Randy," Mills commented.

"Yes, I don't think I'll have any trouble sleeping tonight," I answered, exhausted and looking forward to getting some sleep. "Where should I put my things?"

"In the guest room," Mills answered, as he lead me down a short hall. "I think you'll be comfortable in there. Let's sleep in late tomorrow. I'll wake you for breakfast, if that's okay with you?"

"That'll be great. I'll see you in the morning," I said, as I walked into the room. "Thanks for everything," I added, relieved to be in the guest room and headed for sleep.

Mills gave me a smile "good night" and closed the door behind him. It was nice to be alone after the newness and excitement of the trip and I was glad to see Mills was being a gentlemen. Glancing at a clock that sat on the desk across the room, I noticed it was almost one o'clock in the morning. "They say this is the city that never sleeps," I said to myself, as I walked over to the window, looking down eight stories. The traffic hummed on the avenue below. It was even more beautiful from up here. I scanned the lighted windows of the buildings across the street. Obviously, I wasn't the only soul up at this hour. Outside the bedroom door, I heard Mills walk down the hall and then close a door.

The room was warm and stuffy. I opened a window and reintroduced the smell of the city I had experienced earlier. The winter's coldness rushed into the room. For a second, unsure of the night and the strange surroundings, I thought of escaping through the window and scaling down the building. Deeply breathing in the city, I undressed and climbed into bed, positioning the pillows under my head so I could still see out the window. The hum of the traffic was even louder now with the window open, horns blew as cars whisked by on the wet street below. I reached to turn out the lamp on the bedside table; my eyes were getting heavy. I laid there looking out into the night, still not believing I was in New York for the first time, and at a fine address at that. Feathery snowflakes fell against the panes of the window, trying to come into the room. The ones making it through the opening lasted only a second or two before the warm air from the apartment intercepted their delicate intrusion and melted them. Happily anticipating the next few days, I laid in the bed listening to the music of the city.

The next morning I was awakened by Mills' knock. The temperature in the room was now cold from the open window. I quickly leaped out of bed, shivering as I closed it. To my delight, the city had been covered by a thick blanket of snow during my night's sleep. I was in New York and it was snowing. I felt like a little kid.

After dressing, we headed out for the day. Mills planned to take me all around the city; Marcus had the morning off, so we were on our own. Upon exiting the building, a different door man than the one last night greeted us while scrapping snow from under the canopy. The sounds of the street were muffled by the sheet of white insulation on the ground. As I followed Mills down the avenue to fetch the car, all I could think about was how much I liked snow. It had a way of making everything seem calm. It rarely snowed in Georgia when I was little, but when it did, snow was a welcomed peace, if only for a moment, until the heat came out and melted it away.

At the garage, I learned Mills had two more Rolls Royces, different styles but all matching in color. He also had a stretch limo, which he said was used to run around the city during the week. They were parked in a row; a fleet of a rich man's toys. We took the Corniche. I wondered if maybe he would let me drive it while thinking about my poor bandaged car parked outside my apartment in Atlanta. How pitiful it would look next to these with its leaky top and broken window.

Mills drove me on a tour of the Upper East side, around a snow covered Central Park and later into SoHo, where he knew I would be most interested in stopping. A vitality and creativity floated in the air as we walked along, the snow crisply crunching under our feet. If I'm really going to be an artist, then I need to be here. This is the environment for me, I thought, as countless others before me surely had.

I daydreamed as we walked, looking into the large store fronts, which now were artist studios and galleries, remembering just a few years ago being in college and living at home. Even then my dreams were of living in a big city, of being an artist, of having all the comforts of a successful life, and never wanting for anything. This trip to New York could be the beginning of that dream.

My thoughts traveled in reverse to me sitting in my room studying back home in Warner Robins — how I hated that town and the life I had there. From my room, I could hear my mother walking around the house talking to herself. Every few minutes, the sound made by her cigarette lighter flicking on and off filled the house until she got the cigarette lit. She chain smoked from the moment she woke up until the time she went to bed. The echoing pop of a beer can soon followed. She'd finished the bottle of whiskey I had watered down, but there wasn't much I could do about the beer. There were times when enough was enough and I would empty the whiskey in the kitchen sink with her fighting me to take the bottle. Hardly able to stand with a facial expression of disbelief, like I was pouring out the last drops of a drug she desperately needed to stay alive, she screamed for me to stop. After the first couple of times I refrained from emptying the bottles in her presence and started watering down the booze instead. Generally, she couldn't tell the straight whiskey from the half and half, often times, waiting until she had several drinks in her, then after she had gone to her room to rest I'd make the adjustments.

I sat in my room hoping she wouldn't come storming in yelling like so many other times. And when she did, she usually told me how horrible my dead father was and how she'd wasted her life. Often, busting in demanding I take her to the liquor store so she could get more booze and cigarettes before it closed. Sometimes it would go on all night: Cigarette lighter flicking, beer cans popping, storming in and out of my room. I prayed she would soon go to bed and sleep off her brooding.

I wanted out of Warner Robins and out of that life; I knew I was different, but not really sure how. Tired of always being the caretaker, I wanted someone to take care of me for awhile. I didn't want to be a parent to my mother anymore as I had been all my childhood to both my mother and father. Shortly after my father's suicide, Stephen and Sandra left home. Unable to stand it anymore, they left me alone with her, the beer cans and cigarettes.

There is one afternoon I will never forget. Like bad dreams that never go away, my father's memory had inherited the daylight hours as it had the night. The morning sun was not enough to chase him away to some hiding place until dusk. He was with us each hour, regardless of the hour. I saw his madness in the eyes of my mother and I felt it in myself. The morning had been quiet except for Mother's sporadic movement between the kitchen table and her bedroom. I was doing school work and she had let me be for the majority of the time. Occasionally, she walked back to my room and just stood in the doorway holding on to its frame.

Not saying a word, she just looked at me with those large eyes, the eyes of my father as if she was looking at him and I was not there. Of course she was drunk. I knew this because of her continuous opening of the cabinet below the kitchen sink, where the whiskey bottles waited for her. And from my room I could almost hear her twist the bottle cap off and hear the liquor spill into the glass.

The visits to my room increased as the day grew long. Mother's ritual of coming in and out of my room yelling, made it hard to concentrate on my studies. As usual, she went on and off for hours like a light switch. Where my father left off with the yelling, name calling and the abuse, Mother picked up with reliving it everyday. It soon became apparent that the death of my father wouldn't be the death of his abuse. His ghost was alive, living in each of us, haunting us in death as he had in life, especially in Mother. You cannot run away from a ghost. I would get up from my desk and escort her from the room. But Mother would soon return and the escorting became pushing as I tried to avoid her swinging arms. I knew she was trying to hit him and not me. Mother became hysterical, her yelling filled the house and I became frightened of her.

Suddenly she was behind me and I felt her tug at the hair on the back of my head. As I turned in my chair, she yanked and I heard the fist full of hair rip from my scalp.

"You're a sissy like your father," she screamed.

"What are you doing?" I yelled at her, as I felt the back of my head. It stung.

Mother stood a foot from me, her fist still closed tight, clutching the hair.

"I wish you were never born...I wish none of you were ever born...I should have never married that bastard...and I regret the day I met him," she screamed, out of control.

I didn't know how much more I could take. Like a reflex, my hand shot at her and before I was aware of what happened, I had slapped her across the face. The vision of that moment never leaves my mind. Mother's body stumbled back into the hallway as she felt the cheek of her face. Her eyes were large and seething, looking like they would shoot fire at any moment. Unable to regain her footing, mostly due to the large amount of alcohol she had consumed, and regrettably due to the force of my hand on her angry face, she fell to the floor. My father had become alive in me. I was no longer the little boy shaking in the corner, eyes filling with tears, watching my father beat her, watching her fall. I was now the cause of her pain.

Mother lost her balance and landed on the small bathroom floor off the hallway. Her head rested at the base of the toilet. For a few seconds I stood over her in shock and disbelief of what I had done, afraid she was dead. And when the realization hit me, I wanted to be dead. My stomach became sick as if I was going to throw up. I could not take a breath and my heart seemed to stop beating.

Her body moved and I could hear her say, "Look what you have done to me!"

I leaned over to help her up, trying to stay clear if she took another swing at me. But I wanted her to. I wanted her to hit me hard.

She appeared to be okay. The most damage I'd done was to her pride, but now my heart was damaged forever. We stood in the hallway not saying a word. I put my arms around her and began to cry.

"It's alright," Mother said, as she rested her head on my shoulder. After a few moments, I went back to my room and Mother went into the kitchen. I heard the cabinet door open, and then the whiskey bottle hit against the glass. By the next day she seemed to have forgotten the incident. I would never forget.

Once bottles emptied, the beer cans stopped popping, and she went to bed, I would be left to concentrate on my studies. But, it would only be a matter of time before she woke up. I listened for her, listened for the flickering — for the popping, as I sat at my desk. Looking at my reflection in the mirror on the dresser to the right of my desk, I told myself that someone would come along and take care of me, someone would love me and share their life. I guess I thought someone taking care of me would be the trade off for dealing with all the shit of my father, and then reliving it with Mother. A reward for surviving — for making it through without becoming them, and for coming out alive. Perhaps that is why I stayed when things got bad enough for my sister and brother to leave. There is no reward. You just keep staying in bad situations for the rest of your life. I've come to realize the only reward for surviving is just that.

"Randy, this gallery is owned by a friend of mine. Maybe she's in and you can meet her," Mills said, as he pulled at my arm through the door.

I snapped back to the present and my dark thoughts left me. Maybe Mills would be the person to save me from my past, maybe he would be the person to love me. My brother had been out of my life for sometime now. We barely talked to one another over the past years after he quit school and moved out of the house. Of course, I saw him at work until I left after graduation. Dennis wasn't able to replace my brother; Roberto left me confused; Ted was a fantasy come to life for a few hours, but one that brought with it reality; and Gilbert left me in the night. But Mills, he could fill in the missing puzzle piece of my life where the others couldn't. I could do worse, and besides, look at the kind of life I would have living in New York, not having to struggle anymore. Pierce was right, Mills could do things for me. Mills would be my reward. I would be worth something now, as good as anyone else. While we walked through SoHo in the falling snow, Mills noticed I wasn't wearing gloves. He took me into a store, instructing me to pick out any pair I wanted. I tried on a wool pair and said they would do. He instead picked up a pair of leather ones lined with fur and handed them to the salesmen.

"We'll take these," Mills said, as he handed them to me and paid the salesmen.

Some of Mills' friends came over for drinks that evening

before the whole group went out to dinner. Pierce, who was at least sixty, was accompanied by his twenty-three-year-old boyfriend. Definitely a stereotypical, rich, May-December lover arrangement. "Who said money can't buy love," Pierce would say. "Well, maybe not real love. But if a warm, beautiful young man is willing to spend time with me, among other things, then I'm willing to let him spend a little of my money. That's all the love I need."

Admittedly, I really didn't know what to think of Pierce at first. But, as I got to know him, I came to believe Pierce was a genuinely good person. I liked his personality more than Mills' dry demeanor and he knew exactly where he stood with this twenty-three-year-old. Pierce was in partnership with his brother in a lucrative manufacturing business. Things had become shaky between the two over missing money from the company's account. Increasingly, the finger was being pointed at Pierce, and he was known for spending money by the wallet fulls.

After he converted one bedroom in his home into a walk-in closet, Mills referred to Pierce as "the clothes horse." He was also married and had three sons — two attended an Ivy League school, the oldest nearing graduation. Like Roberto and Gilbert, no one in his family knew of Pierce's secret life. Mills said Pierce's wife probably thought something was going on, but they'd been married for a long time and she was too well taken care of to make a fuss over Pierce's outside interests. Before we left for dinner this particular evening, Pierce made a call to inform his wife he would stay in the city for the night, returning home the following day.

There were six of us at dinner: Pierce and his boyfriend Tim, Richard and Carol — a married couple, and Mills and myself. Mills thought Carol had a thing for him. I thought rather, she had a thing for his money. The restaurant was full of beautiful and stylish people. The maitre d' called Mills by name and seated our party immediately. The tables were buzzing with conversation, as was ours. I felt out of place, thinking I didn't belong in such a nice setting and I shouldn't be wearing the fine clothes on my back. As in first starting college, I was apprehensive I would be found to be an impostor. I silently sat at the table hoping not to be discovered. All the time hoping the truth of my past wouldn't come oozing out of my pores, fearful the maitre d' would come back to the table to insist I leave. Being the shy person I was, I sat back and listened, only talking when someone directed a comment to me. Several people came up to the table and exchanged greetings. By the end of the night, I couldn't remember the names of all the people I'd met.

After we finished eating, the waiter brought the bill to Mills. I glanced at the check as Mills laid it down on the table in front of him. The total was close to six hundred dollars. He paid in cash: Seven one hundreds and a twenty dollar bill. To me, that was nearly two months rent.

Once again, Marcus was waiting for us outside the restaurant. We all got into the Rolls Royce, the biggest of the three, and proceeded to drop Richard and Carol at their brownstone. Marcus drove the rest of us to The Garden Room, a gay bar in the Village. Outside, the street was filled with men, many heading toward the bar.

"Hello, Mills. How are you tonight?" greeted the bouncer at the door.

"Just fine, Frank," Mills acknowledged. "Say hello to my friend, Randy, from Atlanta. You know Pierce and Tim, don't you."

"Yes. Hey guys. Nice to meet you, Randy."

I politely said hello to Frank as Mills lead us through the crowd of men watching music videos on big screens set up throughout the bar, many of which acknowledged Mills.

"Mills, you sure know a lot of people here," I stated. "You must come here a lot."

"I guess so," Mills responded, to my surprise. "I own the place and several more in the city. Come downstairs with me for a minute so I can check on things while we're here."

By now Pierce and Tim had disappeared in the crowd. I

followed Mills to the rear of the bar and down a narrow staircase leading to a large basement filled with cases of wine, liquor and beer.

"Randy, you can move to New York and we'll set you up a studio. In fact, maybe you could use the basement of one of my bars for now until we can find a more suitable place for you to paint," Mills suggested.

"Don't think I can afford to move to New York just yet, Mills," I commented, as he unlocked the door.

"I have lots of room, Randy. You can stay with me and it wouldn't cost you anything," Mills promised. "Think about it."

It was getting clear Mills had thoughts of something romantic happening between the two of us. I wasn't foolish enough to believe he would offer me a place to live and studio space without any "strings attached." The idea of moving to New York filled my head, the brief taste of glamour was sucking me in. To live in New York, right on Park Avenue, and be chauffeured around the city would be grand, a nice reward. I could work in the heart of the art world, but I was sure Mills wanted more than a roommate. It was something to think and dream about. I'd been a dreamer all my life, but this time, one of the dreams stood a chance of becoming reality. Perhaps, I could get a studio in SoHo. My imagination took flight.

Pierce and Tim took a cab over to another bar across town; I was ready to leave and call it an evening. Mills made his way back through the bar with me following close behind. After being stopped by a dozen more guys, we finally made it out the door. Trusty Marcus was waiting. The street was still busy with people walking in and out of the bars and restaurants. Several of them were checking us out as Marcus got out of the Rolls Royce to open the door. Having the door opened for me made me feel a little silly. I surely didn't mind being driven around New York in a Rolls Royce, but if there was any possibility of me moving into this lifestyle, the door opening had to stop.

"Did you have a nice time, Sir?" Marcus asked me.

"Yes, I did. But please, call me Randy," I corrected. "You're old enough to be my father. I should be calling you Sir."

Marcus was actually old enough to be my grandfather, with seemingly a good-natured disposition. It struck me then that in that type of work, one was paid to pleasantly offer a lot of "yes sir, no sir" stuff, besides opening and closing doors. There was something about him I liked. If I moved to the city, we were going to be good friends.

On the way back to the apartment, we stopped at a Haagen Dazs ice cream shop to get my favorite: Chocolate-chocolate chip. It all seemed like a fairy tale, like something out of a movie I'd seen as a child: The camera closes in, the Rolls Royce pulls up to an ice cream store; the driver gets out to get the order; poor boy makes it big and finds true love in the big city. Actually, I went in and got the ice cream myself while Mills and Marcus waited in the car.

Returning to the apartment, Mills said he wasn't sleepy and asked if I would like to watch television with him in his bedroom. His room was very Grecian — dark colors, two columns flanked the window looking out over Park Avenue, and a huge Romanesque bed filled most of the room. Mills opened the doors of the Biedermeier armoire facing the bed, revealing a television screen.

"Hop up, Randy," Mills requested. "I won't bite you," he reassured, as he laid down on the bed.

I sat at the edge of the bed, absently looking at the news program on television as Mills adjusted the pillows behind his head.

"Come on up here and make yourself comfortable. I promise, I won't do anything you don't want me to do," he said, as he patted the bed with his hand.

I slid over toward him leaving two feet between our bodies.

"Here, take a few of these pillows," Mills offered, as he handed one to me.

He began to channel surf.

"Doesn't look like there's very much on tonight. How did you like your first day in New York?" Mills questioned.

"I had a very nice time," I answered appreciatively. "Thanks for being such a wonderful host."

"Well, there's a lot more to see and do, and it'll take more than a few days to take it all in. You should stay longer," he maintained.

Mills kept talking, occasionally commenting on what was on television as he continued to flip the channels. I closed my eyes. The bed was very comfortable and I knew I could easily fall asleep at any moment. Suddenly, I felt Mills' hand touch my arm. I flinched.

"Randy, I think you know I like you. There are a lot of things I could help you with," Mills advised. "Why don't you sleep in here with me tonight. What do you think?"

I knew Mills could do a lot for me. It had been in the back of my mind all day, and I will admit, probably subconsciously there since Pierce introduced the thought to me at the beach. I suddenly felt the presence of my father. If he had lived, Mills and he would be around the same age. I began to feel submissive, out of control of the situation.

Mills began rubbing my arm, inducing a panicked feeling inside me. Atlanta was a long way away now. I was in a strange city and I had nowhere to run. I wanted to say no, I wanted to go to sleep in the other room. But if I said no, what would be his reaction...rejection? Would he dislike me? He moved closer. Rubbing my upper body, Mills began unbuttoning my shirt, pulling the tail out of my pants. Again, I wanted to get up, but I couldn't. I felt trapped in my father's grip, unwillingly obedient.

Lying on Mills' bed, I tried to reconcile the situation. He was older, he had money and he could introduce me to a lifestyle not a lot of people from my background got to live. I had nothing. It seemed like someone was always trying to buy me anyway. I was a commodity. I may as well take the best offer. The rumor that I was an expensive date had no truth to it until tonight. Mills began kissing me as he moved his body on top of mine. I didn't want him there so why couldn't I just get up and leave? Why was I letting him do this to me? I pretended to enjoy the moment. Could I fake my way through this? Was I that good of a liar? Yes, I lied myself through childhood, through my life up to now, and I could keep lying. I wanted him to like me. I wanted us just to be friends, but "friends" didn't get to live on Park Avenue.

It was hard to keep an erection. I kept my eyes closed and concentrated as Mills drove his tongue into my mouth. He lifted himself up on his knees over me; my skin freed from his. He directed my hand to his penis, encouraging me to rub it. Mills began masturbating me, fondling my chest with his free hand. My hand grew fatigued from stroking his penis. Finally, with a gasp he released himself on my stomach. Surprisingly, his semen was cold, it brought no warmth to my skin. I was shaking on the inside. It was a familiar feeling revisiting from a past life.

The next few days resulted in a year of commutes to New York from Atlanta. On my second trip to New York, Mills took me upstairs to his bedroom of the Park Avenue apartment. On the bed was a large gift-wrapped box. He looked at me saying, "I got you a little something." Motioning for me to walk over to the bed, Mills then said, "Go ahead, open it. You may need it tonight." It was a beautiful wool overcoat. Somehow, I made myself comfortable with Mills. I wasn't sure what I wanted and I didn't know where things would end up. I decided to take things as they came. I got to know him more and more during my visits and conversations on the phone — not sure yet if I really liked him, even as a friend. But compared to my life in Atlanta, New York seemed like the brass ring. And Mills was offering it in his hand. Everybody used people, I told myself. I'd been used and now I wanted to turn the tables. I realized there was more to know about Mills than what he allowed me to see. I had a lot of questions in my mind, but Mills was not very free with the answers. I began to hear rumors of his past that made me afraid to ask.

Sex was not a big part of our relationship, at least not for me. I avoided it as much as possible and I went through the motions when I had to. After all, I was an actor of sorts. Lying in bed, I played the young lover of a wealthy and possibly dangerous man. No lies were spoken from my mouth, leaving the movements of my body to perform deceptions. As I sensed at our first meeting, Mills had a menacing side, like a shadow that followed him around. Call it instinct — somehow I knew — but I continued to reach for the brass ring held so tightly in his hand. People talked, even in Atlanta there were those who told me to be careful, Todd for one. His friend, Zack, knew of Mills and told Todd I should stay away. But I kept getting back on the plane for New York. I realized I was more caught up in the wealth than I had imagined, along with the things they afforded: The best restaurants, plays, parties, etc. We never had to wait for a table and we walked right in to any club without being delayed in lines that sometimes were blocks long; the Rolls Royce pulled up to the door and we walked right in. I was definitely hooked on the lifestyle. Going to the theater was what rich and important people did back home. On several occasions after the show, as we were leaving the theater, people mobbed the Rolls Royce to see if some celebrity was in it. Someone in the crowd broadcast, "Who are they?" Sorry just us, I said to myself as they peered in the windows finding the undeserved attention a little embarrassing. Mills seemed to be amused by it, I cared they thought I was someone important.

There were parties to attend. I attempted to pull myself from my layers of protective shyness. At one party on Central Park, I met a Broadway producer. He discreetly invited me to lunch with him, slipping me his card while Mills was not around. Finding him very attractive, I called him one morning after Mills had left the apartment. We met at a small restaurant in the village. He was very forward, talking about sex during most of lunch. My naive side was showing.

Our conversation briefly took a turn just long enough to bring Mills up. My lunch date was baffled by my involvement with him. He insinuated I was hanging out with some pretty tough company. But the subject jumped back to sex and he wasn't willing to elaborate any further on Mills.

After lunch he invited me to join him at his apartment for some afternoon play time. Although tempted by this commanding man, I declined the offer. My hands were full with Mills. I was already beginning to feel like his property, it would be a mistake if Mills were to find out. This was a big town, but I was learning in this rich gay community, people talked and I didn't know who might be watching. I kept his number for several months, but never called him again.

Possibilities were opening up and I didn't want the truth to spoil things. Mills introduced me to an interior designer, Webster who commissioned me to do some art for his office and a piece for a client in the Hamptons. I soon discovered he was into drugs. On one occasion, before leaving the apartment to meet with Webster, he called to inquire if Mills had any cocaine or pot around. This was the first time I'd heard Mills' name mentioned in the same sentence with drugs. Mills had already left and I had no idea where to look. I had never seen Mills use drugs while I was around, although I was sure he did. He sniffed incessantly at times, due to what I was sure was a sign of coke usage, to say nothing of the crowd and their habits I was becoming familiar with. And the times! It was the eighties — it seemed everyone was doing drugs except me — another reason to feel different and out of place. My squeaky clean character shone like a beacon even though I tried to cloud it.

When I showed up at Webster's office empty handed, he seemed pissed. Grabbing his coat, he motioned for me to follow. We went outside where he hailed a cab. Webster quickly told the driver where to take us, which turned out to be half a block from a school yard.

"Wait here," Webster ordered the driver, as he jumped

out of the cab pulling me behind him. I followed him to the playground of the school, trying to keep a safe distance from a policeman standing at the corner. Webster told me to keep a look out, as if he thought I'd done this sort of thing before. After he scored from a guy in the yard, I was sure we were going to get caught. We got back in the cab and returned to the office.

When we arrived, a friend of Webster's was waiting in the reception area. We all went into Webster's office where he began to roll a joint. Alice pulled out a little metal boxed filled with coke. I couldn't believe what I was seeing at ten o'clock in the morning. Webster offered me the joint. I pretended to take a drag off of it, looking to see if they were paying attention, hoping they were not. I watched Alice dip her finger into the box and rub her gums with the white powder. She then offered me the box. I mimicked her, but tried to get as little of the coke on my finger as possible. I did as she had done, rubbing my finger over my gums as they watched me. What little of the coke there was on my finger tasted terrible. Why would they want to put this shit in their mouths much less up their noses, I wondered. I began to feel dumb that I'd allowed peer pressure to influence me. I should have said, "No thank you, I don't do that stuff." But I didn't speak up, the pressure was too great. I was loosing it, opening the door to destruction. I had already been drinking more during my trips to New York. I felt the loss of control that had visited me from time to time. If I was going to survive New York, I had to stay sober. I couldn't feed the blood of my parents flowing within me. I was an addict, I couldn't take the fatal powder of addiction. Having already played with alcohol, pushing it to the limits, using it to ease my sexual confusion — sometimes not remembering how I got home or who brought me there. Drinking helped me feel more relaxed, feel more comfortable around other guys, feel more attractive and desirable to them. All my life, I swore to myself I would never fall prey to the addition of drug or alcohol use. I wouldn't become my parents. But, the blood of my parents fought me, until I fed it poison. Here I was using it as a crutch to help me feel I was better than dirt.

Jimmy came to mind as I sat in Webster's office, watching him get high with Alice. I pictured his face as I had seen it in the white picture frame on the coffee table in Mills' apartment. I pictured the blood on the white carpet, as it would have spilled out of his head, and I compared it to the blood of my father on the sofa and a similar carpet. The next time I was offered any drugs, I told myself, I would try to refuse. For all my efforts to fit in, I had a bad taste in my mouth for the rest of the afternoon.

Roy Cohn, the controversial lawyer, was a good friend of Mills. Every year, Cohn gave a New Year's Eve dinner party at his Manhattan brownstone. The place filled with glamorous people all dressed to kill. An older woman in a slinky silver dress cornered me most of the evening, discussing art while Mills was off talking to everyone else. I couldn't get away from her to save myself.

Later in the evening, I noticed Mills talking to a handsome man next to the stairs on the second floor. They were engaged in conversation as if they were good friends. I couldn't believe my eyes when I finally realized Mills was talking to a famous clothing designer. Here I was all the way from the sticks at a party in New York City with this world-renowned person. I'd finally broken away from the woman in the silver dress, but as soon as I put my drink down to walk over to Mills so he could introduce me to the designer, she appeared again. I stood only a few yards from them, irritated and barely listening to what she was saying. My attention was focused on Mills and his famous friend. I rolled my eyes at Mills for help.

Still in her grip, I saw the designer and Mills shake hands good-bye. I tried to excuse myself but there was no polite way to abruptly exit. Plus, she seemed in need of my attention...anyone's for that matter. I'd noticed her husband had been talking to a younger woman all evening. Understanding her loneliness, I stood there with her. Damn, I thought, there goes my only chance to meet this man. Two model-type looking women joined the designer and they descended the stairs. The designer watched me, as I did him, until they reached the bottom floor. He turned for one last quick look before exiting the door. I asked Mills why he hadn't come to save me from the older woman and introduce me to the designer. "I didn't want the designer to steal you from me," Mills curtly said. "He seemed interested in you, asking if I knew you. I said we were lovers."

"You're pulling my leg...aren't you?" I asked.

"He's a big whore and no one is fooled by that straight act...everyone knows. His models talk...he has bedded most of them — the male ones, that is. I can make you happier," Mills insisted.

I couldn't tell if Mills was serious or not. Fat chance I thought, wishing it was true that the designer was interested. Mills then quickly changed the subject and I dropped it, not wanting to seem to curious.

Cohn's staircase was lined with Andy Warhols like wallpaper. I didn't talk with him very much during the evening. He smiled at me a few times, stopping briefly to inquire if I was having a good time. After the party, many of the guests boarded the double-decker bus that Roy provided waiting outside at the curb. The bus headed off to Studio 54 for a private party, where a section was blocked off with a velvet rope for Roy's guests. I had been to the club before with Mills. A very flamboyant place in its time, of course I'd heard about it before ever coming to New York, but I never felt as if I fit in these places. At times, I didn't feel I looked the part for the club scene and, because of my shyness, my heart was never in it.

After that party, I saw Roy several times over the following year with Mills, usually at his brownstone and on a much calmer note. One Friday evening, after I flew in from Atlanta, Roy had invited us to his house for dinner. Due to bad weather, my plane was several hours late, so Marcus dropped Mills off at Roy's before coming to pick me up at the airport. Roy held up dinner until I arrived to what turned out to be a quiet evening. Roy's lanky, handsome, live-in companion was there, along with their Afghan. I noted the dog and the boyfriend had the same color hair. The surroundings were stuffy and dimly lit as the four of us sat at the table. The conversation was light. The dog lounged near by, his collar occasionally jingled in orchestration with the silverware collecting the meal from the china. Cohn cleared his throat several times as they talked about people I didn't know. Sitting in his house at dinner, I travelled back to high school, recalling the part he played in the historic 1950s McCarthy hearings. Now, here I was many years later socializing with him, only slightly aware of the power and control this man still possessed. I sensed the atmosphere of the room was very much like the man himself, dangerous. Mills was in good company.

In the spring, Mills took me to his house at the Pines on Fire Island. As usual, I flew into the city on a Thursday night, taking Friday and Monday off from work. On Fridays, Mills took care of business. He left Marcus with me and we went around the city picking up things for the weekend: Flowers, food and whatever else Mills put on the shopping list. I enjoyed those jaunts through the city with Marcus, they were much calmer than if Mills was with us. By then, I had broken Marcus of the habit of calling me "Sir" and running around the Rolls Royce to open the door. On those trips, we took the Corniche which, in my thinking, was the less pretentious of the three cars.

With the top down and my list in hand, I sat in the front seat next to Marcus. I felt silly riding in the back if it was just the two of us. Once I talked Marcus into sitting in the passenger seat so I could drive around Manhattan. He gave me directions and even though the streets run east and west and the avenues north and south I always got turned around.

"Randy, I don't think Mr. Gunn would approve of you driving me around. That's my job, that's what he pays me for."

"Marcus, don't worry about it. I'm not a bad driver, I won't get in a wreck. Trust me. I won't tell Mills if you don't." I don't think Marcus liked Mills very much anyway.

I pulled up in front of Bloomingdale's and jumped out to run in to pick up a few items. Two elderly women looked at me and then Marcus.

"I think you have things backwards, Son," one of them said. "Isn't he suppose to be doing the driving?"

Marcus shrugged his shoulders with a surprise giggle. I gave them a wink as I hurried into Bloomies.

The interior of the house on the island was mostly white, like the first floor of the Park Avenue address. It had a pool, a sprawling deck hidden away under the pine trees and tall bushes, and a house man who cooked, cleaned, and served drinks by the pool. There wasn't much of the pagan atmosphere associated with the island; Mills kept me away from that. Although there was always a party to go to on the island during the weekends, we stayed in a lot. He seemed to prefer it that way. At Friday afternoon tea dances and island parties, Mills pointed out several producers, actors and models, introducing me to a few. He seemed to like being in the company of famous people. Occasionally, I noticed people from Atlanta, who ran in the "A" social list of gay society there, many of which were friends of Todd's. By this time, Todd and Eric had settled into a domestic life, working on their first anniversary.

We attended a few parties and dinners on the island which usually started late — around ten, and ended by two a.m. for those who wanted to go out. The bar on the island didn't get cranking until three or four in the morning, but that was way too late for me. One Saturday evening, we dined with a friend of Mills' who owned a bar on Christopher Street in the Village. Joe's house was on the beach not far from Mills'. There was just the four of us — Joe, his young lover Bill, Mills and myself. It seemed a lot of the time all the older men I met were paired up with younger ones, but who was I to talk? The dinner went on for hours,

Mills and Joe spending a lot of the evening talking about the bar business. I talked with Bill who was closer to me in age. Throughout dinner, Bill played footsies with me under the table. He was cute and I was interested, but we knew we were playing with dynamite. I was frustrated and I think Bill could understand why. But that was the end of that and we all moved to the living room. All the rest of the evening I fantasized about sneaking off with Bill to the beach. By now, Mills had a tight hold on me and I wasn't about to let go of the brass ring either. I was too close.

So I took my frustrations to the ocean. I loved to walk on the sandy shore at Fire Island and watch the waves crash in on the beach. There was a freedom there. I tried to escape from Mills whenever possible, leaving him back at the house with his friends. On the beach there was no Mills and no money to desire — just the beauty of nature. I was where I wanted to be. I spent a lot of time walking along the beach watching people, wondering who they thought I was and wondering the same about them. There was always something interesting to see. I thought I had begun to leave the past behind me, finding the path to a happier future. Looking up into the houses, I imagined living in this community, knowing the people who lived and played here. Sooner or later, on my walks, I stopped to linger in front of that designer's beach home, wondering if he was inside; Mills having pointed it out on one of our first walks together. Here people could be themselves and leave the prejudices of the world far away. Most of the people who lived here owned a big part of the world anyway. But the freedom I was searching for couldn't be bought with money or power. Unfortunately, I didn't realize this at the time. Occasionally, while on the beach, I'd catch someone checking me out with binoculars from one of the houses. Peering back into the black lenses staring in my direction, I said to myself, "Yes, I belong here, I am one of you."

Mills saw how much I loved the island. He offered the beach house as a studio. Mills would come on the weekends if I wanted to stay during the week. It was a wonderful offer and I would be hard pressed to turn it down. Trying to reassure me, he said we would see how things worked out between us and after awhile, if this wasn't what I wanted, then he would support my decision. He seemed to want me to be comfortable with the arrangement. My dream of having a home and studio at the beach looked to be coming true.

I still had reservations, but I was slowly convincing myself to make the move. It could be an exciting life. I would have all the comforts: A great place to live in the city, an island house as a studio and I wouldn't have any financial worry. Mills would take care of all that. I kept telling myself this would be the best thing for me. What I had dreamed of while in college and living at home, was coming true. Mills would be the one to take care of me. He was the one my eyes were searching for as I looked at my reflection in the mirror on so many nights while studying, while my mother was cursing my dead father, drinking beer after beer, filling the house with her cigarette smoke, trying to escape her own misery.

There were still the unanswered questions in the back of my mind about Mills and his background. There were still the serious whispers I overheard at parties. I was told by several people, including Pierce, that he had a corrupt and ruthless side. I could tell Pierce took to me, although I wasn't sure how much he liked me. He told me several times that Mills cared a great deal for me, but warned I should be careful; always when he had a few too many, hinting of Mills' ties with the Mafia, but I had heard that while in Atlanta. I asked him to explain, but Mills walked back into the house before anything else was said. I brought the statement up to Pierce at a later time, but he told me to forget about it. Mills was a tough man and I knew he could be brutal if he had to. I remember on our way to the island once, Mills made a stop at a house I didn't recognize. The house had a high wall around it and an iron gate. Like a bad Mafia movie, several men hung around the grounds. Pulling the car through the gates, Mills said it would be better if I waited in the car. He grabbed his briefcase and went into the house, coming out forty-five minutes later. I dared not ask any questions and he didn't offer any details.

Tragedy had hit Mills. I was beginning to think he needed me as much as I thought I needed what his money could afford me. His youngest son, Ross was living in California and became gravely ill. He moved back to New York for treatment. In the beginning, the doctors failed to diagnose clearly the cause of his illness. For a time, he was in and out of the hospital with high fevers and abdominal pain, getting weaker and weaker as time passed. Finally, after surgery at Doctors' Hospital to remove Ross's spleen, the doctors ascertained he suffered from complications related to AIDS. It was the beginning of the AIDS epidemic. A hard time for Mills, it was the first time I could remember seeing him unsure of what to do or say. During the surgery, I waited with Mills in the waiting room. Motionless, he sat, not saying much, with his hands folded in his lap and his head tilted down to the green and dingy white tile floor. His eyes filled with tears that never fell to his cheeks. Mills clumsily came to his feet as the nurse approached to inform us Ross had awakened. It had become clear that Ross and Mills didn't enjoy a close father-son relationship. There seemed to be a lot of tension between them and Ross immediately moved back to California after his condition improved.

I felt closer with Mills after he opened up more about his family, perhaps generated by Ross' illness. But Mills talked little about his ex-lover, only that he needed to get on with his life and put that all behind him. The apartment and the Pines' house were still filled with pictures of Jimmy and him together. What little I learned was from Pierce and from others I overheard at parties. Pierce told me Jimmy used a lot of coke and it made him crazy. He'd been in rehab for his drug addiction. Mills came home one day and found Jimmy dead from a self-inflected gun shot through the mouth; he had used Mills' gun. Pierce seemed to grow nervous as I pres-

sured him on more information, saying, "That's all I know."
At a party on Fire Island, someone started talking about
Mills and Jimmy, not knowing at the time I was Jimmy's
replacement. He insinuated there were a lot of questions as
to whether it was a suicide or not. And when I told him my
connection, he excused himself. A casual acquaintance from
Atlanta, who I saw a few times on the island also told me of
the rumor and the drugs. He stated, "I didn't know you ran
with such a tough crowd." I tried not to give much merit to
the story, people just like to talk, I reminded myself.
Besides, I didn't want anything to spoil my new freedom
and my new connection to wealth.

But questions about the suicide would surface several
more times. There were other occasions after that, where
Mills' character and dark side came into focus. At a large
dinner party, I overheard Mills talking about another old
boyfriend. I continued to follow the conversation trying to
do so without any of the participants knowing I was eaves-
dropping. Apparently, the individual under discussion had
run off with a Mercedes and a rather large sum of money
belonging to Mills. From the conversation, I learned this old
boyfriend was eventually found. With a sinister laugh, Mills
interjected in the conversation, "I don't think anyone will be
hearing from him anytime soon." Then noticing I was looking at him, Mills quickly changed the subject, as he had
before when seemingly engaged in a tense dialogue.

No matter what I heard about Mills' past, I continued to
consider it as mere speculation. Mills seemed to want me,
and being wanted was what I needed. Just before my first
visit to New York around Christmas, Mills bought a beautifully decorated Christmas tree at a charity tree auction. He
said it was for me since I was visiting over the holidays. The
tree was silver, covered in clear glass balls with other deco-
rations making the face of an animated man in its body. It
had arms made of aluminum tubing extending out of its
sides. It stood in one corner of the white living room. I
remember Mills saying, "You know I'm not much on Christ-

mas but I thought you might like it." The tree was funny looking but I was touched he'd gone to the trouble.

I was back in Atlanta recuperating from cosmetic surgery, spending the night at friends' so they could keep an eye on me. During my last year of college, I began noticing that my hair line was receding slightly. The thought of losing my hair was disturbing. The first two doctors said not to worry, that if my hair line was going to recede, it would be years from now. But that wasn't good enough for me. I wanted to be perfect, or as perfect as I could make myself. Finally, I found a plastic surgeon that would keep my recession at bay. Mills knew I was having something done, but I was embarrassed about even feeling the need to have cosmetic surgery. So I didn't tell him exactly what the procedure was. And the reason I told him anything in the first place, was because he had wanted me to fly to New York on the Thursday the surgery was scheduled. His comment was, "I don't understand why you think you need anything done. You are crazy to think anything is wrong with you, but if it makes you feel better, then I guess it's okay. Just don't mess up what you already have." I assured him the surgery was very minor and he would probably never tell the difference.

Later, after the surgery and I was resting, a delivery man brought a huge flower arrangement. The attached card read: I hope you are feeling well and I hope you didn't mess up that beautiful face of yours. Love, Mills. P. S. Wish you were here instead. Mills began early laying the bait, setting the trap for me and I was eating it up.

As time quickly passed and the visits to New York blurred together, I began to feel the pressure to move. It was nice being squired by someone who could offer so much and Mills seemed willing to give. Almost a year later, I'd been captured by the glamour of New York and I didn't want to give it up. I felt something for Mills but I knew it wasn't the love I'd always dreamed of. But of course, I could try to love him. Plenty of bonafide marriages operate that way. I'd kept a safe distance between us — the miles between Atlanta and New York. But Mills was trying to shorten those miles. Long weekends, and a week here and there didn't satisfy him any longer. It was a move to New York, or else. It would be foolish to pass up such a chance for a new life — pass up a chance to be loved. Up until now with Mills, I only thought about the present, now I was being forced to think about a future with him.

There was no passion in my heart when I was with Mills. But maybe love was something that would never be in my heart, there was so little love in my history. But could I compromise love for the comfort of money? Until Mills, love had failed me. It was a trade off: Mills got me and I got the lifestyle only lots of money could afford. It wasn't in the bargain that I had to love him, he only had to love me. I better take as much as I could now, because this chance might not come again. I could learn to live without the storybook romance, I thought. Besides, I really wasn't sure what true love was. Other than the confessed love of Dennis and the hint of love from Gilbert, I never received love up to this point and didn't think I was capable of ever feeling it. It was better to move while Mills still wanted me. Yes, I was an actor — I had acted my whole life and I could act in New York. What future there was would be a wait and see situation. As in the past, the future was an unknown. I wanted to live in the present; live in the center of things, live on Park Avenue and walk the beach of Fire Island. What did I care about Mills' past? What did I care about mine? Anything would be better and it would be better on Park Avenue.

And again, I was tired of having to look after everyone else. I had spent most of my life doing that and I was still doing it with my mother; I could help her by moving in with Mills. I wanted desperately for someone to look after me. Of course, the money and what came along with it was playing a big part in my decision to accept his generous offer.

Hesitant, I told Mills I would go ahead with the move. As a present, he would take me to St. Mortiz for two weeks after I was finally living with him. The trip had been booked.

There was the formality of signing insurance papers for the trip, Mills said, which I didn't quite understand when he presented them on our way out to dinner. I signed the paper without any questions. I was about to move into the future in a very comfortable style.

It was Saturday morning and like most weekends during the season, we went to the island. It was overcast, raining sporadically since the night before. Dark clouds threatened thunder storms as flashes of lightning exploded in the distance. While Mills took a nap, I walked the beach. The sun was still trying to break through the graying sky. The waves crashed in as I'd never seen them before. The wind picked up; I could feel it pushing against my back like it was pushing me away from Mills.

The beach was deserted except for me. The pounding surf washed away my foot prints almost before I could take my next step in the sand. I love the beach that way. My ears filled with the sounds of the water and the wind rushing around me. I cautiously looked up to see if the clouds were going to totally block the persistent sun. I felt a few rain drops fall against my face, but I was determined not to leave the beach until the sky opened up and thoroughly soaked me.

My mind was very much on my upcoming move. It was just weeks away, but I turned back and forth in my head as to whether or not I had made the right decision. Surely, I convinced myself, I would have the freedom to develop my art. All I had to do was paint and walk the beach every day. I re-examined my motivations: A dream come true; I could live my passion. My mind was as cloudy as the sky above me. What about the rumors at parties and in the clubs? The lover who committed suicide a month before I met Mills? Was it suicide? And the men outside of the walled house we stopped at on one of our treks to the island, were they connected to the mob? Was Mills? What about Mills' friends? The side of Mills he hadn't shown me, but the one I'd sensed. All these concerns filled every corner of my brain, as did the sense of misgiving I felt numerous times when Mills and I were together. It fought against my desires for a life in New York.

The clouds were winning control of the sky, and it started to steadily sprinkle. Maybe I should head back just in case the rain comes down harder, I contemplated. I turned around. Suddenly, I realized I no longer had the beach to myself. I noticed two men running ahead of me. They were laughing, as if they were laughing at the rain daring it to interrupt their play. One of the guys grabbed the other and pulled him down on the sand. They wrestled and caressed, kicking up the sand. Getting back up to chasing one another, they fell to the sand again. Their laughter was wonderful. I couldn't remember ever laughing like that. It must be wonderful to laugh so freely. They are in love, I thought to myself as the rain continued to slowly fall from the sky. At that moment, my heart began to hurt. I felt trapped and incomplete. What about Mills? What about love? Could I ever feel that way about him? Would we ever laugh like those two guys in the sand? Did I have a love for him or had I confused love with fear; as in the fear I had carried for my father?

The sun made one last successful attempt to break through the unrelenting clouds stopping the rain briefly. Suddenly, everything brightened on the exact spot where the two lovers hovered. The sun shone on their bodies as they laughed the clouds away. Yes, they were in love, I thought, and the heavens knew it. The sun came out to celebrate their love and push the clouds from their path.

With a renewed clarity, I realized I was selling myself. If I moved to New York, I would trade any chance of finding happiness and love. I would become a prisoner to material things, an empty shell riding around in the back of a Rolls Royce; an empty shell walking along the beach, which I so loved, no longer able to feel freedom and see true beauty. I would have everything in the world that money could buy, except love. A feeling deep inside my soul told me I was putting myself in danger, more danger than I'd ever known before, and I knew I wasn't shrewd enough to survive. At least not yet.

It wasn't fair to Mills and it wasn't fair to the person inside of me, the person I had yet to know, the one still running from my father's world. I still wanted someone to take care of me, but now I realized what I needed resembled those two I'd just seen on the beach. I needed to feel the love inside of me, the kind no amount of money could replace. And love shouldn't come with fear. At least it shouldn't anymore. As much as I wanted it, I didn't belong here; at least not now and especially not under these circumstances. It was a long walk back to the beach house. I had to say goodbye to my dreams and hope I would meet them again.

west

If this be our last kiss, then take it slowly from me.
Allow our lips to linger together in wetness, so I won't soon
forget the
sensation, for I will need to recall it from memory many
years to come.
Let it be hard at first, and press firmly on me.
Breathe deep into my lungs with your sweet breath, so I can
share its life
with you one more time.
Don't pull away too quickly, but stay close until our mouths
are dry.
And as you feel the need to pull away, do it slowly, for to stop
too quickly
would surely be my death.
Kiss me softly now, so I can feel the tenderness, take your
tongue upon my
lips and taste the passion still there for you.
Make this last kiss live forever on my lips, for it may be the
last breath I
take.

On the way home from the doctor's office, we pulled into a Wendy's drive-through to get Todd a hamburger, fries and a Coke. He sat up in the back seat and wolfed them down while complaining about my driving. I heard a hint of the old Todd in his voice from years ago, before any of us knew the word AIDS. Catching a glimpse of a smile on Todd's face as I looked at him through the rear view mirror, somehow brought a smile to my heart and a little bit of hope. He wanted to be his funny self again.

"Randy, you were never that great of a driver," he joked, as he stuffed another French fry into his mouth. "Hey...watch where you're going."

"Okay, okay," I replied.

The traffic was heavy on Peachtree Street as I drove north. I turned off onto a surface street, trying to take a short cut to Todd's house. Sitting up was tiring for him. Todd made a sigh of relief as the car pulled into the driveway. The front yard was partly dug up, where months before, Todd had begun planting shrubbery. It had been a project that he'd started with his second partner, Don. Eric and Todd had split almost two and a half years ago. Eric met a guy in England, where he often traveled on business. The news came over the phone from the foggy streets of London, a week after Todd's father died. Two weeks later, Eric came back to the States, packed his belongings and moved. The news, although heartbreaking to Todd, wasn't a shock. Todd confided in me he thought something was up. Eric's timing though, sucked.

He called me shortly after he got off the phone with Eric. Jokingly, he said, "Well, I have an opening, this is your chance to be my lover, Randy." Eight months later, Todd and Don met. I remember being cautious about their relationship, not wanting Todd to get his heart broken again, especially after the sudden loss of his father. I had helped them move Don into Todd's house. In the beginning of their relationship, I had the impression Todd was contributing a lot more, both emotionally and financially, than Don. And I knew it was because Todd didn't want another failed marriage. But, that was his business and I dismissed it as being overly protective of Todd. He was an adult, and I was sure he knew what he was doing. And maybe, I was a little jealous of Don.

A year and a half later, just several months before Todd went into the hospital, Don left him. One afternoon I received the phone call. Todd was devastated. He kept asking me why. "How could Don leave me? I love him. He is my best friend. What am I going to do? I gave him everything." The questions just kept coming. When I asked him Don's reason, Todd tried to explain that it was because Don thought they had grown apart. I really didn't believe that explanation. We both knew it was the illness. But Todd wouldn't admit the real reason to me, he was still trying to hide it. I don't really know how long he'd been sick. When I first noticed a change that made me suspect he was ill, I shrugged it off. I didn't want to think my oldest and dearest friend in Atlanta had fallen prey to this wretched virus. He was still in denial, and in a way, so was I for him. Don wasn't the kind of guy to stick around when things got tough. I knew Todd loved Don a great deal, but Todd didn't want to admit to himself Don couldn't deal with his having AIDS. He didn't want to face the fact that Don's love wasn't strong enough. Don was running scared.

I spent a lot of time with Todd after Don moved out,

often going to dinner and talking on the phone. He was recovering from a growth on his face, related to the virus. Todd tried to tell me it was an infection from digging up the front yard. The strain from the breakup had taken its toll on him, something I believe played a large part in his rapid deterioration. With Don's leaving, Todd had lost most of his passion for life. I could tell Todd was fighting to put his life together and look ahead, but it was a constant uphill struggle. I tried to open the door of my friendship wider, but he still wouldn't confide he was sick, so I continued to respect his privacy.

After some time past and for awhile, Todd did begin to look better. He was hopeful of starting a new life and moving on. That was what he presented on the outside, but I knew in his heart he wanted Don to come back to him. Todd started working out with a trainer, gaining a positive attitude about himself while getting in shape, both physically and emotionally. Then it happened — I got the call from Marie.

"When you get better, Todd, I'll come and help you finish the front yard," I said, as I carried him back to his bedroom. The home care nurse helped me get Todd comfortable in the bed. The suffering in his face was obvious, as we painstakingly positioned him.

"I don't care about that front yard now that Don isn't here anymore," Todd said.

"Just let's wait and see. You'll change your mind," I responded.

"You know what it's like to love someone Randy...I know you do. To care for someone like I care for Don. What about West? Do you ever hear from him?" Todd pried, taking the focus off of himself.

Most of the men I had spent any time with had slipped by Todd's knowledge. I had always been private about them. Mostly because in the beginning of our friendship, I knew how Todd cared about me. I didn't want to rub anything in his face. Another reason was because of the shame of being with another man out in the open. It was easier to keep that life in the dark. But Todd knew all about West. I had opened up my world a little and by doing so, let my little world know of West. I brought West into the circle of friends Todd had earlier allowed me in. At the time I wasn't sure, but I took a chance to touch the one thing in life I wanted. That being love, and I hoped the reflection of the past would not show itself in the mirror.

It is true: You live the life you earn. And it is a life mastered in the precious years of childhood. If you go about it the wrong way, and run from the truth, it doesn't matter how hard one fights to remove oneself from an undesirable past and find a better instruction through life, the past is always there, right behind you. The faster one runs, the closer it follows. Running is never the answer, because sooner or later, the past catches up to the present. It is like a built-in instinct keeping you running in circles. That's why some of us, including myself, keep repeating the same mistakes over and over again. Familiarity keeps us so busy running, we don't stop to see what we are running from; it's usually ourselves, and no matter how hard you run or how far you go, you can never run away from yourself. And when you look into the mirror, you see it standing behind you.

I was still running so fast from the past that I ran right into it again when I met West. It seems like another lifetime now, in someone else's life. This summer night, I was on a quest to find relief from the heat stirring inside of me. A Saturday night not different from many others. I spent several hours getting ready to venture out into the night to drown myself in the music and crowds in the gay bars of Atlanta, and if I was lucky, maybe find someone to hold me until the morning. It became a common practice, someone I could lose myself in for awhile and not be reminded of where I came from or the void in my soul. I thought I was looking for something different, but my instinct subconsciously ran me in circles.

I walked along the dimly lit Seventh Street, where I had parked my car, turning my head occasionally in response to the sounds in the night. There were muffled voices around me coming from shadowy figures scattered on the street. I heard an outburst of laughter and noticed a figure of a man standing in the window of his second floor apartment looking down at the street, to see what the commotion was about. I turned the corner at the same point I had turned it many times before, on the same search. Just a block ahead of me was my destination. The lights from the building illuminated the night, silhouetting the men gathering in the doorway of the Armory. And next to it was Backstreet. Both bars faced the same parking lot, drawing men from all over into their doors for hours upon hours of play until well after the sun rose the next morning. The faint hum of the music inside drew them in like the Pied Piper. I was anxious. Faces of the men became clearer to my eyes as I came closer, and my ears could now understand parts of their conversations. They where young and old, in groups of two and three and some alone, like me. The music grew louder with each step I took towards the bar until I could make out the familiar song playing.

I shuffled in with the Backstreet crowd, deciding to skip the Armory for now, looking around to see who was there in the bar. My eyes raced from side to side, trying to scan the room without seeming too obvious. I had been eyeing one guy for some time. Was he there tonight among the hundreds of other people? And if he was, I wondered what I would do when I saw him.

His name was Doug. I first noticed him at the YMCA where I worked out. I remember the first time I laid eyes on him: He came into the weight room as I was finishing my workout. Oh God, please let him be gay, I recall thinking to myself. He was six-feet-tall, with light hair and a muscular body. My type. After that, I decided to hang around and do a few more sets.

Something told me this man was gay. Maybe it was wishful thinking. Everything about him said not.

It was a week after I had first seen Doug at the gym that

I was in the Pharr Library, and there he sat at a table with a group of three men and a woman. My intuition had proved to be correct. I pointed him out to Todd and he gave me the thumbs up.

After a few weeks of seeing Doug out and at the YMCA, I mustered up the nerve to meet him. The invitation to his bed came soon after. I quickly became in awe of him, but that was easy for me to do. The stronger the man, the more I wanted him. However, I wasn't sure what Doug's interests were in me. The woman who had been sitting with him at the bar was his house mate. I had heard she was in love with him and, after spending time with them, I could tell it was true. How could I blame her? I was falling for him too. I decided he was trying to live a double life and wasn't completely sure of his own sexuality. I'd been in that place before. It made me wonder what chance I might have to be special to him. I knew very early I wanted to know him for more than sex. I wanted Doug to fall in love with me. I didn't want to be just another guy he would feel no passion or love for. He was everything I was looking for; but I couldn't sense any emotion from him. My track record wasn't so swell. I was tired of going from man to man, from brief relationship to relationship, and yes, from one-nighters to one-nighters. I wanted one that would last. All the men, so far, had very similar qualities, and I thought, by now, I knew what I was looking for. I wanted to be in love with someone for more than a night and I didn't want someone who belonged to someone else, like Roberto and Gilbert had. Doug could end up like them. Nor did I want to fear them like I had my father and Mills. Money wasn't the issue either, for I wanted someone, unlike myself, who felt good about who he was, especially sexually. And if he felt good about being gay, then I could. I wanted to feel the passion I felt with Ted but I wanted it to last. Someone, perhaps like Doug. The truth of the matter was that my insecurity was always the issue, blinding me to any emotion that might have been there. Doug was a good catch, a perfect man in my eyes. I was afraid I wasn't perfect enough for him. And, if I was, what about the girl? I couldn't deal with someone else's wife or girlfriend again. I had made love with Doug. But she was there in the house. And that bothered me.

Nervously, I made my way through Backstreet. Going out on the weekends was becoming a late night habit, so much that there were several months where I never saw much of the daylight on Saturdays and Sundays. The same faces filled the bars weekend after weekend. Friendships revolved around the gay bar scene. Once again, it was close to midnight and the bar was packed with men on a mission. Some were there to drink and have a good time, and the majority, like me, were looking for comfort in someone's arms. As always, I fought my shyness, and it was hard for me to be there, but my need for companionship won out over timidity. Sometimes I drove around the bar a dozen times, before getting up the nerve to park and go inside.

As I look back, I can't help but think my shyness may be why I'm still alive today. That question of why I haven't fallen prey to the virus, as Todd has, is in the forefront of my mind as I sit with him on my visits. There were many upon many nights when I'd get ready to go out but stayed home because I was so critical of the way I looked. I'd believed I was just too ugly and not worthy of another person's interest — so why bother. I know now that my lack of self-esteem was due to childhood and the abuse I experienced. But still, if I'd gone out on any one of those countless nights, instead of staying home, I would surely have increased my exposure to the AIDS virus. I was so desperate for love, I would have gone with any big guy who wanted me, making it more likely I would have been a statistic today. Ironic that my negative feelings and pain may have saved my life.

But before I gathered the courage to get tested, I waited for my number to come up. For several years gay men were dropping like flies around me. And with my own mortality staring me in the face as I witnessed Todd's life slip away, I believed it was just a matter of time before it was my turn.

After one of my visits with Todd, I decided to get tested. Waiting in the doctor's office to be called, my heart felt like it was going to jump out of my chest. From the moment the blood was drawn from my arm, and through the following week of waiting, I was so unmistakably sure of what the test results would be. I had imagined every minor pain in my body as a sign of the inevitable. I had played the game and it was my turn to pay the expensive price like Todd was now paying. The doctor's assistant stepped into the waiting area holding a gray folder: Without expression she called my name. I somehow managed to pull myself out of the chair. At that moment, I found myself wishing I had x-ray vision so I could look through the folder to see the results. It was a long walk to the examining room.

"The doctor will be right in," the assistant said, as she placed the folder in the plexiglass file holder just outside the room. She then closed the door behind her. I stood frozen, trying to control my breathing. I wondered whether in the next few minutes I would be experiencing uncontrollable joy or sorrow. An internal buzzing filled my head as I reviewed every sexual encounter I had ever experienced.

After what seemed like an exhausting span of time, I heard the folder being pulled out of the holder: Dr. Rush opened the door and walked into the room. "You're fine, Randy," she said, her eyes reviewing the contents of the folder.

"What did you say?" I asked, as fear in the form of tears filled my eyes.

"You're negative, you're negative," Dr. Rush clarified.

I was standing next to the dance floor looking around the downstairs bar, when I saw Doug. He was a few feet across from me holding a drink and talking to a very good looking guy. Even though I'd been with him several times by now, I found myself trying to gather the nerve to go over. Doug looked at me and gestured a "hello." Just as my courage rose, he put his drink down and the two of them went off to the dance floor. My insecurity set in again and I walked away, thinking he had found what he wanted for the night.

Deciding to go home, I walked back upstairs. Just as I was making it for the door, Todd stopped me.

"Hey, Randy, you wanna go down and dance?"

After a little coercing, we headed for the dance floor. Attempting to avoid flying arms and gouging elbows, we made our way through the tightly packed floor of twisting bodies dancing to Donna Summer's "Last Dance." I was relating to the lyrics, "last chance for romance tonight." After several songs, I'd gotten Doug off my mind for awhile. It was time to find someone else. Ever since the days Monica and I went dancing on Friday nights, there was something about the music that made me feel better. I could lose myself; it was magic. The more I danced, the better I felt. I began looking at the people standing around the crowd of dancers, seeing if I could catch someone's eye. If Doug wasn't available tonight, maybe someone just as good might be. It would be lonely going home later by myself after seeing him. A smorgasbord of men, some talked over the loud dance music, others drank and watched the dancing on the floor. And I wondered was "he" out there tonight?

As I continued scanning the bar and dancers, I noticed an attractive guy looking at me. At second glance, I decided he wasn't that cute, but with a third look, he looked cute again. He appeared to be bigger and taller than me with brown hair. He was not as great looking as Doug, a little thicker around the middle, but that was okay. The better looking they were, the harder they might be to keep. He looked all-American, and he looked like he could make me feel protected. He fit the big brother/father complex that had always governed my selection of men. We looked at each other as I continued dancing with Todd. Like a game: I would look up to give him a little smile and he would smile back, and then I would look away. The exchange of smiles went back and forth; Todd was oblivious to the whole thing. Each time, my smile got bigger. About the tenth time I looked back, he had disappeared. Frantically, I looked all around to see where he'd gone but he was nowhere in sight. I was worried. He looked like he could hold me just right through the long night ahead, and damn, I had let him get away.

I became angry with myself for playing the game too long. I should have stopped dancing and gone over to say hello. While chastising myself, he appeared again. Great! I was in luck. He'd only gone to the bar for a beer. This time, he wasn't going to get away. I excused myself from Todd, leaving him to dance in the crowd, and made my way through the dancers to where this guy was standing. I had to be aggressive, I told myself, because if I wasn't, it would be a long, lonely night. I had to take a chance on getting shot down.

I stood beside him feeling foolish at my loss for words, hoping he would break the ice. My mind raced to find the right thing to say. Just as I opened my mouth, he turned away and headed back to the bar. "What is this guy's problem!" I thought to myself. This could be embarrassing if he wasn't interested.

As I turned away about ready to give up and take my ugly self home, someone grabbed my shoulder. It was him. My earlier observations were correct, close up he was husky, but he would certainly do. The place was steamy hot and he'd gone back to the bar to get a napkin to wipe his brow. What a relief, I didn't feel ugly now.

Introducing ourselves, we tried to talk but it was impossible to hear what West and I were saying to one another over the music. A song he liked began playing so we moved through the crowd to the dance floor. Finding it harder to talk while dancing we just looked back and forth smiling a lot, but this time, much closer. By the time we stopped, an hour had passed and we found ourselves upstairs cooling off with a drink. It was pretty late — around three o'clock in the morning. West coming home with me that morning was the beginning of an exhausting and turbulent relationship.

He was your basic all-American boy, alright: I'd hit the nail on the head. Although West had been out of school for a few years, he was living that summer at his old fraternity house avoiding a commitment of an apartment in Tallahassee while awaiting a possible job transfer. West was a sales rep for a major toiletries company that manufactured shaving and skin creams and he had been in town visiting friends. His job required a considerable amount of travel. While staying at the frat house, he acted as an "on-site of sorts" fraternity advisor for Delta Tau Delta. Later observations lead me to believe he had a hard time letting go of his college life. He was a fanatic about sports and followed his alma mater, Florida State, wherever they played football, the love of his life. Because my father and brother were so into sports, I'd always shied away from such events. I only just learned a few years ago the correct way to throw a football and it took a lesbian friend to teach me. I soon learned West's love of sports was something I couldn't compete with. He bought season tickets religiously, working his life around the Florida State Seminoles' playing schedule.

Thinking back, I realize West had a lot of qualities I wished for myself — still looking for characteristics in other men to remake myself, as I always had. He wasn't your typical homosexual as portrayed by the media. Neither radical nor effeminate, he would never be one of the ones who were called fags. But, neither were any of the others I'd been with. One of the attractive things about West was there wasn't a wife or girlfriend hiding in the background. He had no interest in women, other than as friends and as an occasional cover. But, he proved to be quite homophobic himself. West wasn't out to his parents and had only divulged to a few people he was gay. He told me that while attending FSU, he'd played a major roll in having a fraternity brother kicked out because he was suspected of being gay. Everything about West said "straight male." He got along with everyone and everyone liked him, very much the mirror image of Stephen.

We commuted back and forth between Tallahassee and

Atlanta over a period of three years. In fact, I spent several weekends in the Delta Tau Delta Fraternity House with West during the first part of our relationship. West was filled with such a fear of his sexuality being discovered that we had to watch our every step. He grew concerned that I was going to give away his secret. I continued to be guarded and tried to act and talk like my idea of a straight male, pulling from the characteristics I coveted over the years. I thought my voice was a dead giveaway, so I consciously practiced making it sound deeper.

It was fall and football fever was in the air. The first weekend I went to visit I was nervous. We had been running around at Florida State partying with some of West's friends before the game. I found it hard to fit in but I pretended to have fun. It was too uncomfortable trying to act straight and pretend I was having a blast at the same time. I may as well have been back living with archer. A few years earlier, it would have been easier, but I knew what I was now. But for West, I walked back into the closet.

The fraternity hosted a party after the game. By then, West and his brothers hooked up with some Delta Tau Delta little sisters. One of them, Dawn, took a liking to me and we danced a few times. She was cute, I enjoyed being around her. This gave me a chance to fantasize a little about being a part of the Greek college life, something I always wanted to experience, but didn't participate in at Mercer. Back then, I would watch the frat boys hanging out at their houses, wanting desperately to go inside and be a part of it, but not feeling good enough. Silently I coveted their sweat shirts displaying their Greek letters, much like I had Stephen's lettermen sweater. Many evenings before leaving the campus, I stood off in the shadows in envy as they escorted their dates to formals. Instead, I drove home to look after my mother. As the party progressed, Dawn started getting friendlier with me, holding my hand and playfully kissing me on the cheek. This seemed to excite West.

"This is perfect," he told me. "Play it up with her so no

one will suspect anything about us." I wondered how far he wanted me to go.

It was late when the party ended. I stepped over frat boys passed out in the hallway as we headed for West's room on the second floor. He was pretty "well served" himself, and I was not far behind him. Only having a twin bed, West insisted we make a fake bed on the floor out of blankets so no one would suspect we shared his.

That night, West got kinky and wanted to shave my body to try out one of his company's new shaving cream products. While I was laying nude on the bed, he made several trips from the room to the common bathroom, getting water in a discarded plastic beer cup to rinse the shaving cream from the razor. At one point, West became afraid someone was going to walk in and catch us. I was nervous myself, but more so, with his abilities of operating sharp instruments under the influence — and so close to delicate areas of my body. I made the suggestion he lock the door, but West said if someone tried to come in and found the door locked, they really would suspect something was up. Evidently, frat boys don't lock their doors...hmm?

The relationship with West progressed quickly. To my surprise I did see Doug a few times after, and I possibly could have dated them both. An easy thing to do with West living out of town, but I wanted to be with just one person and not have to do a juggling act. I decided a relationship with West had a better chance of lasting. I really didn't have anything to base my feelings on, maybe because Doug was so good looking and West was so-so. I could keep West, but Doug may not stay around as long. Doug told me years later I should have given him a chance. Who knows what would have happened if I'd chosen Doug over West? Doug wasn't the settling down type, or so I thought, and I needed someone to be there for me.

But, a lot of truths had yet to hit me in the face and I looked forward to West coming in town for the weekends. I stocked the refrigerator with his favorite foods and stayed up late the night before his arrival cleaning the apartment. His habit was to come into town late on Friday and stay until Sunday evening, sometimes not leaving until Monday, giving us another night together.

It didn't take me very long to fall in love with West but I held back on telling him. I wanted West to tell me he loved me first. When he finally did, I didn't hold back my emotions. Believing I was in love with West helped ease my discomfort about sex. No matter what great pleasure I'd gotten from being with other men, I still found myself crippled by guilt from the confused memories of childhood and current attitudes on homosexuality.

Apparently free of any sexual hang-ups, except other than of being found out, West was very aggressive in bed, and like everything else, I soon came to learn he had to have things the way he wanted. He wanted me the traditional way a man wants a woman. I'd played that role with men in the past, and by the time West came along, I was anything but a virgin. And as with the others, we worked with what was available. I know some people find the thought of anal sex abhorrent. Perhaps I did it because I felt I lacked an important element concerning manhood. I looked like a man, had all the equipment, but something missing made me feel less than a man. Having another man's penis inside of me made me feel a little more complete. I didn't always like the act itself, although it is the closest two men can physically get in the most intimate of circumstances. When you are hungry you eat, when you are thirsty you drink, when you are tired you sleep and when you need comfort you find it where your desire tells you. And, when you love someone you are willing to do whatever it takes to get as close to that person as possible.

I wanted West to have whatever pleasures he could in my body. Having West inside of me at times was pleasurable. Unlike the others, I truly thought, this time, West was mine to keep. For me it wasn't an act of sex but one of love. I wanted to show my love for West by giving him what he wanted and I took the part of him I thought I needed. It was a very private sharing experience between two people. I let him enter me and spill his semen inside my body without a condom. I took his word that he would be mine and only mine, so there were no concerns about contracting any diseases. Before hand, we had talked about AIDS, understanding we were both free of the virus and felt that as long as we were monogamous, we would be safe. With West, I thought my search had ended. He didn't have money like Gilbert or Mills, but money was never a part of my quest. I could and was making enough for myself. Art was selling and the future looked bright. I had finally left the job in Visual Merchandising, taking a part-time sales position in the store to keep the health benefits.

What started out as every other weekend progressed to every weekend. I looked forward to the day when we could be together more often, not thinking anything could ever come between us. With West, I began to feel better about my sexuality because he was big and strong and a match for any straight man. Todd and the rest of my friends seemed to like him. And besides, he wanted me and it was all going to work out.

Things were close to bliss until, one weekend, I visited him in Tallahassee. I arrived late on a Thursday night. By then, West had moved from the frat house and was sharing a house with two other guys who were also gay and closeted. He worked on Friday so I stayed around the house.

I was at his desk paying bills when I noticed a stack of cards and letters. I started thumbing through them because they looked like they were from me — most of them were. I had a habit of often sending him cards, wanting him to always know I was thinking about us. In my rummaging around, I noticed one from another guy. Curiosity got the better of me and I opened it.

I was brokenhearted to see it was a love note from a man in Baton Rouge, Louisiana. The guy had included some photographs of the two of them and an added bonus of a nude

Polaroid of himself. He wrote below the photograph: "For your eyes only, West." I was miserable that West betrayed me. The guy appeared to be well endowed but that could have been from the camera angle. He was nothing pretty to look at. At that point I wanted to grab my things and drive back to Atlanta. I probably should have left and never looked back but I was in love with West and had to find out what this was all about. I thought we had a future, the potential for a strong relationship. But the real reason, looking at the pictures, I imagined I wasn't good enough for him anymore.

I waited for West to return home from work. My emotions were running hot and cold. I didn't want West to think I'd snooped through his mail, so I decided to make a little accident. I took a jumbo glass of water and poured it over the top of the desk, soaking the mail. Then I laid the mail on the bed, like I was trying to dry it.

By the time he got home my story was complete: I was sitting at his desk paying bills. I accidentally knocked over a glass of water and, in trying to dry things out, I discovered Mr. Porno with his "big" self. West appeared to buy the story. His only explanation was he'd been out of town on a business trip and was lonely. He missed me. He was sorry and it would never happen again. I gave in and forgave him. Little did I know it was only the beginning of years of lies and deceit. He had deeply disappointed me, but by then, I was emotionally tied to the relationship and willing to believe anything. I told myself no one was perfect, that we all make mistakes. I forgave the disappointment as I had forgiven those when I was a child.

After that incident, our relationship was up and down. One weekend we were on, the next off. A few months later, West called one evening and said it was over. Then a few weeks later he called again and came to see me. The first thing he said after walking in the door was, "How did I ever think I could be happy without you?" I confided in Todd, he told me to move on, but I took West back.

Months and months went by, and then a year. The commuting continued. I could never really be sure West was faithful after my discovery of the pictures. But my distrust was really learned in childhood. I told him, trying to take control, if we were going to stay together, our relationship had to be monogamous, as we'd talked about in the beginning; reminding him there was a deadly disease out there taking a lot of unsuspecting lives. I didn't want us to end up that way. The passion continued for awhile, but it was never without fear I would lose him to someone better than me. When things were shaky, like with my father, part of me wanted him to go and never come back, and another part wanted to forgive and for him to stay. I uncomfortably felt needy of him and uncertain of my role in the relationship.

As time passed, it was my turn to visit him in Tallahassee. We spent most of the visit in bed trying to make up for lost time. As always, he was aggressive and powerful, climbing on top of me. Insatiable, he fucked me angrily as I felt intense pain inside. Not wanting to displease West, I resisted pushing him off. His body suffocating rather than comforting as it had once been. All instilling a sense of familiarity. Sunday evening, after another sexual encounter, this one on the bedroom floor, the pain returned. I waited until he was finished and hurried to the bathroom in a concealed panic. I discovered I was bleeding. The toilet water was bright red, oddly making me think of the day my father died. The bleeding quickly stopped. The next day everything appeared to be fine.

West had suddenly turned into a beast. He was quick to raise his hand or push me like he was a bully back in grade school. As I had done with my father, I tiptoed around him not wanting to induce his anger. The roller coaster continued when a month later we broke up again; West said we would never get back together — he didn't want to feel tied down. I was devastated, having grown so dependent on the relationship; I believed we would be together forever. I couldn't understand how West could walk away from all the things we had talked and dreamed about. Like my father, he used me and then abandoned me, or at least that's how my emotions reacted.

The next eight months seemed endless. I didn't date and didn't go out to the bars. It was all I could do just to go to work and make myself workout at the gym. Loosing interest in everything including my art — I hit an all-time low seeing myself as worthless again. If West didn't want me, no one else would either.

In the midst of things I was experiencing physical problems. After being examined by the doctor, I found out West had severely torn the inside of my rectum and it was infected.

Betrayed by West, and now dealing with this lingering pain, I felt ashamed and alone. Maybe I deserved whatever happened to me; I felt like trash as I told the doctor what I had done with West. Antibiotics hadn't cleared up the problem. The doctor said I needed surgery to keep the infection from becoming worse and avoid getting blood poisoning. But, by then, I really didn't care what happened to me. And then there was the question from the doctor of whether I had used a condom. In my shameful state, I lied, not wanting her to think I was a fool as well. A bust of nausea came over me as I sat in her office and realized how stupid I had been.

As the infection worsened, three months had passed and I hadn't spoken to West. I wanted to talk to him as much as my friend as my former lover. I tracked him down at his parents' home near Tampa, Florida and we discussed my situation. Ever so melodramatic in those days, that evening, I charged a round trip ticket on my American Express Card not knowing how I would pay for it when the bill came. Anything under a seven day advance purchase on a ticket is murder on the pocketbook, but all I could think about was seeing West again.

He couldn't pick me up at the airport, but luckily, Thomas, a friend who lived nearby met me. Arriving in Tampa, Thomas took me back to his apartment so I could settle in and call West. West had dinner plans he couldn't break, but we agreed to meet at a bar called Tracks; it was the last place I wanted to be. Unfortunately, it was the only option open.

I stayed anxious about seeing West. I was hoping once he saw me again he would realize what a mistake he made in breaking up and we would get back together. It didn't take me very long to locate West in the bar. As I walked over to him, he seemed a little cold, although he'd been fine on the phone. We went out to his car to talk. All I could do was cry when he said he really didn't care what happened to me — he couldn't be bothered.

Humiliated, feeling like a cocktail waitress who had gotten pregnant by a customer and was trying to get money from him for an abortion, I returned to Atlanta the next day and tried to pull myself together. A friend, Ginger, with deep southern religious roots moved in to share the two bedroom apartment. She was a beautiful woman who had been trying to make me straight for some time. On many occasions, I reminded her my sexuality was not a choice, but her strong religious background fueled her attempts to convert me. And meanwhile, after what I'd been through with men, I thought of trying to be straight again myself. Ginger wanted to save my soul from hell and damnation. She read scriptures and left notes strategically placed in the apartment trying to show me the road I was on was the wrong one in the eyes of her god. But, she had a wild side, racing her souped-up black Trans Am around town clubbing. That's how we met, at Backstreet two years before on the dance floor. God would forgive her sins, but those of a homosexual were another story. Ginger aspired of becoming a religious singing star, but was having trouble gathering the nerve to get out there and do it. The talent was there, but no drive. She shopped during the day and went dancing most nights of the week on her daddy's money made from the Florida citrus business. A big business from the size of her closet. Even though her attempts to change me were sometimes annoying, I liked having her around. And besides, I didn't need the wrath of someone else's god to instill contempt in myself, it was already there; fueled by West's apparent aversion for me.

After the surgery, I vowed never to do anything to put myself in such a vulnerable position again. I was putting my life back together and putting West behind me. Ginger told me he'd called a couple of times to see how I was doing, but asked her not to tell. In the meantime, I received a card from West many months after our last conversation expressing he was sorry things between us hadn't worked out. Indignant, I responded, writing: There never was a "me and you", there was only me in our relationship. It had all been in my head, then I tore the letter up.

It was almost a year since I'd flown to Tampa. Ginger and I were talking about one of her new boyfriends, she had given up on saving my soul from the devil, when there was a knock on the door. It was West.

In town visiting a fraternity brother and his wife, he didn't call first because he thought I wouldn't want to see him. It was a great shock to see West standing at the door after such a long time. All he could say was he'd been thinking about me a lot and wanted to see me. Deep down I was happy to see him but I didn't want the old feelings to start up again. We sat and talked for less than an hour before we were back in each other's arms. It was as if the last year never happened, and I hadn't learned very much.

West had since taken a job transfer to Connecticut. The rest of the weekend was spent talking about things that had happened over the last year. On Sunday evening, I took him to the airport, where he asked me to seriously consider visiting him in Hartford. I told him I would think about it.

Watching his plane taxi out into the darkening horizon from the departure gate, I had a strange feeling there was something left to understand and maybe another chance. I was glad he was back in my life, but I was also sad. I'd almost gotten over him and now he was back. When my father killed himself I knew I would never see him again.

The memories were still with me, but with him gone, it was easier to go on. When I returned from Tampa, I acted like West had died and it, too, was easier — now West had returned from the imaginary grave I'd dug for him.

He called me over the next couple of weeks encouraging me to visit. Soon, summer was over and I was on my way to Hartford. He'd made arrangements for us to take a short trip to Newport, Rhode Island. At a romantic setting by the water we sat on the rolling lawn as sailboats passed by. I felt as if I was dreaming; it really seemed like a fairy tale. West said he had pulled his life together and he was sure of what he wanted now. He wanted to spend the rest of his life with me. I tried to make light of it but he forcefully grabbed my arm and said, "I love you Randy, I really want this to work."

Walking back up to our hotel room, I caught my reflection in a large gold framed mirror on the landing of our floor. I remember thinking to myself, I was more handsome now that West wanted me again.

Returning to Atlanta, our commutes began again. Before long, West brought up the idea of me moving. He was devoted to his career, and because I am an artist and had more freedom, West decided I should move to Hartford. We began looking for a house and set a moving date for me to shoot for. The house hunting didn't go very well, it was difficult to find something we both liked. West then decided we would temporarily take a larger apartment in his building. I didn't really care for Hartford but it was close enough to New York that I could visit the city often and perhaps find an outlet for my art. I'd kept in touch with Mills, developing a friendship after the brief rough period when I told him I wasn't moving. West wasn't as sophisticated as many of the other men in my life, but I saw this as a good thing. I wanted a quiet, private life and, this time, I thought we could have a good one together. He had changed — everything behind us now, the future looked bright.

Two weeks before my move to Connecticut, West called

saying there was a change in plans. Turned out he didn't like Hartford either and felt Atlanta was the better place for us. He was giving up his job for me and I felt this meant we would make it. I had already sold most of my belongings for the money I would need to get re-established up north. West told me not to worry, he could carry us both for awhile. But now he was coming to me and I liked that. With the money I'd made, I went out and bought new furniture. Ginger had moved into her own place shortly after West and I started seeing each other again. It all seemed to click.

About the same time West moved in, Mother's drinking got totally out of hand again, interfering with the medication she was taking for depression. She'd increasingly spent more time in the hospital since I'd left Macon and now my sister was showing signs of Mother's behavior. Sandra would call up crying, denying she'd been drinking, lying to me like Mother had about alcohol. Talking to her was like talking to Mother. Several years back, she dropped out of college and joined the Army, following in our father's footsteps as if we didn't get enough of that military shit growing up. She was working on her second failed marriage. Her first was to a Deputy Sheriff who beat her, and the second to JB, an Afro-American, also in the army, whom she met while stationed in Germany. I didn't care that her husband was black, I'd found myself attracted to men of African heritage; I saw them as strong and powerful. But Stephen felt differently, saying it was wrong for people of different races to marry. Sandra knew I was gay. I told her after West and I had first started dating. She said she knew I was when she was sixteen or seventeen years old, not really knowing what gay meant. That realization came at twenty-one.

She wrote me a letter: "I blamed myself for years, thinking I caused you to be gay because I always asked you to play with me when we were little, to fix my hair and help me dress my dolls. You were always my savior. Thinking about the past, you were always there. We were so close, life at home was so terrible. You took good care of me. Remember early in the mornings, I used to sneak in your room, and you'd switch to the top bunk scared I'd fall off. You rolled my hair one night. I wanted to be pretty like the other girls. Father called to us to get ready for bed. We couldn't get my top off over the hair rollers. I refused to let you take them out, so you got the scissors to cut my top off because I was so adamant about my hair. You accidentally cut me, a scar I still have today on my left forearm, but a good memory in a way. Oh God! We were so scared that Father would find out. He hated for you to play girl stuff with me. But we prevailed and my hair was so pretty the next day and Father never found out.

I never told Mother or Stephen that I was gay. Although, I tried to tell Mother once, half way through spilling my sexuality, I decided she couldn't handle it and I backpedaled. I quickly remembered how she had reacted to Sandra telling her about Father. I didn't want Mother to take on any blame when there wasn't any for anyone to take, especially her. In her eyes it would be one more betrayal and she would find a way to blame herself. And, I didn't want Stephen to know either, didn't want him to think he was right all the times he called me a sissy when we were kids. Of course he wasn't right, but I knew he wasn't capable of understanding or accepting the difference.

He told Sandra that her children, if she ever had any with JB, could never play with his own. And, our grandfather told her outright never to step foot in his house again. How's that for a big helping of good old southern Alabama ignorance? I told Sandra, "Fuck Stephen and our grandfather and their racial selves...to hell with their backward asses. If you love the man, then be happy." But she had too much of that negative southern thinking in her and the pressure of an interracial marriage was getting to her. The comments made by Stephen and Grandfather and those made by our father degrading other races were not easily forgotten. Her marriage to JB lasted four years, most of it in Germany where racial problems were less of an issue for her. Getting married to JB might have been a way of Sandra trying to get back at our father. She, as I had, heard the racism of our lineage. No race is better than another, but because of our upbringing, somewhere deep inside Sandra's head, she may have felt she wasn't good enough for a white man.

Ever since moving to Atlanta, I'd hidden my family problems from friends and especially from West, never explaining the true dilemma that awaited when I had to go home for a few days. On many weekends, I found myself in Warner Robins cleaning up the beer cans and whiskey bottles from under my mother's bed and kitchen cabinets, emptying ash trays and tin cans overflowing with cigarette butts. Weeks' worth of dirty dishes overflowed in the sink and spilled out onto the counter tops. Roaches scrambled for food left in open tin cans and on plates, some swimming in the dish water that had been left standing for days. I didn't want that past to contaminate the present, and I didn't want West to know what I came from.

West and I lasted two years together in Atlanta. It didn't take long for the deceit to start up again. I had a feeling it never stopped. West was working at a new job and traveling a lot again. An old boyfriend of his, Bill, moved to town, which was fine as long as they were just friends now.

One evening West said he probably wouldn't be home until after ten o'clock the next night; he was meeting two new clients for dinner. The next afternoon he called to remind me. West had a private line for his work, which he usually kept the volume off on the machine. I became suspicious again of his faithfulness so I checked his machine. There was a message from Bill: "West, come by at six-thirty instead of five-thirty. I'm running late. Look forward to seeing you."

Sick to my stomach at catching him in another lie, I didn't know what to do. At that point, I remembered Bill only lived a few blocks from our apartment. I drove over and saw West's car in the parking lot. Disgusted, I returned home and paced the floor for the next two hours. In the meantime, I saved Bill's message and phoned West's number, making the message light flash so he wouldn't know I had tampered with it. On his desk, I noticed the sheets of season football tickets West had ordered. Frustrated and feeling vindictive, I took them into the bathroom and flushed each one down the toilet as I nervously waited for West to come home.

At nearly ten o' clock I heard a banging at the door. It was West with his hands full of paperwork, his tie undone and his clothes wrinkled. I tried to remain calm.

"How was your evening?" I casually questioned. "Did you get any new clients? Are you hungry?" I rambled.

"I had drinks with one client earlier," he said. "And then met another client and his wife for dinner."

I just looked at him for a moment.

"How can you stand there and lie to me? I know where you've been!" I screamed like an hysterical housewife.

By this time he was standing in his bedroom over the answering machine about to push the button to retrieve his messages. When he realized it was Bill, he tried to turn the volume back down. I told him not to bother.

"How can you lie to me?" I repeated. "You say you love me but you sure do have a strange way of showing it." I began pacing the floor again. "I thought we left the lies behind us the last go around. What do you have to say for yourself?"

"I've been caught," West replied, shrugging his shoulders. "But we didn't do anything. In fact, we talked about you all night. I didn't tell you I was having dinner with Bill because I thought you'd be jealous," he said reassuringly.

I knew he was lying. I had told him before any of his friends were welcome in our lives. He must really think I'm stupid and I thought to myself, he was right.

I told him this was it. I wanted him to move out. West's response was, "I'll leave when I'm good and ready and not before." He quickly turned into a bully trying to degrade me both verbally and physically. West pushed me to the floor. I became scared and I began to feel worthless again, as I looked up and saw the face of my father.

After a week of nonstop fighting one of his fraternity brothers, Lee, offered to let him move in with him and his wife. They were talking in West's room while I was in my room. I couldn't help but overhear their conversation. We had separate bedrooms because West thought it was better for appearances in case a client came by or his parents were in town.

"The only thing I'm concerned about is changing my office phone and the confusion it might cause," West said to Lee.

I knew this was for the best. I would be better off without him, but I still couldn't stand the rejection, and I couldn't let go of the past. At that point I came out of my room and started crying.

"After all we've been through, the only fucking thing you're worried about is getting your damn phone changed over!" I wailed. "The last five years haven't meant a thing to you!"

I ran for the bathroom and sat on the edge of the tub still afraid of losing him. West followed me and sat on the floor. We both started crying. Lee suggested we should try to work this out. He then left us alone in the apartment. I told West there was nothing keeping him here in this relationship. It was up to him whether or not he wanted it to work. He stayed.

Apparently, it didn't sink in. The Fourth of July weekend was approaching and we'd planned a trip to Miami. We soon decided it was too far to drive for four days so West asked if it was alright if he flew to Pensacola on a client's private plane to play golf. I said, "Yes, if that's what you want to do." At the time, I had suspected he was messing around with Paul, a golfing buddy.

On Friday afternoon, I met West to drop off his car at a repair shop. Driving back to the apartment with him, I noticed Paul driving down our street. This struck me as odd since Paul didn't live even close to us. West was ready to leave for his golfing trip and Paul was suspiciously in the neighborhood. I thought it was peculiar because the day before, West had inquired as to what time I was going to workout on Friday. I told him right after we dropped off his car. Arriving home, West seemed just a little too anxious to get me off to my workout. So I thought I would hang around for a little while. I stuck my head outside the back door without West knowing and saw Paul driving around the block again. I knew I'd caught West in another lie.

I went into the bedroom where West was watching television waiting for me to leave. "By the way, who's playing golf this weekend?" I asked.

"Just me and my client with the plane," he answered. "You can go ahead off to the gym, he'll be here soon to pick me up."

In the meantime, the phone rang and when I answered it, the caller hung up. It happened twice. I asked West if he was sure Paul wasn't going to play golf, too.

"No, you're just paranoid," he responded adamantly.

"Well, I think it's rather strange Paul has been driving around the block for the last thirty minutes," I said, as I looked out the window. "The only reason he hasn't come up is because my truck is still in the parking lot, right."

West denied it all and I left the bedroom.

A few minutes later he came in the living room where I was pretending to be busy.

"Look, I'm sorry," he apologized. "I lied to you about Paul."

No shit, I thought.

"There's nothing between us," West professed. "I thought you'd be jealous because I'm going off to Pensacola with Paul to play golf and not staying here with you."

Where have I heard that before, I thought. I reminded him our relationship wasn't worth anything if he couldn't tell me the truth. I suggested he go down and tell Paul the gig was up. Paul came up appearing to be embarrassed. I tried to play it cool.

"Have a good weekend," I said, trying not to sound too sarcastic. "Hope you play a lot of good golf," I told them as they left.

You would think, by then, I would have grown tired of the deceit — that enough was enough. But, I was too dependent and believed if I was alone I would be worthless. The next few months things were not the same. West left for Texas on business for a couple of weeks. Before he left, West said, "I do love you, Randy, and we'll work things out when I get back."

While he was gone, a mutual friend of ours, Alan, while on a business trip came to visit overnight from South Carolina. I put him up in West's room. It was a Thursday evening. Alan and I went to dinner and then stopped by Blakes', a neighborhood gay bar. It was packed for a Thursday night. We were standing around when I noticed a really good looking guy who was about 6'2," 240 pounds, with blue eyes and black hair. Alan and I looked at one another and said simultaneously, "This guy has got to be lost."

The stranger and I started looking at each other and the game of look and look away started. Alan said, "Go talk to him." But I reminded my friend that I was in a relationship. Alan commented that, in his opinion, my relationship with West had been over for some time.

"You're a fool not to talk to this guy," Alan urged. "He obviously thinks you're cute, he keeps looking over here at you."

While Alan purposely excused himself for a minute, the stranger walked over.

"Hi, my name's Mickey," he said eagerly. "I'm from Hawaii and in town for a doctors' convention."

Mickey was doing his residency in Philadelphia, where he would be returning the next afternoon. When Alan came back, I introduced them. After their introduction, Mickey excused himself to the restroom.

"Randy, if you need me to check into a hotel tonight, I

will," Alan said, with a grin on his face like a house cat who had just swallowed the pet canary.

Again I reminded my house guest I couldn't do anything with this guy because of West. Alan, who is considerably shorter than me, grabbed me at the elbow and pulled me down to eye level with him.

"You're crazy if you don't get together with this guy," he said.

Mickey returned and we all talked until Alan glanced down at his watch. He had an early appointment so I asked Mickey, at Alan's coaching, if he wanted to come by the apartment. The three of us left. Alan went to bed while Mickey and I sat in the living room.

There was no doubt things had been rocky with West for a long time, but I didn't want to face it in my heart. Mickey was hard to resist. I told him about my relationship and he still wanted to stay the night. I had to work the next day until three o'clock and wouldn't be able to spend any more time with Mickey before his plane left. He decided to stay and take the last flight back to Philadelphia. Mickey met me at my apartment a little past three o'clock and we went to lunch. He invited me to visit him in Philadelphia before his residency ended. I told him I would think about it. We returned to my apartment and fooled around until nine o'clock. It was hard to say good-bye to this tall, dark, gorgeous man with whom I'd just relived a fantasy very similar to the one with Ted. But West was very much on my mind the whole time. Foolishly, I still tried to hold onto an ill-fated relationship.

Feeling guilty, and covered in the juices of Mick's and my evening together, I called West in Texas. Leaving out the details, I only divulged that Alan and I had met a really great guy and that we should go visit him in Philadelphia. I was becoming the deceiver West had been. He'd been a good teacher.

Avoiding the topic of our intimacies together, I spent a lot of time talking to Mickey over the phone, resulting in making plans to visit him. But I would wait to see how things were when West returned. I still hadn't told West the whole story and I was trying to fool myself into thinking I would visit with Mickey as his friend.

In the meantime, West came back from Texas but the absence hadn't changed things between us. We had sex a few times, but it felt as empty as the times I had spent with women. I was now thinking about Mickey. West encouraged me to go even though I would be away on his birthday — he was just going to work all weekend anyway. I gave West his presents early and, hesitantly left to catch my flight.

Arriving at Mickey's apartment by taxi late in the evening, I was tired and confused. Luckily, he had an early day at the hospital. We decided to go right to bed. I took the sofa while Mickey slept in his bed.

The next day, while Mickey was at work, I looked around the city. His small efficiency wasn't far from the hospital. We met back at the apartment early in the evening and headed off to dinner at a Cuban restaurant, where over beer and Jell-o shooters, the conversation focused on my relationship with West. I'd left a message for West as soon as I got to Philadelphia the night before, and was sad, but not surprised, he hadn't returned my call. Upon returning to the efficiency, the conversation continued on the sofa. Suddenly, Mickey got up and started rubbing my back and massaging my shoulders. I was feeling weak, lonely, and very foolish. Mickey said, "You should forget about West and just enjoy yourself now." Before I knew it my shirt was off and Mickey was on top of me. After rolling around on the sofa, Mickey took my hand and led me to his bed. Within minutes the rest of our clothes were scattered on the floor and Mickey was squeezing body lotion over my nude body. The lotion was cold hitting my skin but quickly warmed to body temperature. He was an awesome sight standing over me squeezing the contents out of the bottle. And, for a brief moment, I forgot West. I had known West for years and this man for only hours.

Mickey laid on top of me, the lotion oozing between our bodies. He kissed me. I was trying to lose myself, but I couldn't. Again, he told me to relax and forget about everything except the moment at hand. Whispering in my ear, Mickey said, "I want to slide myself inside of you." He rubbed between my legs, spreading the lotion until his finger penetrated me.

"This is right where I want to be," Mickey softly spoke, as he moved his finger in and out. "I know you want this too... you're making me so hot."

I looked into his eyes, again thinking about West, thinking of all the times we had done this as a couple. I knew West hadn't returned my call because he didn't want me anymore. "Yes, I want it too," I said faintly to Mickey.

Mickey kissed me on the mouth as he pulled away. My eyes followed him as he walked away from the bed toward the light of the bathroom. I should be happy, I thought, as I watched his broad back and strong round ass move away from me.

The apartment was deadly quiet. As Mickey disappeared into the bathroom, I heard a cabinet door open and then close. Then, the sound of hard plastic crinkling. A second later, Mickey reemerged adjusting the condom on his hard dick as he walked toward me. My eyes focused on it and then he was on top of me again. Now, our eyes met as he adjusted our bodies so he could enter me. I felt the head of his penis pushing into me as Mickey lifted my legs up off the bed. I panicked. My mind flooded with all kinds of thoughts. I realized I was destroying every belief I had. West had been unfaithful to me many times and I tried to convince myself I was doing nothing wrong. But my self persuasion was not working. I kept thinking, here I was, in the height of the AIDS epidemic running rampant across the country and I was rolling around in bed with someone I hardly knew who was about to put his penis inside of me. Pulling myself from under Mickey, I got out of bed without saying a word and went to the bathroom. I showered for what seemed like hours wishing I hadn't come. Mickey was sitting up in bed when I finished. He claimed to understand when I told him I was sorry, that this was just too hard for me.

The next day Mickey had his rounds at the hospital. While he was gone I decided to fly back to Atlanta early. It was West's birthday and I felt guilty about what had almost happened last night. I waited for Mickey to return to tell him I was leaving. His eyes teared up a little, which touched and surprised me, because we hardly knew one another. I was afraid I might be making a mistake by leaving, but I told myself, I couldn't be with someone else until it was officially over with West.

The flights were all open that day, so I had no problem booking a return. I arrived in Atlanta around six o'clock, just before West was leaving for a basketball game. The minute I walked in the door and saw his face, something inside told me I should have stayed in Philadelphia. I was confused and felt sick at my stomach.

West went ahead to the basketball game. We made plans to go out and celebrate his birthday with friends later in the evening. After he returned, I suggested we stay home and watch movies but he insisted on going, promising to be out for only an hour. I told him I would wait for him. He never came home that night. The phone rang at ten-thirty the next morning, it was West. He said he'd too much to drink and stayed at a friend's house. I felt like such a fool. I knew it was over for good.

The next couple of weeks were violent ones, introducing me to a side of West I didn't know he had. He yelled like a madman, and for the first time in years, I heard the irate voice of my father echo in my ears. A fight resulted in West hitting me above my right eye and fracturing his hand in the process. We both ended up in the emergency room in the middle of the night, I with stitches and West with a cast on his hand. I was ready to let go no matter how hard it was, I had lost all respect for myself, I didn't know who I was anymore. It was time to end the lies and let the healing begin. I had to get my self-respect back and let go of the past. Ironically, Mickey called me the very night West moved out. He said I should come back to Philadelphia and pick up where we'd left off. He would be there another two weeks before returning to Hawaii. I asked Mickey if he would come to Atlanta instead on his way back home. I wanted to be with him, but I was through running to someone. I knew I had to stop running; they had to run to me.

*The past few months as well as many absent days over the
last years has
taught me that there was never a "you and me."
As much as I hated to face it, I know now in reality there was
only me in this
relationship.
I try not to look back anymore and have stopped trying to
understand.
Though I can't help but remember, I only hope that with
time, as I fade from
this earth, so will those memories gradually fade from my
mind and free me.
I must now find freedom from the love I hold dear to you.
If I am to survive, this love must die from my heart.*

matthew

The news from the doctor continued to forecast the worst. There was nothing else to do except make Todd comfortable for the duration. Most of his medication was discontinued a few days later because it was too harsh on his kidneys and other organs. The drugs were just prolonging the inevitable and causing more discomfort. Over the next week, Todd's body became swollen and sensitive to the slightest touch. Time became a waiting game, and with it he grew very restless.

Mrs. Weaver had moved into Todd's house while he was in the hospital. She wanted to be close to him and oversee his care. Her concern now was that her son be at peace and, when the end did come, Todd would slip away enveloped in a loving atmosphere.

Shannon spent countless hours by Todd's bedside. He was sitting in the living room with Mrs. Weaver, when I walked into the house. Shannon was telling her how his brother had pulled through several times when his own family thought the end was only hours away. And he hoped the same would be true for Todd. I stood behind Mrs. Weaver as she tried to stay strong.

"Life is like a silk scarf. So beautiful, yet so delicate at the same time," Shannon said, continuing to share his personal experiences. Todd was like a silkworm spinning out beauty into the world. And like the scarf, he was easily torn. AIDS had infected the fibers he had so beautifully spun, and now they were rapidly breaking apart. Just a few days after Shannon's visit, Richard was rushed to the hospital. Shannon was alone in the waiting room when one of Todd's brothers, Stan, and a family friend, Thomas, came to see Shannon in a show of support. The two men walked up to Shannon and embraced him.

"We both have something in common, Shannon," Stan said. "We both have brothers with AIDS."

Before Todd's illness, Stan and Thomas, were separated by a wall of ignorance. They never questioned the stereotypes of gay men. Stan all along thinking his brother, Todd, was an exception. And now his exposure to Todd's gay friends shone a new light. Sharing the grief of another man — another man who happened to be gay brought with it a new understanding to Stan and the rest of Todd's brothers. With all the misunderstanding and hatred expressed in our society today toward gays, this was a light of hope and compassion. Two men, Shannon and Stan, from two different cultures coming together in an embrace to console one another. One gay man and one straight man, whose brothers were fighting a tremendous foe. There was what seemed an instant brotherhood of two brothers with the same concerns and love for their own sick male siblings. They were on the same side now. Suddenly, in the realization of it all, they had all become warriors in the battle against death and prejudice.

The emotional breakup with Don weighed heavy on Todd's mind. A big part of his restlessness. Mrs. Weaver didn't want Don anywhere near the house. She saw Don as a cold, heartless demon who had left her son when he needed him the most. Her distaste for him was magnified by Don having snuck into the house at the time Todd was in Intensive Care. Don took a painting Todd had so loved. Ironically, if Don had waited, he would have gotten it after Todd had died; Todd left it to him in his will. Mrs. Weaver filled the empty space on the wall with another piece of art; hoping Todd wouldn't notice the thief on his return home. She wanted to keep any more pain out of the remaining days of his life. The cover-up was unsuccessful. When Todd returned, the first thing he noticed was the missing painting. He was crushed by sadness. Apparently, Don and Todd had both shared a love for the work of art; having purchased it together. To Todd, it was a symbol of a happier moment of the life they had shared. And memories were all he had left. Now, it was another crack in his already broken heart. Mrs. Weaver hated Don for violating her son like that. We all did, except for Todd.

There were obviously issues left unresolved between Todd and Don. Todd knew he was dying, and with that realization, his agitation continued to grow. Without hope of any change in his condition, he wanted to see Don again. Todd knew his mother wouldn't allow Don to walk into the house they had once shared. In her mind, she was just trying to protect her son. But Todd had to see Don one more time.

When Mrs. Weaver was away from the house. Todd called the nurse into his room and pointed to the drawer of the bedside table where she would find the address book. He then asked her to dial the phone. Todd stared out the window into the back yard waiting for Don's arrival. His heart pounded, mostly from anticipation of the meeting, and from worry his mother might return sooner than planned. Todd had made arrangements with Marie to keep Mrs. Weaver occupied until six o'clock.

Don stood in the doorway of Todd's bedroom. This wasn't the lover he had left. Instead, there was a frail body resembling no one he knew. Don looked into Todd's eyes, the only thing he recognized. He tried to stay focused on them, struggling not to examine the horror before him and reveal it to Todd.

The nurse, getting the signal from Todd with a faint smile of appreciation, stepped out of the room. Todd began to cry. For two hours, Don knelt by the bedside and rested his head next to Todd's.

The visit went well and it seemed to help ease Todd's mind for a moment. The nurse said they both cried a lot together. It doesn't really matter what I thought or what Mrs. Weaver thought, or what anyone else thought about the situation between Todd and Don. The important thing was, it was between the two of them, and if Todd wanted to see Don again, then that's as it should be.

All that could be done for Todd now was to keep him on morphine to ease the suffering and send him into Dreamland. Family and close friends came to say what needed to be said, because within a matter of days, he would quickly become unaware and eventually go into a coma. We held onto every moment, as if it would be the last. Todd began to talk about his father. It had been a strong, loving relationship and Todd had missed Mr. Weaver terribly. He talked incisively, rambling as he looked up at the ceiling of his room. Todd seemed unaware of the changing light outside the window, or perhaps he was more aware than we were. He recounted some of the moments Todd and his dad had spent together: Their trips to the beach; times his dad helped him on different projects for school; camping trips where stories were told around the fire, while crickets sung under warm, clear night skies exploding with stars.

The sounds made by crickets on a summer's dusk in the South are like no other heard by the human soul. I think God planned it that way like He plans so many other things in our lives. It is a soothing language of a species removed and unconcerned with humans. There is a communication that is indistinguishable to mankind and yet it speaks subconsciously to our mortal ears. A foreign voice softening the harshness of the heat of the long southern summer days. It is part of the universal language of the earth that we humans have yet to mature enough to understand. So, we sit and listen for the music of the crickets without realizing the story they sing is one of comfort with the night. But in our ignorance, we are comfortable with ourselves until their song is sung.

It was just such a long summer day being called to an end by the sweet song of the crickets when the memory of my father revisited me, and that world came full circle again. The sun was making its escape from the sky as we sat on the expansive screened porch looking down onto the cove of the lake. The song filled the air as the crickets sung the sun to sleep.

Sitting there with Matthew, we listened to the sounds ending the day and introducing the night. A Daddy Long Leg spider hobbled across the floor and escaped through a crack in the baseboard. I felt secure in the moment like the spider relishing its crack of safety. The crickets' serenade continued into the night and, for a time, it seemed the world was at peace. Our conversation was hushed and sparse; it didn't seem right to break the noises of the evening with human voices. It was nature's time to speak and we couldn't have added anything of importance to the conversation taking place under the stars, along the lake and in the trees.

Robert, Matthew's lover, was asleep in the bedroom of their huge lake house. His sleep, however, was not induced by the sweetness of the music in the lake air, but by the confluence of one too many drinks during a long, hot day. It was a way of life for him, the melodious life of the bottle, which sometimes turned sour. Sleep was but a temporary relief.

They had become my substitute parents. Some of the elements I was already familiar with were present in this relationship, especially Robert's drinking and his angry side. Timely reminders of my family life — a lot of booze and a lot of anger but there were also the good things, things I wasn't familiar with. A sense of love and of friendship. In a way, they had taken me into their family. Out of all the people I'd met since moving to Atlanta, besides Todd, there was finally some sense of relations around me. I cried on their shoulders, particularly Matthew's, about the men who'd come and gone from my life. In their home, I found protection from the confusion of the world, and especially from the gay world.

We were very much like a family. Robert was the mother nurturing me very much like my own mother had in my early childhood. He was a gourmet cook and made all kinds of wonderful things for me to eat, taking great pride in his talents in the kitchen every time I came to visit. It got to the point where I had dinner with them two or three times a week. When we weren't having dinner at their house, they would take me out to eat. Robert had many feminine qualities, and could be at times flamboyant in his mannerisms; it was just his nature. He was tall and lean and wore a short toupee parted on the left, that neatly formed to his head. An elegant man, he appreciated the finer things: The finest clothes and jewelry, the best house and car. Several mink coats hung in one of his many closets. And they were worn proudly by this forty-nine-year-old. Matthew, on the other hand, filled in for the father. The opposite of Robert, he was quiet and manly, an engineer by profession working among straight men. Whereas, Robert, had more freedom as a designer. Matthew's fifty-two-year-old frame stood a few inches below Robert's, his head full of salt and pepper hair. He was wise and understanding, always encouraging me in my art. Matthew took an interest and made me feel as if I could meet new challenges without losing confidence in myself, which was so easy for me to do. He was there to keep me on target, pointing me in the direction I needed to go. When I got off course, he was there to help put me back in the right direction.

They met on a gorgeous May day, ironically one month short of my birth in the same year. Enjoying the beautiful mid-spring weather on a Friday afternoon, Matthew went for a drive in his 1949 black four-door Buick Super. Traveling down Peachtree Street on his way to The Tic Toc, a gay bar, he noticed a handsome man waiting for a bus at the corner. Robert was headed in the same destination, and within thirty minutes they were to start a relationship that would last thirty-five years, despite prejudice and southern, good-old boy mentality.

Not long after Matthew had settled at the bar with a beer, the only alcohol sold at The Tic Toc, Robert stepped off the bus and walked through the door. They stared at one another across the bar until Robert walked over to introduce himself. He knew a good thing when he saw it and so did Matthew. After a few beers and some conversation, they left in the Buick Super for The Chinese Camellia Restaurant, which had a bar in the rear frequented by gay men. There Matthew had a scotch and water and Robert had a scotch mist. Six months later, in October, they took an apartment together on Twelfth Street in Midtown. And from there, they built a quiet and discreet life together, forging successful careers, and making friendships that would last a lifetime.

It didn't take me long, in our newly formed friendship to realize Robert had a serious problem with alcohol. After all, I majored in alcoholic studies in my childhood. Many of his actions and characteristics mirrored those of my parents. Robert was a dear man, his angry side surfacing only when he was drinking. That's when I first felt a kinship with Matthew. He was usually the receiver of a lot of Robert's alcohol-soaked hostilities. I knew what it was like to be on the receiving end of such anger, and I had great sympathy for Matthew in those situations. My heart went out to him. Robert's condescending comments would cut deep like a knife, and clearly left a wound on Matthew's soul, deeply hurting him. Robert wouldn't care who was around, whether it was just me or at a dinner party with twenty people.

I guess I always tried to keep a safe distance from Robert like I had my father — especially when he was on a binge. It was one of those survival tactics I developed in childhood. When Robert was sober, he was grand to be around. He was funny, always with a great joke to tell, the center of attention.

Robert had a lot of success over the years as an interior designer. His increasing drinking was affecting his work, only adding to his problems. Yet, Matthew was always there for him. Like a rock, he quietly took all the verbal abuse Robert vented, trying to let the harsh words roll off his back.

As our friendship grew, so too did Robert's resentment

towards the time Matthew spent with me. It usually surfaced when Robert was drinking and felt he wasn't the center of attention. Matthew was just the kind of person who took an interest in those around him. It was nice to have someone like him interested in my life and what I was doing. Someone neutral. Someone to be trusted. I guess I wanted Matthew to take the place of my father and give me the kind of love I'd never received. Robert's love was also essential so I could be part of a family and feel supported and loved. I wanted a place where I could feel safe and protected from the outside world.

The three of us spent many evenings together in their home. We sat and talked or sometimes watched television until late and it was time for me to head home. They told me stories of their life and travels together — they had seen much of the world I'd dreamed of visiting. I listened and dreamed of meeting someone and having a life similar to theirs. Not like the relationships I had been involved in. And most of the time, it was a comfort to be with this couple. On the weekends, we went to their lake house and spent lazy days on the dock in the sun and peaceful nights watching the moonlight reflecting off the water, listening as the crickets filled the night air with their symphony.

Robert must have been asleep for almost an hour. Sitting on the porch, looking out into the beginning of night, I watched the silhouettes of the trees take shape across the other side of the cove against the blue-blackened sky — not quite illuminated with the first stars of the night. The lightning bugs were beginning to show off their lights, flickering above the ripples on the water made by fish coming to the surface, as the crickets continued to call the night into play.

Well before Matthew's hand moved to my knee, I'd felt uneasy. Perhaps because it was too quiet or maybe because I somehow knew what was about to take place. The peace and comfort had been too good for too long. It was time for something to happen to shake up my world, time for me to be reminded of the past.

Matthew placed his hand on my knee just touching the edge of my khaki shorts. In an instant, my heart stopped; I knew the rest. I dared not glance at him sitting next to me.

"Is this okay with you?" Matthew asked, as I felt his hand rub my thigh.

I sat there speechless not believing what was happening. I began making excuses: Maybe it's the alcohol; everyone had a lot to drink during the day. He's just being affectionate and not really making a pass at me with Robert asleep in the house.

"Sure, it's fine." I managed to get the words out, hiding my discomfort.

My vision tunneled as I stiffly kept my eyes glued to the night in front of me, sending my mind to the other side of the lake, running away from what was happening this moment. I felt like a child again, trapped with nowhere to run. The same hopeless feeling filled every inch of my body until I was paralyzed. If the house had caught on fire, I wouldn't have been able to get out of the chair and run from the flames.

I felt Matthew's hand move to the crotch of my shorts. I wanted to say stop but the words wouldn't leave my mouth. I was afraid to speak, afraid to lose the family I was just beginning to feel a part of. I would be alone again, lost with no one to protect me and keep me safe.

He unbuttoned the waist of my shorts and discreetly pulled at the zipper. I felt his hand slip down into my underwear. Still, I couldn't directly look at him. Motionless, I watched him from the corner of my eye move from his chair to the floor of the porch in front of me. He opened the fly of my underwear and I felt his mouth on me.

My mind was filled with fear. What had I done to make Matthew do this? What if Robert wakes up and finds us? He would hate me. I would lose them for sure. I could no longer hear the sound of the crickets. The reflection of the moon on the water was no longer clear in my sight. My mind was dark, I was somewhere else.

Matthew pulled away and sat back in the chair. I was relieved Robert hadn't stirred, and as far as I could sense, was still asleep. We sat there quietly in the darkness of the porch. The lights from the house were shining from the windows to our backs, casting our images through the screen onto the grass in the yard. I still didn't know what to say. I felt betrayed. Would this be the cost of friendship, or the price to pay to have a family? Would Robert be next? This seemed all too familiar.

I didn't tell Matthew how I felt. I was afraid to share my fear. He was merely fulfilling his desire for me, one I was unaware of until that moment. I knew he never intended to bring sadness into my heart. He couldn't know the responsibility I'd subconsciously placed on him to redeem the ills of my father. It was a task too heavy to place on any man's shoulders.

He took pleasure in a few stolen moments away from his alcohol-soaked relationship with his longtime partner. Robert's drinking and anger sent Matthew in my direction, to find comfort in the innocence sitting there by his side. That innocence had been lost a long time ago, but Matthew didn't know that. He needed to taste the sweet pleasure of skin not spoiled by the disgust of the bottle. He was driven by the realization of his losing Robert to the demon of drink. Matthew had tasted it one too many times from Robert's lips, as I had, from the lips of my father.

How could I turn Matthew away and leave him without the comfort he needed at that moment? If I had, in a way it would be like turning my back on myself. It was still too much for me to comprehend. I felt responsible now for Matthew as I had for my father's needs. My search for a father in Matthew had been betrayed. The memory became all too clear. All it took was a touch from Matthew to bring the fear of my father back into my heart, when of course it had never really left.

"Randy, sleep naked for me tonight." Matthew said, in a low voice, as if to be sure Robert couldn't overhear such desires from his sleep.

It was now another secret to keep inside the walls surrounding me. I have kept this secret before in another lifetime, I thought to myself, as I said my good-night and left the porch for my room on the other side of the house.

I closed the bedroom door behind me. Should I lock it, I asked myself, looking at the waist band of my shorts still unbuttoned. The windows over the bed allowed the moonlight to drift into the room. It was late. The sound of the dock down below repeatedly hitting against the water wall of the lake carried into the house. The crickets were silent and now the night was dead.

I stood there next to the bed. Slowly pulling the t-shirt off over my head, letting it drop to the floor at my feet. It smelled from the day on the lake. Still partially unzipped, I slipped my shorts off with the underwear still in them. I was doing as I had been instructed.

Matthew must have gone to bed, where Robert was still sleeping off the drunk he had acquired earlier in the day. Maybe he would fall asleep next to Robert, where he belonged, and not wake until the morning. Everything would then be back to normal again. As a child, the night had a way of forgiving the sins of my father and this night should be no different.

I turned down the bed cover and slipped between the cotton sheets, pulling the top one up around my neck protecting my nude body from the surroundings. The house was hot from the long summer day. I curled up on my side, facing the door to the room and remained like an errant child awaiting punishment. This night was no stranger to me.

I drifted in and out of sleep, reviewing scenes of childhood in my mind. But, it was like a puzzle having several pieces missing, nothing fitting together — an incomplete portrait of the past. The important pieces had been torn from memory, leaving only the rough edges behind as a reminder. Part of me still trying to rip out more memories and another part searching for the answers to the missing story left so evident by the incomplete family album.

This night, I wanted to quickly fall into a deep sleep for if Matthew did wake and come to my room he might not disturb me if he found me asleep. And, if he decided to take his pleasure in the dead of night, then I might remember it as a dream. This time, sleep would be a haven for me. As I moved in and out of sleep, my eyes watched for the door. My ears listened for footsteps crossing the floor outside my room. There was only silence and I fell back into a bleak sleep.

Sometime in the night, before the light broke over the lake, I felt the presence of someone kneeling over me. The sheet was being pulled lightly from me, sliding over the bare skin of my body until I was exposed. I didn't open my eyes and dare wake from my superficial sleep. I was dreaming, I told myself. It is better if I sleep.

The next day, I acted like nothing had transpired the night before on the porch and in the darkness of my room. It was an easy acting job, one of which I had years of practice. As a child, it got to the point where I was acting all the time. After awhile, I lost touch with the real person. In fact, the real me never had a chance to exist. I became an actor to protect the person I was, and now I realized the face of the little boy I see today in childhood photographs is a little boy no one ever knew. He was not even known by me.

I simply blocked the incident from my mind, locking it away in the dark recesses where I put all the other confusing crap from my life. Hopefully, it soon would be a lost memory like all the others. But, this time I wasn't a child anymore. I could have stopped it just by getting up from my chair and saying "no." I wanted to, but my body wouldn't move and the words wouldn't pass my lips to break the silence of the air. In an instant, I was a child in the body of an adult.

Robert wasn't aware of the activities that transpired while he slept. The day came and went without any discussion between Matthew and myself of the night before. I was surely not going to bring it up — already denying in my mind that it had ever happened. Maybe Matthew had as much as Robert to drink and didn't remember what happened either. It would just be a dream somewhere deep in his mind. I would keep the secret for the both of us. My father had blackouts and couldn't remember a lot of things he did while he had been drinking. I would stay away from Matthew the next time we were alone and everything would work out fine. That way I could still hold onto my new family.

But Matthew hadn't forgotten the night of the crickets' song. He had just been waiting for the next opportunity to take pleasure again and find relief from Robert's continued love affair with the bottle. I evaded talking about the incident.

There was a change in everyone. Robert seemed to grow meaner and his drinking increased, and Matthew began showing me much more attention. I stopped coming by the house so much, but it was hard to say "no" when Robert called to invite me for dinner, his voice getting hard and insistent as if I was disappointing him. So many times, I unwillingly accepted.

Unable to refuse his invitations as well, Matthew and I had lunch without Robert knowing. Sometimes when Matthew was on his way out of town on business, we would meet near the airport for dinner. We fell into familiar modes of conversation. Matthew wanted to know all about my latest projects — his interest always filling the void unfilled by my father. It had been several months since that night at the lake house. Nothing else happened, except Matthew might hold my hand if we were in the car alone together. I was still uncomfortable but realized Matthew needed my company and I still needed him to take an interest in my life. He needed someone to remove him from Robert's world of drinking and I still needed the love of a father.

In the meantime, Robert was like a roller coaster with the drinking. He hid his vodka in glasses of iced tea, drinking behind everyone's back, trying to fool us, much as my own mother had done for years. The insults flying at Matthew became worse. And the worse things got, the more Matthew required my company. Eventually, Robert went into the hospital with as damaged a liver as any heavy drinker ever had. The doctor told him he had to stop or he may as well put a gun to his head. That news seemed to slow Robert down, but not for long.

I let my guard down with Matthew and, because nothing had really happened since that night at the lake, I began feeling comfortable again. With Robert sick, they needed me. The three of us were to go off for the weekend to see friends of Matthew's and Robert's in Tennessee. We were leaving early on a Saturday morning so I spent the night at their house in order to get an early start.

I stayed in one of the guest rooms of their stately, white-columned, Neel Reid home in the exclusive in-town neighborhood of Ansley Park. The blue painted room had twin beds, each crowned by large padded headboards covered in gray satin. Across from the beds sat a huge Empire dresser with an ornate mirror. To the right of it was a skirted table accompanied by two gilded French chairs. I felt like I was staying at the royal palace. The room had two doors leading into it — one to the main hall of the upstairs and the other to an adjoining bath and dressing room between the guest room and Matthew's bedroom. Robert's room was down and across the hall. They had kept separate bedrooms for years.

I was the first to retire. As I was drifting off I heard faint foot steps and doors closing outside my room. I fell into sleep secure in the thought everyone was safe and sound in their beds. We would have a nice weekend.

I don't know how long I had been asleep before I felt wetness on me. I jerked, opening my eyes to see Matthew's head moving below my waist. I lay still, not saying a word. He had come to me again in the night while Robert slept. The room was dark except for the dim, thin stream of light coming into the room from the crack of the dressing room door.

Staring into the darkness of the room, I waited for him to finish, only moving my body slightly as he sucked on me. Matthew was on his knees, his body hidden to the room by the bed. I could hear his faint moans as he took pleasure in his sucking. I touched the back of his head to quiet him as I felt the juice from his mouth run down my hip and onto the bed.

Unexpected, there were footsteps outside of the door leading to the hall. Matthew ducked behind the bed and crawled back into his bedroom through the dressing room like lightning. My heart stopped as the door opened and Robert peered into the room. I could smell the liquor on his breath drifting into the air as he mumbled something I couldn't understand. I didn't acknowledge his presence and pretended to be asleep. The door closed as quickly as it opened and I heard Robert's footsteps fade down the hall.

This couldn't happen again. There was too much at stake, too many emotions to deal with. Although it was Robert's drinking that sent Matthew to me, that was not enough justification for what was taking place within our lives. I couldn't deal with the reminders of my past and I couldn't keep any more secrets. This was all too familiar, like being caught in a time warp.

After one of our private dinners together, on the drive back to my apartment I told Matthew I couldn't do this to Robert — failing to tell Matthew how closely the experiences with him related to my past and of the fear they brought to my heart. I thought it was enough to leave things as they were and not take the chance of hurting Matthew, if it was his belief I'd taken pleasure in his physical attentions.

Wanting a relationship one day, I refused to come between the many years of the relationship they had shared. This might haunt me, and I didn't want to be in Robert's or Matthew's shoes twenty years from now. Matthew held my hand.

"I love you Randy," he said genuinely. "I wish you

would allow this to continue."

"It's just not possible, Matthew. There is nothing to continue," I said delicately.

I thought at that point I would lose his love, that he would turn away and not be there for me anymore. After all, he still didn't know he was filling the shoes of my father in more ways than one.

"I understand," Matthew said. "I'll do as you wish and not come to you anymore. But know if you need anything, I'll be there for you."

I was relieved to see Matthew wouldn't turn away from me because of my decision. I knew then his love for me was deeper than a physical one. He truly cared.

Robert's drinking continued, worsening despite his doctor's warnings. Before, it was Matthew's affections that kept me away. Now the more Robert drank, the more I made excuses and stayed away from them both. I felt some responsibility for Robert's drinking. My dinner visits to their home were not as often. Robert grew upset with me for turning them down. To appease him, I gave Robert a painting he liked. I was so proud he wanted it and hung it over the fireplace of one of the sitting rooms of their home. He offered to buy it, but I wanted to give it to him. I hoped it would bring us closer and, in some way, silently make amends for the few indiscretions with Matthew.

Again, I looked forward to things getting back to normal between the three of us. I no longer worried about the physical contact between Matthew and me; I knew I'd made the right decision. That was all behind us. I felt his love but didn't feel I had to repay it by stripping myself and deceiving Robert. The past was left in the darkness of a few stolen moments in the night. As a couple, they had given me so much comfort. I wanted our friendship to be a strong one, with no secrets.

Matthew mentioned he was interested in buying a condo for an investment. If I wished, I could live in it and pay rent. We found what looked to be a great deal. A developer was renovating an old twelve unit apartment complex into con-dominiums. Matthew began getting things in order. Robert found out and hit the roof.

"There's no way you're going to buy Randy a condo!" he shrilled.

Robert called demanding I return the house keys and never to set foot in their home again. I tried to explain that I was going to pay rent but he wouldn't listen. Matthew told me not to worry, that Robert would get over it and things would be fine.

After all their years together, Robert was talking now of splitting up with Matthew. I knew it was my fault. Matthew reassured me it was just the booze talking and that Robert wouldn't leave. Matthew had been looking after Robert for so long, keeping him afloat, and he wouldn't give up that kind of security. He was just blowing off steam, trying to be the center of attention. Well, he succeeded. Robert called all of their friends and said I was trying to break them up; I was humiliated. Robert took the painting I gave him and burned it in the fireplace over which it had hung. Robert must have hated me so much and I hated myself for the situation.

I told Matthew I wouldn't move into the condo if he bought it. He said he was going to buy it anyway; Robert was not going to tell him how to run his life. After another stay in the hospital, Robert eased up on the drinking and came around. He agreed I should move into the condo and he apologized for burning the painting.

In September, two weeks before the condo sale was scheduled to close, I was awakened by a call from a friend at seven o'clock on a Wednesday morning.

"Randy, turn the television on. Your condo is on the news. It's on fire!" Connie announced.

By the time I reached for the remote control and turned on the television, the news anchor had moved on to another story. I got in my car and drove the two miles to the condo. As I slowly pulled up to the front of the building, I could see the charred remains of the structure. The fire chief said faulty wiring in the unit may have been the cause. Out of all the units being remodeled, this was the one where it started. There was minimal damage to three of the other units in the building.

The odor of charred remains was strong in the air later that same day as Matthew and Robert met me at the condo. We walked through the unit. The roof was gone, as well as the bathroom and part of the kitchen. The hardwood floors of the hallway and one bedroom were almost burned through. We stepped over the piles of burnt wood and sheetrock. Everything was soaked from the firemen's water hoses. Matthew decided to still take the unit after the developer repaired the damages. He said it would be better, like getting a new structure instead of a converted one. I moved in four months later on Christmas Eve.

By March, things appeared to be going well. I had settled in, putting the fire behind me. At first I took it as a bad omen, but Matthew convinced me things worked out for the best. Robert was offering decorating tips, even stopping by to see how things were coming along. Spring was a few weeks early and all the windows were open as I lay on my bed for an afternoon nap. I was enjoying the gentle breeze running through the apartment and soon started to fall asleep. Matthew and Robert were leaving the next day on a short vacation, and Matthew had loaned me a VCR for the time they were going to be away, mine was on the blink. I planned to spend the weekend catching up on movies I'd missed at the theater.

Relaxed, I drifted on the edge of sleep until I heard some rustling noises from somewhere in the condo. Being so comfortable on the bed, I didn't want to get up to see where the noises might be originating; convincing myself they were from outside — one of my neighbors on the back porch. The commotion ceased and I closed my eyes while adjusting the pillow under my head. I drifted off again. Moments later, the rustling resurfaced. Forcing myself to wake up, I groggily rolled off the bed and walked from the bedroom. The noises became louder. As I turned the corner from the hallway into the kitchen, I could see a man holding a large screwdriver climbing through the kitchen window. With a closer look, I discovered it was Robert.

"What are you doing!" I commanded, not believing my eyes.

On attempting his entry, he had gotten stuck. Robert struggled to pull himself through the window, his butt outside, while his torso hung a few feet above the kitchen floor. The window opening was not quite large enough for his stomach, swollen from the years of alcohol. I walked closer to view the spectacle of his squirming like a stuck pig in a farmer's fence, he grunted, not answering, filled with embarrassment of being caught.

I helped him through the window, pulling from under his arms trying to stay clear of the screw driver in his hand. Robert got to his feet inside the kitchen as I took a few steps back. My heart was pounding, as much from dragging him through the window as from the uncertainty of his mission. Robert stood trying to bring order to his appearance, brushing off and straightening his clothes that had been ruffled in the failed entry.

"What do you think you're doing?" I asked again, demanding an explanation. "Are you crazy?"

Robert stuttered searching for words to make sense of his upcoming accounting for his actions.

"Randy, I'm sorry I didn't think you were home," he answered, his speech thick and broken, as he stepped toward me.

"Obviously!" I said, knowing he was close to drunk. "Don't come any closer. What are you doing with that screwdriver?" I questioned, taking another step away from him.

"I'm not going to hurt you. Is that what you think?" Robert said, as he pointed the screwdriver at me.

"Put it down on the counter. NOW!" I commanded.

Robert placed the screwdriver on the kitchen counter

and stepped back.

"See, I'm not going to do anything to you. I came to destroy the VCR Matthew loaned you for the weekend," he shamefully explained.

Unsteady on his feet, his eyes were blood shot. The smell of booze became more prevalent as he continued to explain and I was forced to inhale his breath.

"Why would you want to do a crazy thing like that?" I questioned, still in disbelief of Robert's actions.

"I...I don't know. I was jealous... I guess," he answered, looking back at the screwdriver on the counter.

"Jealous of what, Robert?"

"Matthew is always there for you. He doesn't do anything for me anymore. I can't help myself," Robert said, as he covered his face with his hands.

"He doesn't pay attention to you because you drink too much, Robert," I reasoned.

"I guess you're right," Robert said reluctantly agreeing.

"This is very upsetting, I don't know what to think of this, Robert," I said, as I stroked my head.

"Please don't say anything to Matthew," Robert pleaded.

"How can I help not to? This is some serious shit you're pulling. There's no telling what might have happened if I hadn't woken up... that screwdriver could have been through my heart," I said, as I walked over to it and put it in a drawer.

"No... no Randy, I would have never done something like that. You... you must believe me," Robert implored.

My mind filled with images of my body on the bed with a look of horror and surprise on my face, my blood rushing out of me, soaking the sheets. I could feel the blood oozing from me and the coldness of the steel of the screwdriver in my body. I was relieved, happy I had awakened in time.

"Randy," I heard Robert's voice as I shivered at what I had just imagined.

"I'm not so sure. This is very upsetting to me," I emphasized again.

"I'm so sorry Randy. This will never happen again... just please, let's forget this. I...I can make this up to you," Robert declared.

"The only thing you can do is stop drinking. You need to get some help, Robert... some real help," I clarified.

"I know... I know. You're right. I will," Robert recognized, knowing as I did that he would never really stop.

"Let me drive you home, Robert," I requested.

"No... no, I can make it... really, I'll be fine," he tried to assure me. "Just promise you won't say anything."

"Don't worry about it, just worry about yourself," I urged, knowing the minute Robert was out the door I would have to call Matthew.

I called Matthew at his office and told him what had taken place. He listened on the phone amazed at Robert's actions.

"I'm so...so sorry, Randy, I'll speak to him," Matthew assured me.

"No Matthew! Don't say anything. I'm not sure what he had in mind when he was crawling through the window but he is embarrassed now. You know how he is. I thought it was important you know. Try and get him some help. Will you?" I insisted.

"He has been going to the doctor for years and he has done AA. What else can be done?" Matthew questioned.

"Robert needs to see a psychiatrist. Try to get him to see one," I replied.

"He's stubborn. You know that Randy," Matthew proclaimed. "Where is he now?"

"I guess he went home. I think he was okay to drive. You know, he's going to either kill himself or someone else if he continues. Just like my father, he's going to wind up dead. Alcohol has taken control of him. It killed my father as sure as the bullet did. Robert is going to die by the bottle if something is not done," I told Matthew, as my voice began to shake.

"I know Randy. I know," Matthew uttered. "But Robert has to want to stop," he added.

"I know. It is probably too late," I said, realizing the truth of that statement.

After locking the window Robert had tried to climb through, I returned to my bedroom to resume my nap. With my eyes closed, I reluctantly revisited my bedroom back home where a little boy watched his mother and father fight over a butcher knife. I got up and went back into the kitchen where I had left the screwdriver in the drawer. Instinctively, I hid it away.

Robert called me before they left the next day to make amends saying he would stop drinking. Not knowing what to think about the situation, I kept the windows in the kitchen secured and added an extra lock on the outer doors.

I knew then things would never be the same, but that was something I'd always known in my life. Peace is often short lived. Robert filled his glass with only iced tea for awhile after, but his need for alcohol soon won over his desire to quit. Its hold on him was too powerful. I suppose I knew all along he would never stop, just like my father never could. They both needed alcohol like the very blood in their veins.

We all wage wars; we all battle issues in our lives. I was really never sure of the one Robert was fighting. From what little he told me over the years and from what I could determine, I think it had a lot to do with his childhood and being gay. Deep down, he never felt like he fit in anywhere, and now he was growing old. His drink served as a shield to protect him in the combat of life. Like my father, the fight was too fierce and there were too many battles lost. The last soldier fell as the last glass emptied. In the end, the foe won. One year later, Robert died of cirrhosis of the liver. I remember the last moments I spent with him before he went back into the hospital for the last time. Matthew had called me to their house to come and sit with Robert for awhile.

I sat quietly in the sitting room across from Robert's

bedroom, watching him in a restless sleep. The heavy draperies were drawn tight keeping the world at a distance. The light outside was too bright for the harsh realities of what was taking place in the room. He was dying. He had taken a similar road as my father and now he had almost reached the end of his journey.

Whereas my father had ended his journey sooner, Robert's death was slow. The final drinks Robert had taken served as the bullet entering my father's head. For a moment, the world began to turn backwards again. The roles Robert and Matthew had played for me were reversed now. The morning I stood in the kitchen many years ago in a not so distant place, and heard my father call out to me before he pulled the trigger, had come around again. This time I had a chance to say good-bye.

randy

*Today I noticed the clouds had a wondrous texture I had
never seen before,
as they slowly drifted over my head.
They looked as if they had been painted with vibrant brush
strokes.
And as the sun broke with brilliant color, I felt its warmth
smiling down on
me.
The trees appeared greener and the spring flowers more
beautiful than I ever
remember seeing them before.
I stopped and wondered for a moment why things seemed so
different, today
of all days.
Then it became very clear to me.
It was a new spring and Todd was needed to adorn all of
heaven and earth
with his brilliant talent as he had once shared briefly with us
here.
And now I will always know.
When the sun breaks through the cloudy days we will see his
smile and the
brightness of his eyes chasing sadness from our hearts.
As the green sea rises to meet the blue sky, we will remember
him, for he is
dancing somewhere on the horizon.
We will feel his love in the greenness of every tree and in the
beauty of
every flower.
And when the sun breaks through the cloudy days, we will
look up and smile
back at our dear friend as he continues his work for all of us
to see.*

My friend was drifting off. Todd could hardly talk anymore. My only wish now was for him to find peace in his dreams. I knew there was so much more he wanted to accomplish in this life. As any of us would, he was fighting the end so hard and I was overwhelmed with anger, wanting to scream out for him. He had to know the end was close at hand; we could all see the fear in his face. I tried to tell him things would be okay.

"I'm afraid Randy, afraid of what I'm going to be missing. I don't want to leave my family and friends and the good times together," he said, with great sadness in his eyes. "I will be missing so much."

Lying next to Todd in his big, white bed, I told him he would never leave us, he would always be here with us, and when the end did come, it only meant the beginning of a great adventure for him. He was going to a place filled with wonder and new experiences. Todd struggled to speak, his words barely breaking a whisper. The warm spring sun shone through the double-windowed doors filling the room with light. Outside, fresh yellow daffodils sprang up indiscriminately among the grass in need of cutting a week ago. Four wooden posts stood in the ground where a deck had been planned in the once well manicured backyard. But in the disorder there was a sense of peace and freedom. The sunlight filtered through a collection of pictures placed in carefully selected frames on the bedside table. An anthology, telling a story covering the years of a young man's life: A picture of Todd's mother and father; that of four brothers standing arm and arm, all young and handsome; a wedding picture of his older brother with his bride; a picture of a niece; another of a nephew, named Little Todd and pictures of friends. And among them, rested a picture of Todd and Don arm in arm with their dog, Kipper at their side.

"Don't be afraid. You're just going on a great journey where you'll be seeing things your family and friends could only dream of," I said, trying to sound reassuring. "One day we'll all meet again in a celebration of friendship and love in a much better place than we are today." I hoped he believed me. I hoped I believed it myself. Todd looked at me and said he would be our guardian angel.

On Wednesday, April 14, at five o'clock in the morning, before the first light of day broke the darkness of what seemed to be an endless night, Todd left us. I will always remember the stillness of the air that morning; much like the one some eighteen years ago. The phone woke me from a light sleep. Before I picked it up, I knew the news. Marie's voice was on the other end. The last few months of Todd's life as I knew them flashed through my mind; the years of our friendship as well. His pain and uncertainty were over. Todd was finally free of the mortal anxieties he dealt with for so long. The day I met Todd became as clear as the day he died. So very many days had passed into years since that meeting. I had just started my search — a search for a father, a search for love and a search to find peace within myself in understanding who I was. Between our meeting and Todd's death, I came to meet many men, but none of them left the impression on my soul as he had done. I could now see us as lovers, as partners in life as he had, but now it was too late. My search was in the wrong direction and it had lasted too long. I had overlooked the one person who perhaps I should have been looking for all along. I had outgrown my need for a Goliath, but it was too late for Todd and me. But the gift of a true friendship is something I will always be grateful for.

In a way, Todd's passing gave me a new life. He was a
gift I will never be able to repay. My outlook on life is much
different now and my appreciation much greater.

It was not enough to pick up his frail body, overtaken by
the AIDS virus in my arms and carry him to the doctor; it
was not enough knowing he probably wouldn't live to see a
cure. He was still with us then, alive, and there was always
hope. It took me walking back into his house and into his
bedroom, and seeing his empty white bamboo bed so beautifully made, without him in it. Two large gray silk pillows
embroidered with small stars laid where his head once had.
Later that day, I wanted to pick up the phone and call him to
see what he was doing over the weekend, but I knew there
wouldn't be an answer at the other end. I dialed his number
anyway, just to hear his voice on the answering machine.

"Hey Todd, I'm going to miss you," I said quietly after
the beep.

I dare not presume I comprehend the enormous hopes,
fears and realities Todd was faced with during his struggles
with AIDS. I was angry that he, as well as so many before
him, and many more after, had to face this death. What an
unthinkable waste of life and love. I asked myself why do so
many have to die because they reached out for the touch of
intimacy in what can sometimes be a cold and lonesome
world. In the human search for love and comfort, AIDS
would be the end reality. It is a price that shouldn't have to
be paid. There is no answer to such a question. On the outside, Todd had tried to be so strong, but somehow I know on
the inside he was as fragile as the very heart beating in all of
us.

Today, because of my friend Todd, I try to see each day
as a new beginning for me. The light that once shone so
harshly as a constant reminder of the experiences in my
childhood is less intense. I see each day as a chance to find
peace with the past and look at the gifts each sunrise brings.

I truly look for the beauty in the beginning of each day,
in the warmth of the sun on my soul and the breezes that

brush by my face. I realize it is there for us all to see in the sunrises and in the sunsets, in the way the clouds roll by through the sky, and in the way the stars light up the heavens. There is beauty to be seen even on cloudy and rainy days.

I won't take another moment of life for granted. I won't worry about another small, insignificant detail. I will welcome each day and wish on every first star I see in the night's sky, and I will forever be grateful for the love and friendship of a tender dear friend and the lessons he has taught me. May his winter sleep be filled with sweet dreams of a new spring.

Until now, I have lied my whole life. But things are different today. Todd's last months battling AIDS forced me to recount my life. As I walk in front of the house where I first lost myself, even the breezes that brush by me feel differently than I remember as a child, when I once made the same footsteps in this very place. Somehow, the memories carried on them have lost their harshness in the midst of all the pain lived here, they are not as vexing as I recall, nor as intense. Time has staled them.

The discarded leaves of October, from the same seasoned trees, serve as silent witnesses to all that took place here. They will forever hold their silence as they stand seemingly frozen, quietly inching their roots deep into this earth. But I will no longer remain so. As I pick up one of the leaves just shuttled to the ground, I can see a little life left in it. There is still some softness as in the flesh of men. There is still a hint of green, still a hint of hope, but apparently not enough to hold this one leaf strong on the tree. The fight is now over for it. It has let go and placed its faith in the trusted wind to take it safely to the ground — to its resting place. I will take the greenness left as a sign of hope for me.

Even the air seems different, but I can still detect a faint scent of how things used to be. I know it's really me who has changed — not the place. I am different now as I am also the same. It must have been a gradual transition from all those silent years, and the realities of this moment have finally caught up with me. It's hard to believe so much time has passed undetected and, with it, the realities and dreams of a young man left behind. Is it those dreams I detect in the air triggering something in my mind? They are still here, rushing up to greet me, the breezes carrying them to me. Broken and left behind in the madness, it is as if they have waited a long time for my return and now I am here to collect them. In running from them, I have run into them again.

Like the leaves falling from these trees around me, falling from their home, I too must let go. I have come back here again to collect those dreams and face the realities, to finally let go once and for all. It is now time to realize what has happened in the silence of my life and let the wind carry me in the direction of those dreams and realities I almost left behind forever. I wasted a tremendous amount of time and effort looking for love and comfort outside of myself. In the process, I bypassed myself as a person. I overlooked the love I was capable of giving myself for the longest time, unaware it even existed. I have learned love starts here, with me, inside of me and for me, before I can find it with another person. I'd heard of loving yourself before — how important it is, but I had to learn it in my own time. It's a lesson that has taken a long time to learn and I'm still learning.

From the beginning of my life, there was a vast emptiness inside of me. I may not always clearly remember particular incidents, but I know I always felt different. Removed from what was happening around me, left behind and out of sight of the others, I was a stranger to everything, emotionally distant. Sensitive, maybe too sensitive, longing for something but never sure of what. Knowing I was different, I struggled to be like the others. My life became an endless search to become something I was not capable of, something impossible for me to be and still be true to the being I was born.

Now I know part of the truth. To be anything other than what I am would be a lie. It is time to stop and live the truth.

No one can make me feel wrong for feelings that live inside me. This I know. They are held in the same deep place as all human needs — the soul. And, if I am wrong, then we are all wrong for following our hearts.

My inner desires have brought me into the arms of many men. It was a journey borne from following my heart while running from childhood demons. The map I followed was never laid out clearly. The directions I took were not consciously made. I blindly felt my way through. The journey continues and a new light leads the way into the future.

There were many times I laid naked beside the men in my life and felt ashamed. I felt I was a lesser person than even the men in my company. I will never again allow such thoughts, stimulated by past experiences or our suppressive and unknowing society, to enter into my mind. The comfort I seek is the comfort I require and there is no shame in any two people sharing with one another.

I hope I am a wiser traveler now, knowing what obstacles to avoid on my trip through this life which is mine, and only mine to live. After all this time, I realize I have a companion in myself. This companion is shrewder and confident; he won't lead me astray. As for the men I have loved and shared my nakedness with, in the most intimate of circumstances, they have taught me well. Not all the lessons may have been welcomed at the time, but I realize their instruction made me the person I am today. As my teachers, they have taught me how to love and how not to love. And as a result of their lessons, I have grasped how to love myself when I couldn't find it anywhere else. It has been an intense schooling. I am lucky to have survived as any of us are with mind and body intact. My spirit has been broken on some occasions but faith has mended it time and time again. Even in the darkest moments, I always held onto one true friend, forgiveness.

The blood soaked sofa from my father's last violent act is no longer positioned in the living room. It was replaced and the stained carpet cleaned. The room stands quiet as if locked in time. The door to that room is seldom opened. On occasions, returning to visit my mother, I have walked past that door. The few times I dared to enter, I found myself traveling back in time. The smell of my father's blood has never left that room.

He could have gone elsewhere for death. My father choosing to shoot himself in the house somehow ensured none of us would forget. At first, I saw my father's death as freedom for us. But none of us will ever be totally free. Even though the physical evidence is gone, the stain of his blood remains on my soul, as I am sure it does with my mother, sister and brother. With the memory of his violence clearer, I have learned from it. My father, Wilson, has been the greatest teacher of forgiveness. In order to climb out of the despair I wallowed in for too many years of my life, I had to learn how to forgive his physical and mental assaults on me. I do not look on him any more as the father who broke the trust and responsibilities of the sacred office associated with the duties and obligations of fatherhood.

I remember him today as a sad and troubled soul, many times reminded of him by the smell of the combination of beer and whiskey. Although I do not release him of the responsibilities of his actions, I free him of any liabilities in connection to the present and future events of my life. He showed me what road not to follow. He demonstrated what actions not to take. By surviving him, I learned not to assume the same steps which misled him in his life and finally led to his own self destruction.

I have weathered him. I have the chance to make something better of myself, and by doing so, make something better of him. His chance was lost the day he pulled that trigger. He played the biggest role in making me a survivor.

My brother, Stephen, has given me a sense of hope for the future. The years that passed kept us strangers, but things are changing. I realize now I played a large part in creating the gap between us. I know now there is nothing wrong in coming from one world and living in another, in being dif-

ferent from those you came from. I cannot be the person, or
if you will, the man my brother is. Neither, should I be
ashamed of what his world may think of me. I no longer
question why he turned out one way and I another.

For nineteen years after our father's death, we didn't
communicate. To see one another would have been too harsh
a reminder of our past. Our mother's ongoing struggle with
mental disorder — the two years she spent in a state mental
institution — brought us together. Mother's many years of
mental and physical pain had finally caught up with her. Initially separated by our father, she now has shortened the gap
between two sons. Now we have to communicate to do what
is right for her, to assist in getting the help she needs, and in
doing so, begin to heal the wounds between us.

Shortly before our mother was committed, my brother,
sister and I met with her doctor. It was an unusual sight to
see the three of us in the same room. I sat looking at my
older brother wondering where the years had slipped away.
We were far away from the two little boys fighting one
another, lost in a forgotten childhood. I realized those boys
had grown up and were finally on the same team. We left the
doctor's office and stepped into the elevator together. Standing outside of the building, we said our good-byes and
headed back in our own directions, back to our own worlds.
With my arms opened wide, I reached out to hug Stephen.

"People might get the wrong idea of two guys hugging
one another, you know," he said, with an odd look on his
face.

"I won't worry about it if you won't, Stephen," I said.

It was a brief embrace, not nearly long enough to make
up for all the ones we had missed over the past many years.
But, it was an embrace and a beginning. For so long to have
felt so removed and different from Stephen, I now see a welcomed hint of similarity of the face of a brother in my reflection in the mirror.

Years passed, and with them, the memory and odor of
Mr. Jones. But they returned in the beginning of spring in

my adult years, when the grasses sprang high and the afternoon air filled with the sounds of lawn mowers being pushed through the neighborhoods by little boys. I had grown to dislike the smell of freshly mown grass; its odor permeated the many layers of my soul, sickening my stomach. I heard the high-pitched motors and smelled the freshly cut grass, but didn't understand until years later — as with so many other things, the sickness that came over me.

Because of my father, there wasn't a lot of innocence left for Mr. Jones to take. As an adult, I have not always been as smart as that little boy whose first instinct told him to protect himself. He ran for the right reasons away from danger, but not for long. Perhaps to learn some hard lessons — the kind most children are fortunate to avoid, he put himself right back in situations and continued doing so into adult life. Familiarity could have become a fatal comfort. Just as I had never spoken about the family abuses, I never told anyone what transpired that afternoon I went off with Mr. Jones. Aided by Mr. Jones' death, I displaced the memory, forgetting it had taken place, until years later, when the ghosts came back and the pieces of the puzzle of my life started loosely fitting together.

Dennis became the bridge to carry me across the ambivalent waters raging in myself. Connecting the apprenticeship of my father and its trepidations with the maturing of the man I eventually became. He was the first door of truth I walked through.

My true self was only beginning to stare me right in the face. The day Dennis and Donna moved to Florida, I realized a small part of myself had just opened up. I soon closed it again, confusing my emotions for Dennis with the experiences of my father and even my brother. Only years later would I come to realize Dennis became the first substitute, filling the void of emptiness left from the lack of acceptance of the male influences in my young life. And there would be others to follow. The day he drove away was like my father dying all over again. Things were incomplete as they were when my father died and the search continued.

I was a groomsman in Dennis and Donna's wedding. The night before the ceremony he again professed his love to me but there was no going back. I should have not been there in the first place. I found myself again standing on the street watching the two of them driving away after the wedding. I had been left behind again by my father, brother, and now Dennis.

I drove back from Florida with Fielda and Carl. Sitting in the back seat, sick to my stomach, all I could think about was opening the car door while it was moving down the highway and throwing myself out onto the road to finally end the pain and confusion in my heart.

The marriage lasted barely one year. Dennis moved to Atlanta and, after unsuccessfully trying to make things work out with me for a brief period, he met another man with whom he became partners. By then, I had closed the door and dared not return to that painful room. A lot of lives were interrupted by a marriage that never should have taken place. I have not kept in close contact with Dennis over the past few years. I feel sad for Donna; she should have never been caught in the middle of two men trying to live by the rules of an unaccepting society.

I don't know if Dennis ever told Donna the truth. I hope that wherever she is today, she has found happiness and is deeply in love.

The messenger comes cloaked in our inner yearnings. It is hard to see at first meeting, but they are mirrored by our response of them. I thought my desires were the same as Roberto's, but in truth, they were different. He did amplify them for me, adding a final twist. I was naive to the situation, naive to the new breed of man I encountered. The sweet and sour experience with Roberto left me in even more confusion concerning the appetite of the thoughts that consumed me. After I left Roberto in his hotel room, I was empty. Any understanding I gained by being with him in my struggle concerning my sexuality was lost for the time being.

After that last look over my shoulder at him standing in front of the hotel, I never saw Ted again. Still feeling him inside of me, feeling wet and aroused, my mind reliving the sensation of being with him, I tightly held onto the piece of paper Ted had written his address and phone number on. Even though I would have liked to relive the experience with him, I knew this was just a passing of two individuals. For a few hours, I was lost in his mighty arms. I realized while he slept next to me that there would be no going back. I had experienced who I really was, and whether I was born, made, or a combination of, this was who I was and will always be. It would be foolish to deny the truth and deny my soul the nourishment it required. I had been accepted by a man, regardless of his sexual orientation, who could rival my father, brother, or any other man who made fun of my differences.

The things we did in that white room are not the things I necessarily choose to partake of today, as I did in the past with other men. At the time, it was something I needed, and fortunately I was spared deathly consequences. Somehow, I thought Ted was giving me a part of his manhood. It is a different time now and I wouldn't do it again today. I certainly wouldn't do it without the protection of a condom. Since my meeting Ted, I have walked many a beach feeling the sand under my feet and the warm water rushing over them, remembering the passion he brought into me. I have looked off in the distance to see if he might be walking the same beach with me. I will always remember the moments spent in the room cooled by the breezes from the turquoise waters of Acapulco.

Gilbert was trapped when he realized there was more to his encounters with men than he first thought. He couldn't turn back — either because he was unselfish or afraid, or maybe a good bit of both. His family, social standing and his great-great-grandfather's firm accumulativeness held a tighter grip over what rested in Gilbert's heart, so he continued to live a lie. In the end, I was fortunate not to fight his decision to end things, knowing from the beginning there would be no life in it for me either.

If we had allowed it to continue, my life would have consisted of waiting for moments to be with him, and that is no life for anyone. Able to let go because I never tried to hold on, I knew I had met Gilbert before in Roberto. I didn't want what was someone else's and didn't want the danger of losing anymore of myself foolishly. Gilbert helped me understand there was no definite black or white when it came to sexuality. He made me feel better about what were choices and what were not. Even though I had questioned mine over and over again, I was relieved I hadn't been born ten years earlier knowing the truth about myself and ending up married. I don't believe Gilbert ever found real happiness. Although he acted on his desires, they were severely suppressed by the life his father wanted him to live.

When I moved from the apartment, I left Gilbert's painting in the closet along with the tapes he had brought on his visits. It was a brief memorial to our time together, moments stolen from his other life in Columbus. I couldn't constantly be reminded of a man I so wanted but could never have — the odds were against me. Other than Todd, out of all the men I have been with intimately, I know in my heart something about him touched me greatly. He was the ideal man, maybe the man I wanted to be. Or maybe it was his music. Gilbert died a few years ago, I heard he had "cancer" and shot himself at the beach house.

It took me several days to break the news to Mills that I wouldn't be moving to New York after all. Fear made me wait until I was safely back in Atlanta. Declining to mention that fear, I tried explaining I wasn't sure if my feelings were deep enough — that what he had to offer financially shouldn't be the reason to make the move. He called aggressively for a week saying I should give him and New York a chance. "At least for awhile," he said. But Mills couldn't convince me. I hoped he understood my decision and possibly respected me for not taking advantage of him, and for not taking the easy way. He had seen young men pass in and out of his life, but they always took something of financial value. I wanted Mills to see all I wanted was his friendship.

That friendship continued at a distance for two years. It was not long before someone new came into Mills' life. He was like so many who came before me, like the person I had almost become. He saw what Mills had to offer and grabbed for it. In the end, Mills' heart was again broken. His new infatuation bounced back and forth between Mills and an old boyfriend; it was hard on Mills not knowing where he stood. I couldn't help but be a little jealous. Mills had let me go too easily compared to the desperation he expressed over this man returning to the arms of someone else.

Mills phoned often requesting I come for a visit. I had never seen Mills so sad as when I arrived. I came in on Friday night. Marcus had left and Mills found a new chauffeur, a virile Brazilian with a smile that fantasies are made of. I instantly took a liking too him but kept it to myself. On a cool April Sunday morning, we drove out to take the ferry to Fire Island for the day. The beach was as I had left it. I walked with Mills and visited with friends I had made: The sand, wind and water, not so long ago. The wind and water rushed to greet me as the sand cushioned my steps. It was nice to see and feel them around me once more.

Mills and I talked about his situation. I told him there were no solutions, only that time, as I had found, would ease the pain he felt inside. Somehow it was so clear, he had to let go. The insidious fact was this man only wanted an older man's money while Mills wanted a younger man's love. But I couldn't tell Mills those words. I couldn't hurt him with the truth he was blind to. Perhaps that was my mistake.

As we drove back to the city, the Corniche broke down. Leaving the car at a garage, we took a taxi to the train station. Mills and I sat on a bench eating Haagen Dazs ice cream bars and waited for the train to take us back to the city. Mills smiled, remembering the times I had made Marcus stop for ice cream.

"I still wish you had moved to New York back then, Randy," Mills said.

To me it seemed so long ago.

"My life was better then," Mills added, and then he was silent.

It was a solemn ride. Mills was obviously despondent. The frozen ice cream couldn't match the coldness in his heart. My heart ached for Mills, for the love he wanted from this man. And, in a way, I hurt as well. I hadn't found the love I had been searching for since I left Mills. I wanted someone to love me as much as Mills loved this man. But it was a desperate, lonely love. A place we have all been, some of us more than once, and for a moment I felt better I was leaving the next morning.

I left New York on Monday, hoping Mills would be alright. I told him to visit me in Atlanta to get away from things. On Wednesday evening, Mills allegedly attacked the old boyfriend of the man he loved. The details were vague. There was very little media coverage on the case and none outside of New York. Within a week of the killing, a friend phoned to say he had heard a rumor Mills was involved in a murder. Apparently, the boyfriend of the young man Mills loved was dead, the boyfriend's roommate wounded, and the police had shot Mills. I couldn't believe it when I found out the murder happened just two days after I had left him in New York. Friends told me to stay clear of the mess after Mills was charged with murder, but I had to find out what had happened.

I called the Park Avenue apartment. To my surprise, his son, Ross, answered the phone but could only tell me his father was in the hospital and that he'd let Mills know I called. Mills returned my call a few days later. His explanation was brief, telling me of a fight that spiraled out of control. Mills maintained he was only defending himself. He was still in shock and couldn't talk about what had happened — not believing it had happened himself. The only thing I had to go on was Mills' word. At that point, I thought it was best to distance myself from his predicament.

There was a trial, Mills pleaded self defense and the jury was hung. Mills called me to come back to New York. Against my better judgment, I went. Perhaps I was trying to make up for all those young men he desired to have who couldn't return his love, but always took his money before leaving him alone. Maybe our rejection after getting our fill of riches turned Mills to madness and that turned him to murder. Maybe in some way we are responsible. While Mills and I ate breakfast at a coffee shop, he told me the District Attorney's office planned to retry him. He was afraid they would convict this time and wondered if he should leave the country.

"They just want my money. They are out to get me and my attorney is milking me. Lawyers!" Mills exclaimed. "He insists my driver pick him up for court," Mills said, going on and on.

Mills was like a caged animal trying to find a way out, anguished over a life of confinement.

"Randy, I just don't feel good about this. I'm telling you, it was self defense," he declared. "Why can't they just drop it?"

At the time, I wished he hadn't told me of his plans. I didn't want to know anything. I wanted to believe him but now I was not so sure. My fear of Mills grew as I sat listening to anger spill from his mouth. His expression was hard and fierce as I looked at him, trying not to stare at his right eye. It sagged and fell out of alignment with the left eye — a result of the policemen's bullet. All I could think about was my first plane ride to New York four years earlier and my next one out.

As Mills pleaded with me to be his friend, my mind flashed back to a frightening experience at my apartment in Atlanta. One night — well after midnight, after I decided against moving to New York, two men came banging at my door. They were trying to kick it in. I'd been asleep and woke to them demanding I open the door. Fear filled every part of me. I was in danger. Mills' repeated phone calls the week after I'd canceled on moving had an edge of force as he tried to convince me otherwise. There were no clear threats made, just that I would be making a huge mistake.

Crouched by the bed with a stretcher strip (wood to frame a canvas) in my hand to use as a weapon, I overcame my fear long enough to call the police. Their kicks became harder as the wooden panels of the door began to give way to the force. I prayed for them to leave. As the patrol car's lights flooded into the windows of the building, the men bolted. What if they had been successful in kicking the door in the first time? Was there a connection to the break-up with Mills?

Before the incident, I imagined someone was following me. I noticed a man hanging around the apartment building. More than once, from my bedroom window, I saw him sitting in a parked car facing my apartment. On several occasions he appeared, once while I was in a restaurant and another time at a bar. I couldn't tell through the peep hole whether one of the men kicking at the door was the same stranger I'd seen hanging around before. Nothing happened after that night. I never considered a possible relationship between the calls from Mills, the two men at my door and the stranger, until that moment sitting across from him during breakfast. Did Mills send someone to spy on me, to find out if there was more to why I was not moving? Was he a cold-blooded murderer? Just the thought of a connection disturbed me. Plus, I had signed an insurance policy. What was that all about?

Toward the end of breakfast, Mills asked me to send him the telephone numbers of two pay phones where he could reach me.

"Randy, don't ask any questions," he said. "If you believe me, you'll do as I ask. All my friends are deserting me. I need to be able to count on you."

Obviously paranoid, Mills wanted to call me at home

and instruct me as to which one of the pay phones to go to so we could talk without fear of being recorded. I came back to Atlanta and did as he asked. If he was a murderer, I wanted to make him go away as quickly as possible.

Only a short time passed until I heard from Mills again. He called asking for that big favor I had always known would be the payoff.

"No questions, just listen to me," he instructed. "I need you to send a telegram to my lawyer here in New York. He's bleeding me dry. I have been meeting with him everyday getting ready for the retrial. I'm sick of looking at his face. He just wants more money. I need a break from this, just a few days not to have to think about this mess. Okay?" Mills said angrily. "Pay cash and send it from me. Remember... pay cash Randy, I'll send you the money. It will cost about thirty bucks. And Randy, send the telegram tomorrow at exactly ten a. m.," he added.

The content of the telegram to Mills' lawyer in New York was as follows: I am in Atlanta. A good friend was in a near fatal car accident. Will be back in New York on.... signed Mills Gunn.

"Randy, you do that for me. I need you to do this... you won't get into any trouble," Mills assured. "I just need a few days away from that lawyer," he repeated.

I asked myself, what harm would sending the telegram do? It is just a telegram. And what harm might come to me if I said no? The latter concept stuck in my mind, and not wanting to make him mad, I sent the telegram. Mills just wants to get a breather from his lawyer, that is all I thought or wanted to think. I wasn't used to running for help. I would take care of myself and get him out of my life. One week later I received a card with some cash postmarked, New York. He wrote:

Dear Randy,

You have always been a wonderful friend and I want you to know I appreciate and love you.

Mills

I have never heard from him again.

I am a long way from the Park Avenue address I almost called home and from the beach of Fire Island I loved, yet I know I made the right decision. Once I had more information on the murder, I was in shock. The gruesome details of a brutal knife fight, instigated by Mills, made me sick to my stomach. After Mills went on the lam, there was a second trial. He was convicted in absentia of first-degree manslaughter. I always knew he was a dangerous man. That's probably why I tried to stay on his good side, why I sent the two telephone numbers and why I sent the telegram. After all, he told me he was going to leave the country. Better to protect myself, I thought. I wanted to make it back to Atlanta and I didn't want anyone coming after me because Mills told me he was going on the lam. What if he thought I might betray him and call the District Attorney's office about his contemplating skipping town, thus blowing his plans? Would he snap and send someone for me or come for me himself? He had connections. Yes, I thought about calling the police, but they couldn't protect me from my father; and something told me that they couldn't protect me from Mills either: They would think I was just some "fag," and I didn't want to become any more involved. But Mills must have trusted me. How many people would he tell he was about to make a break for it? I was too scared to say a word, and perhaps, he knew it.

Mills' son had died during the first trail due to complications from AIDS. When I last saw Mills, he portrayed himself as a broken man who had lost a son and lost at love — but wasn't a murderer. Maybe he was a better actor than I was, or maybe I wanted to believe the man who seemed to care so much for me could have never killed anyone intentionally.

I thought all I needed was someone to take care of me, to give the best life had to offer and show me the world. If I had moved to New York, I'm sure the dream I had wanted would have turned into a nightmare. I could have ended up as the others had in Mills' life. At twenty-five years of age, I could have made the worst of all choices. So tempted to fall into a material world where alcohol, drugs, beauty and money were gulped in vast amounts by those who wanted to be "somebodies." I almost did, by the invitation of a dangerous few.

My relationship with Mills had nothing to do with love. I had the attentions of an older man. My young eyes were filled with glitter and I almost felt I was worth something. Luckily, I realized acquiring things with other peoples' money couldn't buy me love and acceptance. Mills was about those things in the reverse and look what happened to him.

Rumor is that he went to Brazil by way of Hong Kong, possibly with his Brazilian chauffeur who looked more like a bodyguard than a driver to me. Mills would be close to seventy-years-old now, if he is still living.

When West and I split up for the last time, I thought I would never find love again. I had never loved anyone until I met him. I was desperate for it; I was dependent on it. I handed over to West every part of me, including my soul. He knew my heart better than any other person in my life. It was as if I cut myself open with a knife and let every emotion pour out of me and he poured salt into my gaping flesh.

I believed every promise of love and devotion he spoke. I was a fool to have believed the sentiments he betrayed time and time again. Every time I caught him in a lie, he begged for forgiveness, just like when my father got drunk and abused me. He said he was sorry and it would never happen again. It was all I knew so I always forgave.

I don't blame West for what happened between us. I should have left long before I lost respect for myself, long before the lies mounted. There are takers and there are givers. West was a taker, but in the end he gave me freedom. Once I was able to come to terms with the realization that I was replicating my father in West, I became free of past dependencies. In a way, I was trying to make things right with my father through West; I was trying to win his love through West. That's why I kept going back. Somehow trying to make up for all the abuse, still feeling it was my fault. It all hit so close to home.

West moved out on a Saturday night. Six years before, it was a Saturday night that we had met. There were no goodbyes, just two voices yelling — mine screaming, "Get Out!" West struck me and threw me against the wall. I found it hard to breathe, a combination of panic and a few cracked ribs. A girlfriend picked me up so I wouldn't be there while West and a friend removed his belongings. My heart sank when I returned hours later to find his room empty. I spent a sleepless night telling myself, over and over, this was for the best. At five-thirty in the morning, I sat in the middle of his empty room. They had all left me: My father, the men after him, and now West was gone as well. Panicked, I drove over to the house where West had moved in with Lee and his wife. The sun was just breaking over the horizon as I turned onto the street. Stopping in front of the house, I saw that West had left most of his furniture under the carport. I slowly pulled my truck down the long drive. Everything told me no one was up at this hour, at least I hoped that was the case. Quietly, so as not to wake anyone, I proceeded to load up West's bed, desk, chest of drawers and a dozen boxes onto the back of the truck. Making two trips, I put everything back into his room as if it had never been moved. I hoped by filling his room with his belongings the way it was before, I could fill the emptiness inside of me. The panic subsided after I had his things back with me. Then, I hoped he would come back too.

West was not happy when he found all his things gone — at first thinking they had been stolen. After a few weeks, I gave everything back. Months passed. Memorial Day weekend found me with friends in Pensacola Beach. A migration of what seemed like thousands of men found the gay beach area and with them was West. We saw one another on the beach the first day, but I didn't acknowledge him. Later that night at a club, The Office, I saw him again. The bar was packed to the rafters with an influx of men there for the holiday weekend. I had been dancing all night with Chris from Kentucky. The dance floor was wet from the sweat rolling off the dancing bodies. Intense body heat filled the bar. After dancing elbow to elbow among the sweaty bodies, Chris and I went to the roof deck of the bar to get out of the heat. The roof was as crowded as every inch of the bar below. Chris and I had taken off our shirts, mine was tucked in the waist of my shorts and Chris had lost his on the dance floor. The cool air felt good as it hit our wet bodies.

While on the roof, I was concerned if the structure was strong enough to support all the people. But those thoughts vanished when I noticed West standing a few feet away — almost close enough for me to reach out and touch him. He was with a group of guys I didn't recognize. As I talked with Chris, I pretended not to notice West. I was close enough to hear one of his friends referring to me, "Take a look at that guy in the red and white shorts... man...nice body." At that point, I saw West out of the corner of my eye shrug his shoulders and bolt from the group back downstairs. Looking good is always the best revenge, and being with a good-looking guy didn't hurt either.

A few weeks later, back in Atlanta, I ran into West at Blake's. He said he missed me, that he was leaving for Florida in two days on business for a month, and wanted to get together upon his return. I got home around one o'clock in the morning. Shortly after, the phone rang. West was on the other end wanting to come over. He spent the night. The next night I went to his place, not because I needed him, but because I felt he needed me. In the morning while we were in bed, West said he still loved me, and when he got back to Atlanta he wanted to try things again. Until then, he would call while he was away. West did call, but I never returned his calls. That morning, like the time I put him on the plane for Hartford, I was relieved he was going. But this time, unlike before, there was no going back.

I held on to West for so long because I was used to turmoil in my life. It was all I knew. I was running in circles, looking for something better than me. I had grown up that way. Anyone else would have walked away much sooner. Every time West lied to me brought disappointment. Something inside made me fight harder to win his love so he would stop hurting me. The truth was he wasn't hurting me, I was. It was an unhealthy way to live. I saw myself through his eyes. If I thought West loved me one day, then I would love myself. If I thought he hated me and didn't want me anymore, then I hated myself and wanted to be someone else. Like being beaten by my father, I always came back for more.

Being beaten, violated, or just mistreated was synonymous with love. Six years is a long time to love someone and hate yourself at the same time. For those wasted years, I should have loved myself better. I think I have finally stopped running in circles, finally stopped running from myself. Up to, and mostly including West, in some twisted subconscious way, I picked men who like my father, weren't destined to stay in my life. My father's suicide left an impression on me — not wanting anyone to stay for very long in my life, but still tied to the fear of abandonment. Sooner or later they would leave. I would feel the void and panic left by my father each time someone left, leaving me to look for him again. I found my father again in West, hopefully for the last time.

Matthew has given me back the ability to trust, something I had lost long ago. I learned to deal with the word love with a lot of skepticism early on in my life as a child. My distrust was reiterated when West lied and abused the love I gave to him so honestly and freely. If someone said they loved me, it usually meant trouble and they would probably not be around for long.

On the other hand, I realize Matthew's love will always be there. He wants nothing in return except my happiness. He reminds me from time to time in a phone call, hug, or card, that I can trust the word love again. Matthew has watched a lot of men come in and out of my life. He has stood on the side lines just in case I needed him. His shoulders have been soaked on numerous occasions with my tears and heartaches.

In a letter, he wrote: Thanks for being the person you are. Never feel you are unloved or unappreciated. There are so many who do care for and love you, but remember, I love you the most.

It has been several years since Robert's passing. The lake house was sold and I'm sure the crickets still serenade the nights on the lake, but they are singing someone else's story. I know a huge part of Matthew's life was lost when Robert died. Matthew had been a valiant friend, companion and lover to Robert for many years. They had stuck it out together as heterosexual marriages fell by the wayside. I know they had many good moments, as well as some bad. Matthew was always there for Robert, even in the misery of the bottle, and Robert had been there for Matthew in better times. Matthew set an example for me not to run away from the past as he played a part in bringing it back to me.

Things didn't change after Robert's death. Matthew never relived those few stolen moments in the night as Robert slept, as I believe he may have desired. I choose to believe what Matthew brought to me were memories from the heart of better moments with Robert.

Matthew has carried the weight of my father for many years now, and I am sure he has felt its load. He is a constant in my life and will always be the human light leading me to a safe haven in the darkness of my endless nights. By knowing his unconditional love, my life has been a better place to live. My rejection of his desires would have sent many men on their way, leaving me to stand alone. He is not that kind of man. His is a selfless love. I am the selfish one.

I sat at the kitchen table, feeling odd in my suit, as I waited for John's car. We were driving to Athens with Marie and Bill for Todd's funeral. The *Atlanta Journal* newspaper was scattered on the table and floor. And in my hand, I held on to the front page. A controversy was raging in Cobb County, a bedroom suburb of Atlanta. A group of its citizens didn't want the city to fund any organizations connected to the arts involving homosexuals. The arts have always been a venue for people "different" from the mainstream to express themselves, a free berth to develop, and from which to share their special talents with everyone from all walks of life. Todd had used that avenue.

A picture of an elderly man holding a protest sign with "thank God for AIDS" written on it dominated the front page. I found myself wondering if this man realized its impact. I wondered if he had ever met a mother, like Mrs. Weaver, or a father whose beloved child had endured the cruel and heartbreaking death associated with the disease. And I wondered if this man had any idea of the misery and hardship. I thought of Mrs. Weaver and hoped she had not seen the paper; especially this day of all days. I had seen the pain in her eyes, heard her screams and cries behind a closed door as she watched her child deteriorate and succumb to an agonizing death.

I thought of my father — this man appearing to be Wilson's age if he had lived. I thought about war and hate and sacrifice. And I wondered if this man had fought next to my father or even Todd's father during World War II. What happened to the freedom that countless fellow Americans, as well as other allies, died for? Was it fought in vain? And I wondered what we have learned from our histories and the histories of others. Had we not learned anything as a society? And, if not, were we all doomed? This man felt some justification in Todd's death and the death of so many others. Sitting there looking at the wrinkled paper, it seemed to me that the destruction of one society is the destruction of all. And again I wondered how long we would have to wait before we learned and ended the senselessness of the fear of others, different from ourselves. If we are to fight a war for freedom, then it certainly should be for the freedom of all and not the freedom of a select group. The love Todd and I shared for humanity was for just that: Freedom to be human, freedom for the quality of being human and for being ourselves. We interpreted the signals that each of our life experiences gave us, and then, taking the translations into account, we followed the signals from our souls.

In Todd's recording of thoughts, it was his wish that there be support and compassion for his family and for other people infected with this disease. Todd not only had to deal with the realization this virus was taking over his body, he also had to live with the unwarranted shame that came hand and hand with AIDS. Incubated by a few men who wrongly call AIDS the wrath of God, Todd's burden, like so many others, was unimaginable. Fools walk this earth and they are regrettably followed. If God loved any man, then he loved Todd.

afterword

Though we are strangers and come from different places, I invite
you to walk with me among the fields where the tall grasses grow
and the wild flowers flourish.
Regard how different the flowers are; so many colors, shapes and
variations for our own different eyes to see. Notice how differently they grow.
Behold the beauty their differences make and attend the peace in
the fields where they sow.
Like two different flowers, sit and ponder quietly with me in the
tall grasses.
How is it that they, the wild flowers can grow so differently,
but live so peaceful in the tall grasses? Yet we, you and I
fight and wage war amongst ourselves because of our differences.
I guess this is why they have been here long, peaceful in the
fields and will remain here long after we are gone.

In a way, I owe the completion of this book to Todd. While he was sick, he told me he was one of three people who knew the real Randy. I should have asked him who the other two were. Todd urged me to share myself with more people and let my friends really know who I was, to get on with my life and do what I was put on this earth to do. His last words to me were from a recording of thoughts to his family and friends, of which I am proud to have been included in. This is what Todd wrote: "The next person is Randy...Randy and I have grown up together, believe it or not...probably my oldest friend in Atlanta...we go way, way back, Randy. We are both artists, we both love the beauty of man, or humanity, I should say...what it has to offer every person, and what it has to offer to us, which is really crucial and important...because not all of us get the same signals, and that's what is so great about the world, is that we don't always get the same signals. You are so talented, you are so deep, and you have always been there for me. Keep your talent alive and well, keep your faith...you've got a deep, deep emotional faith...and if I can give you any advice, I would say to open it up more. Let more people know what you are thinking, because they are there for you, too. Thanks for being a very important part of my life. And for being a part of so many people's lives. You've got a lot of capacity, Bud...a lot of understanding that you haven't even tapped on. So tap on it...get going, and thanks."

It took me almost a quarter of a century to find my first friend. I miss him immensely. I owe the deepest gratitude to Todd for being a true friend, for seeing through the barriers I surrounded myself with for so many years, and for helping me regain the importance of seeing each day as the gift it truly is.

Examining your life takes courage. The kind of courage you need to turn and face yourself. The courage to accept others, and the courage to say different is not necessarily wrong. The courage to believe in ourselves despite some emotions which set us apart from others in our society.

Without a doubt, life is a complex emotional situation. You have a world full of diverse people trying to coexist with a lot of emotion flying around. It is full of many groups, all thinking their way is the right one, their emotions should be everyone else's. Which, in turn, makes for a world full of prejudice. Wherever you look, it seems as if someone is always trying to take charge, to make everyone else live by their rules and emotions. And it has been this way from the beginning.

There are more ways than one to live, love or believe. We should have the courage to accept our differences and go on. Life is about going forward, progressing, filtering preju-dice out of our lives so that every human can live as they feel they must. We free ourselves of prejudice by not allow-ing our beliefs, developed from our own emotions, to spill over into judging others. We are all here on this earth by some power greater than our own and that power made all these differences. Our lives are full of experiences which mold us into the individuals we are today. Our biological make-up is a delicate balance of many factors. As a result of this, no two of us are really the same. Because of our differ-ent make-ups, many varieties on the theme of human exist, and as you are, I happen to be one of those variations also.

Whatever factors made me the person I am today, the simple fact is, I am that person. There is no going back. I don't have to understand the whys anymore. Being gay is not a matter of government or religion. It is a matter of the heart and soul. And if I am to be judged, then let it be by God and God alone. I have to follow my heart.

Denying someone or some group the right to live their lives as they feel they must without causing harm to another is like clipping the wings of a bird and placing it in a cage. Who gave anyone the right to do such a thing to any creature, much less a human being who has done harm to no one?

I have been fortunate and blessed in my journey, even on its darkest roads. My wish for you is that your journey will be one of truth and freedom. Never forget the history of man's journey filled with its horrors and always hold your authenticity close to your heart. Life is not about building skyscrapers, conquering lands, becoming a king or ruling over a country. Life is about looking up to the sun and realizing there is a power greater than any one person can imagine or obtain. Life is about extending a hand to someone in need of help and holding someone close who needs comfort. Life is about feeling the coolness of the green grass under bare feet and hearing the sounds of the sweet songs of the earth.

Man has inflicted so much pain on this world I am surprised we cannot hear the continuous screams of horror echoing through the heavens and I am surprised we cannot see how man's hate has bloodied the blueness of the sky. It is a shame people have been so foolish, including myself, in closing their ears and turning their backs on one another. It is a simple truth, one of sharing a gift of such beauty and magnitude of this world with plenty of room for everyone. In the end it does not matter what color, race, gender, size, shape, nationality, religion or sexual orientation one is. In the end it does not matter who you loved, but only how deeply that love was felt.

My mind and eyes are beginning to see clearer. The truth emerges and I am feeling a sense of freedom for the first time in my life. I no longer am ashamed of who I am. I set the best example and do my part in making this world a better place in whatever small or larger way I am able, and under no circumstances accept or allow any form of prejudice to stand in the way of my happiness. I won't make the same mistakes again. I learn from the past.

If the society I live in won't accept me for the person I am, then I will accept myself. My search for love has finally come to an end. I found it in myself. I had to believe my life was worth something, no matter how different I was from everyone else. The truth is, we are all different and we are not alone. We are all looking for love on this earth, what each heart needs is, after all, the wonder of life. Find it where you can, and if it is in *The Arms of Adam,* then so be it.

*There will come a day when the sea is calm, the sky so blue
and the grass so green, and the sun will warm our souls.
There will come a day.*

*There will come a night when the stars are so bright that
darkness will be no more.
There will come a night.*

*There will come a time when the strong will pick up the weak
and hold them close to their breasts and there will be no
judgment, no fear, no hate. There will come a time.*

*There will come a moment when all people will join hearts
and put their efforts toward that which is true and real and
when that moment comes our pain will end and new life as it
should be, will begin. There will come a moment and that
moment will be eternity.*

*This will come when each and everyone of us, you and I,
believe this must be the way and take steps to make it so, by
our own deeds and actions. This will come.*

*There will come a day when the sea is calm, the sky so blue
and the grass so green, and the sun will warm our souls. Yes,
there will come a day.*